DICTIONARY
of FIBER & TEXTILE TECHNOLOGY

www.kosa.com

To the best of our knowledge, the information contained herein is accurate. However, neither KoSa nor any of its divisions or businesses can accept liability of any kind for the accuracy or completeness thereof. Final determination of the suitability of any information or material for the use contemplated, of its manner of use, and whether the suggested use infringes any patents is the sole responsibility of the user.

Copies of this book may be ordered through your KoSa representative or from:

KoSa
Communications and Public Affairs
P.O. Box 32414
Charlotte, NC 28232-2414
704-554-2769
FAX 704-554-2626

Acknowledgements

We wish to express our gratitude to all whose contributions to this edition of the *Dictionary of Fiber and Textile Technology* have helped to make it current and accurate.

Dr. Edward A. Vaughn, Professor
School of Textiles, Fiber and Polymer Science
Clemson University

Mr. Jos K. Vandermaas
Retired Hoechst Celanese employee

Special thanks to the numerous KoSa employees who contributed terms and reviewed the changes in this edition.

Foreword

This *Dictionary of Fiber and Textile Technology* is intended to be a convenient reference for textile terminology. Although it covers all types of textile terms broadly, its special emphasis is on manufactured fibers — what they are, how they are made, and how they are used.

Formerly the *Man-Made Fiber and Textile Dictionary,* earlier editions were published to provide a reference source for our employees. The later editions were published in response to numerous requests from customers and others in the textile industry for an up-to-date glossary of terms encountered in the manufactured fiber and textile trades. To enhance its usefulness, the dictionary was expanded and illustrated.

This current edition has been updated and further expanded to cover recent developments in fiber-forming polymers, new commercially manufactured fibers, high-performance fibers, textile equipment advances, and new applications for textile materials. New diagrams have been added to illustrate these developments. Coverage of natural fibers has also been expanded. We have attempted to convey as much information as possible without making the book cumbersome.

As in previous editions, generic terms such as dyeing and knitting are handled comprehensively with specific terms presented under one heading. The more widely used manufactured fibers are listed by their Federal Trade Commission generic names and definitions, in most cases followed by a brief description of their manufacture, characteristics, and applications. The appendix gives abbreviations, equivalent weights and measures, and various conversion tables and formulas needed by the textile technologist.

We hope that this dictionary will help to familiarize you with the language of textiles. Only through you can we determine its value, and we therefore invite your comments.

About KoSa

KoSa is the world's complete polyester resource. We manufacture commodity and specialty polyester products as part of five global businesses: Intermediates and Polymer, Packaging Resins, Technical Filament, Textile Fibers and Tire Cord. With global headquarters in Houston, Texas, KoSa employs more than 10,000 people worldwide. For more information, visit our website at **www.kosa.com**.

A

AAMA: Acronym for the American Apparel Manufacturers Association.

AATCC: Acronym for the American Association of Textile Chemists and Colorists.

AATT: Acronym for the American Association for Textile Technology.

ABACA: A tough bast fiber from the abaca plant. The long, strong fibers, off-white to brown in color, are used primarily in ropes, mats, and coarse fabrics. The abaca plant is native to the Philippines and is of the banana family. Also called MANILA HEMP.

ABNORMAL CRIMP: A relative term for crimp that is either too low or too high in frequency and/or amplitude or that has been put into the fiber with improper angular characteristics.

ABRADED YARN: A filament yarn in which filaments have been cut or broken to create hairiness (fibrillation) to simulate the surface character of spun yarns. Abraded yarns are usually plied or twisted with other yarns before use.

ABRASION MARK: An area where a fabric has been damaged by friction.

ABRASION RESISTANCE: The ability of a fiber or fabric to withstand surface wear and rubbing.

ABRASION TESTERS: Several types of instruments for simulating frictional surface wear of a textile material in actual use. Abrasion tests for fabrics are flat abrasion, flex abrasion, and edge abrasion.

ABSOLUTE HUMIDITY: The mass of water vapor present in a unit volume of air. (Also see RELATIVE HUMIDITY.)

ABSORBANCE: The ability of a substance to transform radiant energy into a different form, usually with a resulting rise in temperature. Mathematically, absorbance is the negative logarithm to the base 10 of transmittance.

ABSORBENCY: The ability of one material to take up another material.

ABSORPTION: The process of gases or liquids being taken up into the pores of a fiber, yarn, or fabric. (Also see ADSORPTION.)

ACCELERANT: A chemical used to speed up chemical or other processes. For example, accelerants are used in dyeing triacetate and polyester fabrics.

ACCORDION FABRIC: A patterned circular knit fabric of two or more colors produced on single-needle machines. The pattern is achieved by combinations of knit, tuck, and welt stitches.

ACCORDION PLEAT: A series of narrow, regularly spaced, pressed folds in fabrics, usually running in the lengthwise direction in skirts and dresses. Accordion pleats show the entire upper surface of the fabric, as opposed to true pleats. (Also see PLEAT.)

ACETATE FIBER: A manufactured fiber in which the fiber-forming substance is cellulose acetate (FTC definition). Acetate is manufactured by treating purified cellulose refined from cotton linters and/or wood pulp with acetic anhydride in the presence of a catalyst. The resultant product, cellulose acetate flake, is precipitated, purified, dried, and dissolved in acetone to prepare the spinning solution. After filtration, the highly viscous solution is extruded through spinnerets into a column of warm air in which the acetone is evaporated, leaving solid continuous filaments of cellulose acetate. These filaments are simultaneously twisted and wound onto a bobbin in the form of yarn which is ready for use without further chemical processing. In the manufacture of staple fiber, the filaments from numerous spinnerets are combined into tow form, crimped, cut to the required length, and packaged in bales.

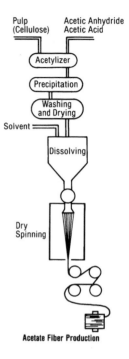

Acetate Fiber Production

CHARACTERISTICS: Acetate fabrics are fast-drying, wrinkle and shrinkage resistant, crisp or soft in hand depending upon the end use, and luxurious in appearance.

END USES: The end uses of acetate include lingerie, dresses, blouses, robes, other apparel, linings, draperies, bedspreads, upholstery, carpets, umbrellas, formed fabrics, and cigarette filters.

ACETIC ACID: An organic acid (CH_3COOH) widely used in textile applications. It is used in textile wet processing, dyeing and printing, and in the manufacture of cellulose acetate and cellulose triacetate.

ACETIC ANHYDRIDE: Anhydrous acetic acid [$(CH_3CO)_2O$]. It is used in the acetylation process in the manufacture of cellulose acetate.

ACETONE: Dimethyl ketone (CH_3COCH_3). One of the most powerful organic solvents. Acetone dissolves secondary cellulose acetate and other derivatives of cellulose. It is miscible with water and has a low boiling point (55–56°C).

ACETONE RECOVERY: A process for reclaiming the acetone solvent from acetate fiber or plastics manufacture. Usually the recovery process consists of adsorption by activated carbon and redistillation.

ACETYL: The radical ($CH_3CO–$) of acetic acid.

ACETYLATION: A chemical reaction whereby the acetyl radical is introduced into a compound, as in the conversion of cellulose to cellulose acetate.

ACETYLATOR: A chemical-reaction vessel in which cellulose pulp and acetic anhydride are combined to form cellulose acetate.

ACETYL VALUE: A measure of the degree of esterification or combination of acetyl radicals with cellulose in acetate or triacetate products.

ACID-DYEABLE VARIANTS: Polymers modified chemically to make them receptive to acid dyes.

ACID DYES: See DYES.

ACID FADING: See GAS FADING.

ACIDIC: A term describing a material having a pH of less than 7.0 in water.

ACID RECOVERY: A reclamation process in chemical processing in which acid is extracted from a raw material, by-product, or waste product. In the manufacture of cellulose acetate, acetic acid is a major by-product. Acid recovery consists of combining all wash water containing appreciable acetic acid and concentrating it to obtain glacial acetic acid.

ACID RESISTANCE: The property of withstanding contact or treatment with any acids normally encountered in use. The type of acid should be stated (i.e., organic or inorganic).

ACRYLIC FIBER: A manufactured fiber in which the fiber-forming substance is any long chain synthetic polymer composed of at least 85% by weight of acrylonitrile units $[-CH_2-CH(CN)-]$ (FTC definition). Acrylic fibers are produced by two basic methods of spinning (extrusion), dry and wet. In the dry spinning method, material to be spun is dissolved in a solvent. After extrusion through the spinneret, the solvent is evaporated, producing continuous filaments which later may be cut into staple, if desired. In wet spinning, the spinning solution is extruded into a liquid coagulating bath to form filaments which are drawn, dried, and processed. The forms produced are staple, tow, or top.

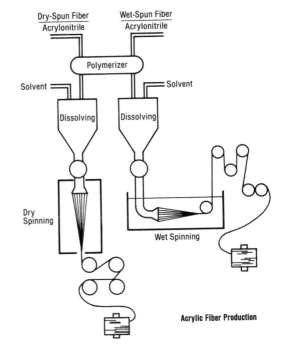

Acrylic Fiber Production

CHARACTERISTICS: Acrylic fabrics have low moisture absorbency and dry relatively quickly. In general, acrylic fibers are resistant to the degrading effects of ultraviolet rays in sunlight and to a wide range of chemicals and fumes. They provide warmth in fabrics which are lightweight, soft, and resilient. Acrylic fibers have relatively poor flame resistance compared with other fibers. (Also see MODACRYLIC FIBER.)

Some acrylic fabrics, particularly knit types, approximate the hand of fine wool. Because of the composition and cross section of the fiber, fabrics made from them have a high bulk to weight ratio. This is further enhanced with the so-called "high bulk" spun yarns. These are produced by two methods: (1) staple blends of regular acrylic fiber with a higher shrinkage acrylic fiber, and (2) bicomponent fiber, with regular and higher shrinkage acrylic polymers extruded in a side-by-side arrangement. Both types bulk when treated to induce shrinkage.

END USES: Acrylic fibers are used in apparel, such as sweaters, simulated furs and other pile fabrics, socks, dresses, and exercise wear. Other end uses include floor coverings, draperies, upholstery, and blankets.

ACRYLIC RESIN: A polymer of acrylonitrile, used in the production of manufactured fibers, as a fabric finish and as a size.

ACRYLONITRILE: A colorless, volatile, flammable liquid (CH_2=CHCN) used as a raw material in the manufacture of acrylic polymers and fibers.

ACTINIC DEGRADATION: See ULTRAVIOLET DEGRADATION.

ACTINIC RESISTANCE: See ULTRAVIOLET RESISTANCE.

ACTION STRETCH: See POWER STRETCH.

ACTIVATED CARBON: Charcoal, mostly of vegetable origin, of high adsorptive capacity. It is used for decolorizing liquids and other adsorption purifications. Usually made by carbonization and chemical activation.

ACTIVEWEAR: Garments designed to provide properties such as comfort, support, insulation, and wear resistance required for vigorous exercise or sports activities.

ACTWU: Acronym for the Amalgamated Clothing and Textile Workers' Union.

ADDITION POLYMERIZATION: A reaction yielding a polymer in which the molecular formula of the repeating unit is identical with that of the monomer. The molecular weight of a polymer so formed is a simple sum of the molecular weight of the combined monomer units. Combination occurs by means of rearrangement of the chemical bonds.

ADDITIVE: A supplementary material combined with a base material to provide special properties. For example, pigments are used as dope additives to give color in solution dyeing.

ADD-ON: The weight of solid material applied to a textile after drying, usually expressed as a percentage of the dry weight of the textile before the addition.

ADHESION: The force that holds different materials together at their interface and resists separation into two layers.

ADHESION PROMOTERS: Products used to treat the smooth fiber-face of closely constructed base fabric to provide a chemical bonding site for subsequent coating. This step is done because it is difficult to get good coating adhesion via strikethrough and mechanical bonding in closely constructed fabrics. Products containing the isocyanate group are the most widely used promoters. (Also see DIP TREATING.)

ADHESION TEST: In coated and laminated fabrics, a test to determine the force per unit length required to separate the layers.

ADHESIVE ACTIVATED YARNS: Yarns treated by the fiber manufacturer to promote better adhesion to another material such as rubber and/or to allow easier processing.

ADHESIVE BONDED FABRICS: See BONDING, 1.

ADHESIVE MIGRATION: In nonwovens, the movement of adhesive together with its carrier solvent in a fabric during drying, giving it a nonuniform distribution within the web, usually increasing to the outer layers.

ADHESIVES: In textiles, materials which cause fibers, yarns, or fabrics to stick together or to other materials.

ADIPIC ACID: 1,4-butanedicarboxylic acid [$COOH(CH_2)_4COOH$]. It is used in the polymerization reaction to form nylon 66 polymers and in the manufacture of polyurethane foams.

ADSORPTION: The attraction of gases, liquids, or solids to surface areas of textile fibers, yarns, fabrics, or any material. (Also see ABSORPTION.)

ADVANCED COMPOSITE: Polymer, resin, or other matrix-material system in which reinforcement is accomplished via high-strength, high-modulus materials in continuous filament form or in discontinuous form such as staple fibers, fibrets, and in-situ dispersions. (Also see COMPOSITE.)

AESTHETICS: In textiles, properties perceived by touch and sight, such as the hand, color, luster, drape, and texture of fabrics or garments.

AFFINITY: Chemical attraction; the tendency of two elements or substances to unite or combine, such as fiber and dyestuff.

AFMA: Acronym for the American Fiber Manufacturers Association.

A-FRAME: A device used in batch dyeing and finishing to hold a roll of fabric.

AFTERFLAME: Continuous flaming of a solid material after the ignition source is removed.

AFTERGLOW: The flameless, glowing combustion of certain solid materials that occurs after the removal of an external source of ignition or after the cessation of combustion of the material.

AFTERSCOURING: A soaping treatment to remove excess surface color from textiles after dyeing or printing.

AFTERTREATMENT: Any treatment done after fabric production. In dyeing, it refers to treating dyed material in ways to improve properties; in nonwovens, it refers to finishing processes carried out after a web has been formed and bonded. Examples are embossing, creping, softening, printing, and dyeing.

AGAVE: A genus of spiny-leafed plant from which are produced many common bast fibers including SISAL and HENEQUEN.

AGEING: 1. Deterioration of textile or other materials caused by gradual oxidation during storage and/or exposure to light. **2.** The oxidation stage of alkali-cellulose in the manufacture of viscose rayon from bleached wood pulp. **3.** Originally, a process in which printed fabric was exposed to a hot, moist atmosphere. Presently, the term is applied to the treatment of printed fabric in moist steam in the absence of air. Ageing is also used for the development of certain colors in dyeing, e.g., aniline black. (Also see STEAM FIXATION.)

AGER: A steam chamber used for ageing printed or padded material.

AGGLOMERATION: A cluster of particles or fibers.

AGITATE: To stir or to mix, as in the case of a dyebath or solution.

AIR BAG: An automatically inflating bag in front of riders in an automobile to protect them from pitching forward in an accident. End use for manufactured textile fibers.

AIR BRUSHING: Blowing color on a fabric or paper with a mechanized pneumatic brush.

AIR CONDITIONING: 1. A chemical process for sealing short, fuzzy fibers into a yarn. Fabrics made from air-conditioned yarns are porous. Because they allow more air circulation, these fabrics are also cooler. **2.** Control of temperature and/or humidity in work or living space.

AIR ENTANGLED YARN: See COMPACTED YARN.

AIR JET DYEING MACHINE: A jet dyeing machine that uses air jets instead of a venturi to move the fabric through the dye liquor. The machine uses a low liquor ratio, which lowers energy costs.

AIR JET LOOM: A shuttleless loom capable of very high speeds that uses an air jet to propel the filling yarn through the shed.

AIR JET SPINNING: A spinning system in which yarn is made by wrapping fibers around a core stream of fibers with compressed air. In this process, the

Airflow Direction

Air Jet Spinning

fibers are drafted to appropriate sliver size, then fed to the air jet chambers where they are twisted, first in one direction, then in the reverse direction in a second chamber. They are stabilized after each twisting operation. (Also see FASCIATED YARN.)

AIR JET TEXTURING: See TEXTURING, 1.

AIR-LAID NONWOVEN: Fabrics made by an AIR-LAYING process. The fibers are distributed by air currents to give a random orientation within the web and a fabric with isotropic properties.

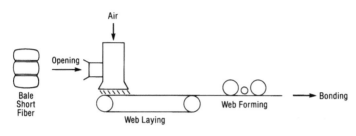

Air-Laid Nonwoven Process

AIR LAYING: A process in which air is used to separate and move fibers to fashion a web such as the Kroyer® process for short fibers, usually of wood pulp; or the Rando-Webber® process for staple-length fibers.

AIR PERMEABILITY: The porosity or the ease with which air passes through material. Air permeability determines such factors as the wind resistance of sailcloth, the air resistance of parachute cloth, and the efficacy of various types of air filters. It also influences the warmth or coolness of a fabric.

AIRPLANE FABRIC: A plain, tightly woven, water-repellent fabric tradition-ally made of mercerized cotton. During World War I, the fabric was treated with a cellulose acetate dope and used to cover the wings, tail, and fuselage of airplanes. Today, similar fabrics made from nylon or polyester/cotton blends are used in rainwear and sportswear.

AIR-SUPPORTED STRUCTURE: A structure supported by internal air pres-sure. The covering material is an application for technical textiles. Entrance and exit is through air locks.

ALBATROSS: A soft, lightweight wool or wool blend fabric in a plain weave with a napped, fleecy surface that resembles in texture, the breast of the albatross. It is usually light-colored and is used in negligees, infants' wear, etc.

ALGINATE FIBER: Fiber formed from a metallic salt (normally calcium) of alginic acid, which is a natural polymer occurring in seaweed. Alginate fiber is soluble in water.

ALKALINE: A term used to describe a material having a pH greater than 7.0 in water.

ALKALINE DYEING: See DYEING.

ALKALINE WEIGHT REDUCTION: A wet process for modifying the surface of polyester textiles by hydrolyzing, dissolving, and eroding the surface of the fibers with a precisely controlled alkaline solution, usually caustic soda. The treatment produces a softer handle.

ALKYLATION: The introduction of an alkyl radical into an organic molecule.

ALLOY: A solid or liquid mixture of two or more metals; or of one or more metals with certain nonmetallic elements formed by fusing the components.

ALPACA: 1. Long, fine hair from Alpaca sheep. **2.** A fabric from alpaca fibers or blends, (originally a cotton cloth with alpaca filling) that is used for dresses, coats, suits, and sweaters. It is also used as a pile lining for jackets and coats. (The term has been incorrectly used to describe a rayon fabric.)

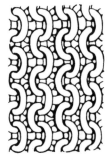

Alpaca Stitch

ALPACA STITCH: A 1 x 1 purl-links stitch that is knit so that the courses run vertically instead of horizontally as the fabric comes off the knitting machine. A garment made with an alpaca stitch is not always 100% alpaca; it can be made of other natural or manufactured fibers.

ALPHA CELLULOSE: One of three forms of cellulose. Alpha cellulose has the highest degree of polymerization and is the chief constituent of paper pulp and chemical dissolving-grade pulp. (Also see BETA CELLULOSE and GAMMA CELLULOSE.)

ALSIMAG®: Registered trademark of American Lava Corporation for ceramic materials. These materials are used in guides and discs on textile processing machines and fiber manufacturing equipment.

ALTERNATING TWIST: A texturing procedure in which S and Z twist are alternately inserted in the yarn by means of a special heating arrangement.

ALUMINA FIBER: See REFRACTORY FIBER.

AMBIENT CONDITIONS: See ATMOSPHERIC CONDITIONS.

AMERICAN SPINNING SYSTEM: A worsted spinning system developed in the U.S. that uses dry combed wool, as opposed to oiled wool, as processed on the bradford system. The American system is a shorter process based on modifications of the cotton spinning system. Considered in the U.S. to be more efficient than the bradford and French systems, it is the most widely used worsted system in American mills. (Also see WORSTED SPINNING SYSTEM.)

AMINE END GROUP: The terminating ($-NH_2$) group of a nylon polymer chain. Amine end groups provide dye sites for polyamides.

AMORPHOUS: Noncrystalline, lacking regular geometrical shape. Used to describe certain regions in polymers.

AM/PAF: Acronym for antimicrobial/producer-applied fluorocarbon.

ANGLE OF LAY: In cordage, the angle formed by strands wrapping the core and the axis of the cordage.

ANGLE OF WIND: On a yarn package, the angle formed by a wrap of yarn and a straight line perpendicular to the axis of the package.

ANGORA: 1. The hair of the Angora goat. The long, fine fibers are so smooth and soft that they must be combined with other fibers in weaving. **2.** The hair of the Angora rabbit. The fine, lightweight hair is warm, and it is often blended with wool to decrease price and to obtain novelty effects in weaving. By law, the fiber must be described as Angora rabbit hair.

ANHYDRIDE: A compound formed by abstraction of water, usually from an acid. Example: acetic anhydride, which is used in converting cellulose to cellulose acetate.

ANIDEX FIBER: A manufactured fiber in which the fiber-forming substance is any long chain synthetic polymer composed of at least 50% by weight of one or more esters of a monohydric alcohol and acrylic acid, (CH_2=CH– COOH) (FTC definition). Anidex fiber is not currently being produced.

ANILINE: A derivative of benzene used in making dyes, among other products.

ANILINE DYES: See DYES.

ANIMAL FIBER: Fiber of animal origin such as wool, alpaca, camel hair, and silk.

ANION: A negatively charged ion.

ANISOTROPIC: Not having the same physical properties in every direction. In the plane of a fabric, it is related to a non-random distribution of fibers.

ANSI: Acronym for the American National Standards Institute.

ANTHRAQUINONE DYES: See DYES.

ANTIBACTERIAL FINISH: A treatment of a textile material to make it resistant to, or to retard growth of, bacteria.

ANTICHLOR: A chemical, such as sodium thiosulfate, used to remove excess chlorine after bleaching.

ANTIFELTING AGENTS: Products that prevent or minimize matting and compaction of textile materials.

ANTIFOAMING AGENT: An additive that minimizes the formation of bubbles within or on the surface of a liquid by reducing the forces that support the bubble's structure.

ANTIMICROBIAL AGENT: A term used to describe chemical agents that kill or retard the growth of bacteria and fungi.

ANTIMICROBIAL/PRODUCER-APPLIED FLUOROCARBON: The application of both an antimicrobial agent and a fluorocarbon to a carpet yarn by the fiber supplier.

ANTIOXIDANT: A substance to retard deterioration (of fiber, fabrics, finishes, etc.) resulting from reaction with oxygen.

ANTIQUE SATIN: A woven fabric resembling SHANTUNG with slubs in the filling direction on the right side.

ANTI-REDEPOSITION AGENT: A substance added to surfactants to keep materials removed from textiles during washing suspended in the wash water.

ANTISOILING PROPERTIES: The ability of textile materials to resist the deposition of dirt and stains.

ANTISTAINING PROPERTIES: The ability of textile materials to resist the deposition of oil- or water-borne stains.

ANTISTATIC AGENT: A reagent capable of preventing, reducing, or dissipating static electrical charges that may be produced on textile materials.

ANTISTATIC PROPERTIES: The ability of textile materials to disperse an electrostatic charge and to prevent the buildup of static electricity.

APPLIQUÉ: A design made separately and then sewn on a cloth or garment.

APRON: A small conveyor belt to support and control the movement of fibers during drafting. (Also see DRAWING, 1.)

APRON MARK: See DECATING MARK.

ARACHNE MACHINE: A machine for producing loop-bonded nonwovens. The fabric is formed by knitting a series of warp yarns through a fiber web processed on a card. (Also see BONDING, 2. STITCH BONDING.)

ARAMID FIBER: A manufactured fiber in which the fiber-forming material is a long chain synthetic polyamide having at least 85% of its amide linkages (–NH–CO–) attached directly to two aromatic rings (FTC definition).

Aramid fibers have high strength and high modulus and retain their properties at elevated operating temperatures. They are available in two types, meta-aramid and para-aramid, depending on their molecular structure. Meta-aramid fiber is dry spun, and para-aramid fiber is dry-wet or wet spun. (Also see META-ARAMID FIBER and PARA-ARAMID FIBER.)

ARCHITECTURAL FABRIC: Fabric used for building construction such as fabric roofing systems. (Also see AIR-SUPPORTED STRUCTURE.)

ARGYLE: A pattern consisting of diamond shapes of different colors knit in a fabric.

ARTIFICIAL TURF: A manufactured carpet having the appearance of grass. Used to replace grass in sports arenas, yards, etc. (Also see RECREATIONAL SURFACES.)

ART LINEN: A plain-weave, softly finished fabric used either bleached or unbleached as a base fabric for needlework.

ASBESTOS: A naturally-occurring nonmetallic mineral fiber that is nonflammable. Asbestos was formerly widely used for flameproofing many textile products such as insulation, theater curtains, and protective clothing. Since it was found to cause respiratory problems and cancer, asbestos is now used only under strictly controlled conditions.

ASPECT RATIO: 1. The ratio of length to diameter of a fiber or yarn bundle. **2.** In tire production, the ratio of the height of the tire to its width. **3.** In a rectangular structure, the ratio of the longer dimension to the shorter.

ASPHALT OVERLAY FABRICS: See GEOTEXTILES.

ASQC: Acronym for the American Society for Quality Control.

ASTM: Acronym for the American Society for Testing and Materials.

ASTRAKHAN CLOTH: A thick knit or woven fabric with loops or curls on the face. The base yarns are usually cotton or wool and the loops are made with fibers such as mohair, wool, and certain manufactured fibers. The face simulates the pelt of the astrakhan lamb.

ATACTIC POLYMER: A type of polymer molecule in which substituent groups or atoms are arranged randomly above and below the backbone chain of atoms, when the latter are all in the same plane (e.g., in polypropylene). (Contrast with ISOTACTIC POLYMER, SYNDIOTACTIC POLYMER, and TACTIC POLYMER.)

Atactic Structure

ATI: Acronym for America's Textiles International.

ATMA: Acronym for the American Textile Machinery Association.

ATMI: Acronym for the American Textile Manufacturers Institute.

ATMOSPHERE, STANDARD: See STANDARD ATMOSPHERE FOR TESTING.

ATMOSPHERIC CONDITIONS: In general, the relative humidity, barometric pressure, and temperature existing at a given time.

ATMOSPHERIC FADING: See GAS FADING.

ATTENUATION: 1. Drawing sliver or roving to make it progressively finer during the drafting process. **2.** The order in which warp yarns are drawn through the heddle eyes in preparation for weaving. (Also see DRAWING-IN.)

ATTRITION MILLS: Machines for reducing materials into smaller particles by grinding down by friction. In the manufacture of acetate and triacetate fibers, equipment used in shredding pulp prior to acetylation.

AUTOCLAVE: 1. An apparatus for carrying out certain finishing operations, such as pleating and heat-setting, under pressure in a superheated steam atmosphere. **2.** Apparatus for polymerizing condensation polymers such as nylon or polyester at any pressure above or below atmospheric.

AUTODOFFER: A stationary or movable device designed to remove full bobbins and replace them with empty bobbins. Automatic doffers are used chiefly on yarn spinning and winding machines. (Also see DOFFING.)

AUTOLEVELLER: A device used in spun yarn manufacture to detect variations in the linear density and feed back signals to adjust the draft to compensate for any deviation from a set value.

AUTOMATED DISPENSING: In wet processing of textiles, a system for automatically weighing and dispensing dyes and chemicals used in preparation, dyeing, and finishing operations.

AUTOMATION: 1. The use of automatic machines or devices to reduce human effort in manufacturing processes. **2.** Integrating a series of batch processes into a continuous process to improve efficiency and reduce labor costs. (Also see ROBOTICS and CONTINUOUS PROCESS.)

AUXILIARY: In wet processing operations, a chemical that improves the efficiency of the operation or helps to achieve a special effect.

AVERAGE STIFFNESS: The ratio of change in stress to change in strain between two points on a stress-strain diagram, particularly the points of zero stress and breaking stress. (Also see MODULUS.)

AVERAGE TOUGHNESS: See TOUGHNESS.

AXIAL YARN: A system of longitudinal yarns in a triaxial braid that are inserted between bias yarns.

AXMINSTER CARPET: A machine-woven carpet in which successive weftwise rows of pile are inserted during weaving according to a predetermined arrangement of colors. There are four main types of Axminster looms: spool, gripper, gripper-spool, and chenille.

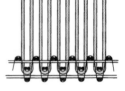

Axminster Carpet Construction

AYSA: Acronym for the American Yarn Spinners Association.

AZLON FIBER: A manufactured fiber in which the fiber-forming substance consists of any regenerated naturally occurring proteins (FTC definition). Azlon is not currently produced in the U.S.

AZO DYES: See DYES.

AZOIC DYES: See DYES, NAPHTHOL DYES.

B

BACK BEAM: 1. The beam from which the warp is fed during sizing. **2.** The beam at the back of the loom from which the warp yarn is fed during weaving.

BACKCOATING: The application of latex or adhesive to the back of a carpet to anchor the tufts, usually followed immediately by addition of a secondary backing material such as woven jute or nonwoven polypropylene.

BACKED FABRIC: A material with an extra warp or filling added for weight and warmth. Satin-weave and twill-weave constructions are frequently used in the design of backed cloth because they are relatively resistant to the passage of air.

BACKFILLING: A solution composed of varying amounts of cornstarch, China clay, talc, and tallow that is applied to the back side of low-grade, low-cost cloth to change its hand, improve its appearance, and increase its weight.

BACK GRAY: 1. In roller printing, a greige fabric placed between the blanket and the fabric to be printed to absorb excess dye paste that penetrates the fabric face. **2.** In screen printing, a fabric used to stabilize lightweight or open-weave fabric to be printed. The face fabric and back gray are gummed together to prevent slippage.

BACKING: 1. A general term for any system of yarn that interlaces on the back of a textile material. **2.** A knit or woven fabric or plastic foam bonded to a face fabric. **3.** A knit or woven fabric bonded to a vinyl or other plastic sheet material. **4.** See CARPET BACKING.

BACK-SIZING: See FILLER.

BACKSTITCH: See PURL.

BACK WARP: The warp which, along with the back filling, actually forms the second face (back) of double, triple, or quadruple fabrics.

BACKWASHING: In worsted processing, scouring of wool sliver or top before or after pin drafting and/or combing.

BACKWINDING: 1. Rewinding yarn or fiber from one type of package to another. **2.** Winding yarn as it is deknit.

BACTERIAL RESISTANCE: The resistance of a textile material to the growth of bacteria on fiber surfaces.

BACTERICIDAL FIBER: Fiber used for medical applications, socks, shoe liners, etc., in which bactericides are introduced directly into the fiber matrix as opposed to fiber simply having a bactericidal finish applied.

BAGGING: 1. A fabric woven in cylindrical or tubular form on an ordinary cam loom and used for grain bags, etc. **2.** Fabric bulging caused by extension at the knees, elbows, etc., of a garment lacking dimensional stability.

BAGGY CLOTH: A fabric that does not lie flat, caused by sections of tight or loose yarns in either the warp or the filling.

BAGGY SELVAGE: See SLACK SELVAGE.

BAIZE: Wool felt used for lining display cases and covering billiard tables, for example.

BAKING: See CURING, 1.

BALANCED TWIST: In a plied yarn or cord, an arrangement of twist which will not cause the yarn or cord to twist on itself or kink when held in an open loop.

BALANCED WEAVE: A term used to describe a woven construction in which the same size yarn and the same number of threads per inch is used in both warp and filling directions.

BALANCED YARN: A yarn with BALANCED TWIST.

BALE: A bag, sack, square or oblong box, or package into which silk, staple fibers, or tow are compressed. The common shipping and storage package for these fibers.

BALLING UP: A defect in which loose or frayed fibers form into a ball and are then woven into the fabric.

BALL MILL: A standard method of reducing water-insoluble substances such as pigments or dyestuffs to a fine state of division. It consists of a cylinder, rotating on an axis, partly filled with steel balls, porcelain balls, or common pebbles. The controlling factors are size of balls, relative volumes occupied by balls and substance, type and quality of substance, and rate and time of rotation.

BALLOON: The curved paths of running yarns about the take-up package during spinning, downtwisting, plying, or winding, or while they are being withdrawn over-end from packages under appropriate yarn-winding conditions.

BALLOON EYE: The guide that controls the apex of the yarn during spinning, downtwisting, plying or winding operations.

BALLOON FABRIC: In lighter-than-air craft, the fabric used for containment of air or gases in cells that perform the lifting function. In hot-air balloons, a fabric that serves as the outer covering of the balloon. Most balloon

Balloon

fabrics today are coated fabrics with closely constructed woven polyester or nylon substrates, laminated with a film backing and sometimes with a rip-stop material in a sandwich construction.

BALLOONING: Entrapment of air by a circular knit fabric to reduce crease formation during wet processing.

BALL WARP: Parallel threads in the form of a twistless rope wound into a large ball. When wound mechanically with quick traverse a ball warp may be made in the form of a large cylindrical package.

BANDING, HEAVY TOW: Nonuniform distribution of filaments across tow-band width.

BANDLE: A coarse homespun linen made on narrow hand looms in Ireland.

BANK: Another name for a yarn creel.

BAR: See BARRÉ.

BARATHEA: 1. A silk, rayon, or manufactured fiber necktie fabric with a broken rib weave and a characteristic pebbly appearance. **2.** A fine, dress fabric with a silk warp and worsted filling, woven in a broken filling rib which completely covers the warp. **3.** A smooth-faced worsted uniform cloth with an indistinct twilled basket weave of fine two-ply yarns.

BAR CODE: Adjacent stripes of varying width used to represent alphanumeric characters. These permit rapid reading by means of electronic scanners.

Bar Code

BAR FILLING: In preparation for weft knitting, the operation of placing one or more rib knit borders or other knit pieces, individually or in succession, on a transfer bar to facilitate transfer onto the needles of a FLAT-KNITTING MACHINE.

BARKING: The removal of bark from wood prior to pulping.

BARRÉ: A defect characterized by bars or streaks, fillingwise in woven fabrics or coursewise in weft-knit fabrics, caused by uneven tension in knitting, defective yarn, improper needle action, or other similar factors.

BASE FABRIC: In coated fabrics, the underlying SUBSTRATE.

BASIC: A term describing substances having an alkaline nature. Bases may or may not be water soluble.

BASIC DYES: See DYES.

BASIS WEIGHT: The weight of a unit area of fabric. Examples are ounces per square yard and grams per square centimeter.

BASKET STITCH: In this knit construction, purl and plain loops are combined with a preponderance of purl loops in the pattern courses to give a basket-weave effect.

Basket Stitch

BASKET WEAVE: A variation of the plain weave in which two or more warp and filling threads are woven side by side to resemble a plaited basket. Fabrics have a loose construction and a flat appearance and are used for such things as monk's cloth and drapery fabrics.

BAST FIBER: Any of certain strong, woody fibers used in making rope, cordage, etc.

BATCH DYEING: See DYEING.

BATCH PROCESS: A general term for any process in which each production lot is handled separately, as contrasted with a CONTINUOUS PROCESS.

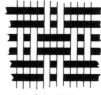

Basket Weave

BATHROBE BLANKETING: A double-faced fabric woven with a tightly twisted spun warp and two sets of soft spun filling yarns. The fabric is thick and warm and its filling yarns are frequently napped to produce a soft surface. Today's blankets are made of spun polyester, acrylic, or polyester/cotton blends.

BATIK: See DYEING.

BATISTE: 1. A sheer, woven, mercerized fabric of combed cotton or polyester/cotton resembling nainsook, only finer, with a lengthwise streak. **2.** A rayon fabric decorated with dobby woven stripes and jacquard florals. **3.** A smooth, fine, woolen fabric, lighter than challis and very similar to nun's veiling.

BATTING: A soft, bulky assembly of fibers, usually carded. Battings are sold in sheets or rolls and used for warm interlinings, comforter stuffings, and other thermal or resiliency applications.

BAYARDERE: A very broad term for stripes that run crosswise in a knit or woven fabric.

BCF YARN: Bulked continuous filament yarn for the carpet trade, usually made of nylon, polypropylene, or polyester.

BEADED SELVAGE: See LOOPY SELVAGE.

BEADED VELVET: Velvet with a cut-out pattern or a velvet pile effect, made on a jacquard loom. This fabric is used primarily for evening wear.

BEAM: A horizontal cylinder usually of metal on which a large number of yarns are wound in a side-by-side arrangement in preparation for slashing, weaving, warp knitting, or tufting operations.

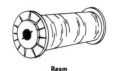
Beam

BEAM CREEL: A large frame for holding weaving section beams from which warp sheets are fed into the slasher for sizing.

BEAM DYEING MACHINE: A machine for dyeing warp yarns or fabrics that have been wound onto a special beam, the barrel of which is evenly perforated with holes. The dye liquor is forced through the yarn or fabric from inside to outside and vice versa.

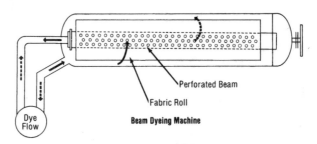
Perforated Beam
Fabric Roll
Dye Flow
Beam Dyeing Machine

BEAMING: The operation of winding yarns onto a beam usually in preparation for slashing, weaving, warp knitting, or tufting. Also called warping. (See diagram on the following page.)

BEAMROLL: See BEAM.

BEARDED SPRING NEEDLE: See SPRING NEEDLE.

BEARDING: Fuzz on loop pile carpets usually resulting from poor anchorage or fiber snagging.

BEATER: 1. The machine which does most of the opening and cleaning work on a fiber picker and opener. Revolving at high speed, it beats against the fringe of fiber as the latter is fed into the machine. **2.** A machine used in the paper industry for opening pulp and combining additives.

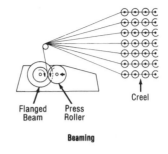

Beaming

BEATING-UP: The last operation of the loom in weaving, in which the last pick inserted in the fabric is "beat" into position against the preceding picks.

BEAT-UP: The number of tufts per inch of length in a warp row of pile, used to describe Axminster, chenille, and other carpets not woven over wires.

BEAVER CLOTH: Made of high-quality wool, this heavy but soft fabric has a deep nap. Beaver cloth is frequently used in overcoats.

BECK: A vessel for dyeing fabric in rope form, consisting primarily of a tank and a reel to advance the fabric.

BEDFORD CORD: A rib-weave fabric with raised lengthwise cords produced by using stuffing threads in the warp. Since the fabric is strong and wears well, it is used for upholstery, suits, riding habits, and work clothes.

BEETLING: A process in which round-thread linen or cotton fabric is pounded to give a flat effect. Beetled linen damask has an increased luster and a leather-like texture. Beetling is also used to give a thready or linen-like appearance to cotton.

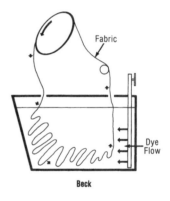

Beck

BENDING LENGTH: A measure of fabric stiffness based on how the fabric bends in one plane under the force of gravity.

BENDING MODULUS: Maximum stress per unit area that a specimen can withstand without breaking when bent. For fibers, the stress per unit of linear fiber weight required to produce a specified deflection of a fiber.

BENDING RIGIDITY: See FLEXURAL RIGIDITY.

BENGALINE: A fabric similar to faille, only heavier, with a fine weave and widthwise cords. Originally, bengalines were made of a silk, wool, or rayon warp with a worsted or cotton filling and used for dresses, coats, trimmings, and draperies. Modern bengalines are made with filament acetate or polyester warps. Also, some bengalines have fine spun warps with 2- and 3-ply heavier spun yarns for filling cord effects.

BENT NEEDLE(S): 1. In a tufting machine, needles that are permanently pushed out of place, causing a lengthwise streak due to off-standard tuft spacing across the width. **2.** In a jacquard loom, a needle that is out of alignment with the punched hole in pattern cards.

BENZENE: A volatile, flammable, colorless liquid hydrocarbon (C_6H_6) used as an illuminant, a solvent for fats and resins, a raw material in dye synthesis, and the hydrocarbon source for many manufactured fibers.

BENZOATE FIBER: Fiber with a silk-like hand made from a condensation polymer of p-(ß-hydroxyethoxy)benzoic acid.

BERBER: Originally, wool carpets in tribal motifs woven by North African tribesmen. Today, the term is used to describe manufactured carpet with a pebbly, homespun appearance. It is made from natural-colored (but sometimes dyed) wools.

BETA CELLULOSE: One of the three forms of cellulose. It has a lower degree of polymerization than the alpha form. With gamma cellulose it is known as hemicellulose. (Also see ALPHA CELLULOSE and GAMMA CELLULOSE.)

BIAS FABRIC: A two-dimensional textile fabric that when oriented in the XY plane contains fibers that are aligned in a different direction, i.e., 45° to the X-axis fibers.

BIAS FILLING: A fabric defect in which the filling yarn does not run at a right angle to the warp. The principal cause is improper processing on the tenter frame. (Also see BOW.)

BICOMPONENT FIBER: A manufactured fiber made from two different polymer components, which may be composed of different polymer types or variants of the same polymer. The two polymers may be combined in several ways:

Matrix Fiber: Several or many filaments of one polymer are extruded in a matrix of the other polymer. One method of producing MICROFIBER is by dissolving the matrix polymer, leaving ultrafine filaments of the second polymer. (Also see ISLANDS-IN-THE-SEA.)

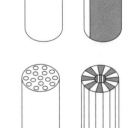

Matrix-Fibril Fiber: Short, fine FIBRILS of one polymer are randomly distributed through a matrix of the second polymer.

Sheath-Core Bicomponent Fiber: One polymer forms a core and the other surrounds it as a sheath.

Side-by-Side Bicomponent Fiber: The two fibers are extruded in a bilateral relationship. Also called bilateral fiber. (Also see CONJUGATE FIBER.)

Bicomponent Fibers

BICOMPONENT FIBER YARN: A yarn composed of bicomponent fibers.

BICOMPONENT YARN: A yarn with two different staple or filament components: **1.** A plied yarn constructed of two different singles yarns. **2.** A core-spun or other wrapped yarn. **3.** A filament yarn combining two types of filaments. (Also see BICOMPONENT FIBER YARN.)

BICONSTITUENT FIBER: 1. A fiber extruded from a homogenous mixture of two different polymers. Such fibers combine the characteristics of the two polymers into a single fiber. **2.** A bicomponent fiber with a low-melting sheath. **3.** See BICOMPONENT FIBER, MATRIX-FIBRIL FIBER.

BIDIRECTIONAL FABRIC: A fabric having reinforcing fibers in two directions, i.e., in the warp (machine) direction and filling (cross-machine) direction.

BILATERAL FIBERS: See BICOMPONENT FIBER, SIDE-BY-SIDE BICOMPONENT FIBER.

BINDER: An adhesive applied with a solvent, or a softenable plastic melted to bond fibers together in a web or to bind one web to another.

BINDER CONTENT: The weight of adhesive used to bond the fibers of a web together. Usually expressed as percent of fabric weight.

BINDER FIBERS: Fibers that can act as an adhesive in a web because their softening point is relatively low compared with that of the other fibers in the material. (Also see BONDING, 2. BONDING WITH BINDER FIBERS.)

BINDING: A narrow folded fabric sewn around a seam or edge to support or protect it or change its appearance.

BINDING GLACÉ: A polished, woven binding, usually of a 3 x 1 twill weave, that is used primarily in men's tailored apparel.

BIOABSORBABLE FIBER: A fiber used for sutures that will decompose and be absorbed by body tissues.

BIOCHEMICAL OXYGEN DEMAND (BOD): A standard test for estimating the degree of contamination of water supplies. It is expressed as the quantity of dissolved oxygen (in mg/liter) required during stabilization of the decomposable organic matter by aerobic biochemical action.

BIOCIDE: A chemical substance applied to textiles or other materials to inhibit growth of bacteria or fungi.

BIOCOMPATIBLE: A term used to describe a material that does not cause allergic or other adverse physiological response on contact.

BIODEGRADABLE: The ability of a substance to be broken down by bacteria so that it can be returned to the environment without posing an environmental hazard.

BIOPOLISHING: An enzyme finishing treatment for cellulose fabrics that uses cellulase to hydrolyze the surface of the fibers. The treatment smooths the fiber surface and reduces fuzziness and pilling potential. (Also see ENZYME FINISHING.)

BIRDSEYE: 1. A generic term describing a cloth woven on a dobby loom, with a geometric pattern having a center dot resembling a bird's eye. Originally birdseye was made of cotton and used as a diaper cloth because of its absorbent qualities, but now the weave is made from a variety of fibers or fiber blends for many different end uses. **2.** A speckled effect on the back of a knit fabric resulting from the use of different colors on the face design.

BIREFRINGENCE: An optical property of many types of fibers that indicates the degree of orientation of the fiber's molecular structure. It is the difference in the refractive index measured in the axial direction and that measured perpendicular to the fiber axis.

BISFA: Acronym for Bureau International pour la Standardisation de Fibres Synthetiques.

BLACK WOOL: Any fleece from sheep that is not completely white but contains gray, brown or black wool.

BLADE-IN-AIR COATING: See COATING.

BLANKET: 1. An unquilted bedcovering with good thermal insulation properties. **2.** The heavy felt band that supports print fabrics in roller printing. **3.** The wide continuous belt of various materials used to convey pulp through a papermaking machine. (Also see PAPERMAKER'S FELT.)

BLANKET MARK: See CORRUGATION MARK.

BLEACHING: Any of several processes to remove the natural and artificial impurities in fabrics to obtain clear whites for finished fabric or in preparation for dyeing and finishing.

BLEB: A blister or bubble on the face of a spinning jet, interrupting the extrusion of the filament from the spinneret hole involved.

BLEB RATE: The frequency of bleb formation in an extrusion operation.

BLEEDING: Loss of color by a fabric or yarn when immersed in water, a solvent, or a similar liquid medium, as a result of improper dyeing or the use of dyes of poor quality. Fabrics that bleed can cause staining of white or light shade fabrics in contact with them while wet.

BLEND: 1. A yarn obtained when two or more staple fibers are combined in a textile process for producing spun yarns (e.g., at opening, carding, or drawing). **2.** A fabric that contains a blended yarn (of the same fiber content) in the warp and filling. (Also see COMBINATION FABRIC and COMBINATION YARN.)

BLENDING: The combining of staple fibers of different physical characteristics to assure a uniform distribution of these fibers throughout the yarn.

BLINDING: Loss of luster of fibers after wet processing.

BLISTER: A bulge resulting from separation of coating or laminating material from the base fabric.

BLOCK COPOLYMER: A copolymer composed of different repeating monomer units linked in blocks along the main polymer chain. (Also see MONOMER and COPOLYMER.)

BLOCK CREELING: A method of creeling in which all of the yarn supply packages are replenished at one time. (Contrast with RANDOM CREELING.)

BLOCKING: 1. A defect in coated fabrics caused when adjacent layers of fabric on a roll stick together during storage. **2.** The process of molding the shape of felt items such as hats. **3.** The effect of a dye or chemical that inhibits dye uptake by a textile material. **4.** See FIRE-BLOCKING LAYER.

BLOCK PRINTING: See PRINTING, 1.

BLOOM: The appearance of brightness of a dyed fabric when the fabric is viewed across the top while held at eye level.

BLOOMING: See OPENING, 2.

BLOTCH: See FINISHING SPOT.

BLOTCH PRINTING: See PRINTING, 1.

BOARDING: A final finishing process for hosiery in which damp hosiery items are smoothed and shaped by drying on heated forms.

BOARDY: A term used to describe a fabric with a very stiff hand.

BOBBIN: A cylindrical or slightly tapered barrel, with or without flanges, for holding slubbings, rovings, or yarns.

BOBTEX® ICS YARN SYSTEM: A process for producing a simulated spun yarn by embedding individual fibers in a thermoplastic or adhesive coating on a filament yarn.

BOD: Acronym for biological oxygen demand.

BODY: The compact, solid, or firm feel of a fabric.

BOILING WATER SHRINKAGE: A test designed to measure shrinkage in a cord, yarn, or high-shrinkage fiber when it is immersed in boiling water while under a tension of 0.05 grams/denier.

BOIL OFF: 1. See SCOURING. **2.** For cotton, a process to improve absorbability by boiling the fiber or fabric in a bath containing detergent, soap, or an alkali such as caustic soda. **3.** For silk, see DEGUMMING.

BOLT: A roll or piece of fabric of varying length.

BONDED FABRIC: 1. A fabric containing two or more layers of cloth joined together with resin, rubber, foam, or adhesive to form one ply. **2.** See NON-WOVEN FABRIC.

BONDED RUBBER BACKING: A secondary carpet backing of latex or rubber foam. It may be applied in strips or seamless widths.

BONDING: 1. A process for adhesive laminating two or more fabrics or fabric and a layer of plastic foam. There are two methods: the flame method used for bonding foam and the adhesive method used for bonding face and backing fabrics. **2.** One of several processes of binding fibers into thin sheets, webs, or battings by means of adhesives, plastics, or cohesion (self-bonding). (See diagram on the next page.)

Bonding with Binder Fibers: Specially engineered low-melting-point fibers are blended with other fibers in a web, so that a uniformly bonded structure can be generated at low temperature by fusion of the binder fiber with adjacent fibers.

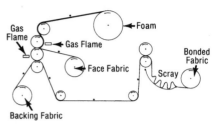

Flame-Foam Bonding Unit

Fusion Bonding: Fabrication of carpet for tiles or modules by a thermoplastic process in which yarns are implanted in a liquid vinyl compound in a sandwich configuration between two backing materials. After the yarn is set in the resin, a knife splits the sandwich to create two cut pile carpets.

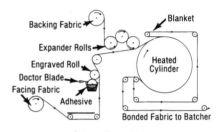

Adhesive Bonding Unit

Point Bonding: The process of binding thermoplastic fibers into a nonwoven fabric by applying heat and pressure so that a discrete pattern of fiber bonds is formed. Also called spot bonding.

Powder Bonding: A bonding method for nonwoven fabric. A carding web is treated with a thermoplastic powder having a melting point less than the web fiber. The web is then heated by hot air, infrared heat, or hot calendering to melt the powder and bond the fibers.

Print Bonding: A process of binding fibers into a nonwoven fabric by applying an adhesive in a discrete pattern.

Saturation Bonding: A process of binding fibers into a nonwoven fabric by soaking the web with an adhesive.

Solvent Bonding: A method of bonding a web by applying a solvent to soften the fiber surfaces and promote fusion with adjacent fibers.

Spray Bonding: A process of binding fibers into a nonwoven fabric involving the spray application of a fabric binder.

Spray Spinning: See SPUNBOND.

Stitch Bonding: A bonding technique for nonwovens in which the fibers are connected by stitches sewn or knitted through the web. Also known as QUILTING.

Thermal Bonding: A technique for bonding fibers of a web with meltable powders or fibers, using infrared heating, hot air, or hot-calendering. (Also see BONDING, BONDING WITH BINDER FIBERS and BONDING, POWDER BONDING.)

BOND STRENGTH: 1. The amount of force required to delaminate a piece of woven or knitted fabric from its backing. **2.** The amount of force required to break the fusion points found in certain nonwovens. **3.** The amount of force required to break the chemical bonds between atoms in molecules and crystalline salts. **4.** The force required to separate the component layers of a BONDED FABRIC or LAMINATED FABRIC. **5.** See PEEL ADHESION.

BOOK CLOTH: Print cloth treated with pyroxylin or starch and clay and used in bookbinding.

BOOK FOLD: A method of folding finished fabric in which the fabric is first folded in half widthwise, then folded back and forth in equal lengths. Finally, the fold edge on each side is folded to the inside, forming a compact bundle equal in length to one-half the width of the goods.

BORON FIBER: A vapor-deposited filament made by depositing boron on a heated tungsten wire. These fibers were developed for use in aircraft and space applications. They can be woven into fabrics.

BOSS: That part of a drafting roll of largest diameter where the fibers are gripped. It may be an integral part of the roll, as in steel rolls, or it may have a covering of leather, cork, etc. In the former case, the boss is fluted.

BOTTOMWEIGHT: A term used to describe fabrics, usually weighing 6 oz/yd^2 or over, that are suitable for garments such as pants and skirts.

BOUCLÉ: A fabric woven or knit with bouclé yarns. Bouclé fabric has a looped or knotted surface and is used for sportswear and coats.

BOUCLÉ YARN: A novelty yarn with loops which give fabrics a rough appearance. Some bouclé yarns have cotton cores with other fibers wound around them. Bouclé yarns may be made from wool, cotton, silk, linen, manufactured fibers, or combinations of fibers.

BOURRELET: A double-knit fabric with raised loops running horizontally across the surface of the cloth giving a rippled or corded effect.

BOW: The greatest distance, measured parallel to the selvages, between a filling yarn and a straight line drawn between the points at which this yarn meets the selvages. Bow may be expressed directly in inches or as a percentage of the width of the fabric at that point.

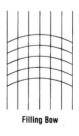

Filling Bow

BOX LOOM: A loom using two or more shuttles for weaving fabrics with filling yarns that differ in fiber type, color, twist level, or yarn size. The box motion is automatic, changing from one shuttle to another. Examples of fabrics made on box looms are crepes and ginghams.

BOX MARK: A fine line parallel to the filling caused by shuttle damage to a group of filling yarns.

BRADFORD SPINNING SYSTEM: A type of worsted spinning system that uses a Noble or circular comb to straighten the long wool fibers and remove short fibers before further processing. The fiber is oiled before it is combed. (Also see WORSTED SPINNING SYSTEM.)

BRAID: 1. A narrow textile band, often used as trimming or binding, formed by plaiting several strands of yarn. The fabric is formed by interlacing the yarns diagonally to the production axis of the material. **2.** In aerospace textiles, a system of three or more yarns which are interlaced in such a way that no two yarns are twisted around each other. **Biaxial Braid:** Braided structure with two yarn systems, one running in one direction and the other in the opposite direction. **Triaxial Braid:** A braided structure with axial yarns running in the longitudinal direction. **3.** A grade of long, coarse lustrous wool used in carpeting.

BRAID ANGLE: The acute angle measured from the axis of a fabric or rope to a braiding yarn.

BRAIDED FABRIC: A narrow fabric made by crossing a number of strands diagonally so that each strand passes alternatively over or under one or more of the other strands. They are frequently used in shoelaces and suspenders.

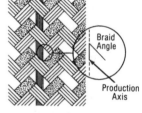

Braided Fabric Showing Braid Angle

BRAIDING: The intertwining of three or more strands to make a cord. The strands form a regular diagonal pattern down the length of the cord.

BREAKER FABRIC: See TIRE FABRIC.

BREAK FACTOR: A measure of yarn strength calculated as: (1) the product of breaking strength times indirect yarn number, or (2) the product of breaking strength times the reciprocal of the direct yarn number.

BREAKING ELONGATION: See ELONGATION AT BREAK.

BREAKING LENGTH: A measure of the breaking strength of a yarn; the calculated length of a specimen whose weight is equal to its breaking load. The breaking length expressed in kilometers is numerically equal to the breaking tenacity expressed in grams-force per tex.

BREAKING LOAD: The maximum load (or force) applied to a specimen in a tensile test carried to rupture. It is commonly expressed in grams-force (kilograms-force), pounds, or newtons. (Also see BREAKING STRENGTH.)

BREAKING RATIO: See BREAK FACTOR.

BREAKING STRENGTH: 1. The maximum resultant internal force that resists rupture in a tension test. The expression "breaking strength" is not used for compression tests, bursting tests, or tear resistance tests in textiles. **2.** The load (or force) required to break or rupture a specimen in a tensile test made according to a specified standard procedure. (Also see BREAKING LOAD.)

BREAKING TENACITY: The tensile stress at rupture of a specimen (fiber, filament, yarn, cord, or similar structure) expressed as newtons per tex, grams-force per tex, or grams-force per denier. The breaking tenacity is calculated from the breaking load and linear density of the unstrained specimen, or obtained directly from tensile testing machines which can be suitably adjusted to indicate tenacity instead of breaking load for specimens of known linear density. Breaking tenacity expressed in grams-force per tex is numerically equal to breaking length expressed in kilometers.

BREAK-OPEN: In flammability testing of protective apparel, the formation of a hole that allows the flame to pass through.

BREAK-OUT: See SMASH.

BREAK SPINNING: 1. A direct spinning process for converting manufactured fiber tows to spun yarn that incorporates prestretching and tow breaking with subsequent drafting and spinning in one operation. **2.** See OPEN-END SPINNING.

BRIGHT: In reference to fibers, the opposite of dull or matte. In manufactured fibers, the term is often used for fibers containing only a very small amount of delustrant, in contrast to clear, which denotes the absence of delustrant.

BRIGHTENER: See OPTICAL BRIGHTENER.

BRISTLE: 1. A short, stiff, coarse fiber. **2.** The hair of the hog.

BRITTLE POINT: The temperature at which a polymer no longer exhibits viscoelastic properties.

BROADCLOTH: 1. Originally, a silk shirting fabric so named because it was woven in widths exceeding the usual 29 inches. **2.** A tightly woven, lustrous cotton or polyester/cotton blend fabric in a plain weave with a crosswise rib. It resembles poplin, but the rib is finer, and broadcloth always has more picks than poplin. The finest qualities are made with combed pima or Egyptian cotton. **3.** A smooth, rich-looking, woolen fabric with a napped face and a twill back. Better grades have a glossy, velvety hand.

BROAD GOODS: Woven fabrics 18 inches or more in width.

BROADLOOM: A term that refers to carpets woven in widths from 54 inches to 18 feet, as distinguished from narrow loom widths of 27–36 inches.

BROCADE: 1. A rich, jacquard-woven fabric with an all-over interwoven design of raised figures or flowers. The pattern is emphasized by contrasting surfaces or colors and often has gold or silver threads running through it. The background may be either a satin or a twill weave. **2.** A term describing a cut-pile carpet having a surface texture created by mixing twisted and straight-standing pile yarns.

BROCATELLE: A fabric similar to brocade with a satin or twill figure in high relief on a plain or satin background.

BROKEN END: A broken, untied warp thread in a fabric. There are numerous causes, such as slubs, knots, improper shuttle alignment, shuttle hitting the warp shed, excessive warp tension, faulty sizing, as well as rough reeds, heddles, dropwires, and shuttles. (Also see END OUT.)

BROKEN PICK: A broken filling thread in a fabric. Usual causes include too much shuttle tension, weak yarn, or filling coming into contact with a sharp surface.

BROKEN SELVAGE: See CUT SELVAGE.

BROKEN TWILL: One of a range of twill constructions in which the twill line changes direction. (Also see HERRINGBONE.)

BRUISE: See ABRASION MARK.

BRUSHING: A finishing process in which rotating brushes raise a nap on knit or woven fabrics. Brushing is used on sweaters, scarves, knit underwear, wool broadcloths, etc.

BRUSH PILLING TESTER: An apparatus to simulate fabric pilling propensity in actual use. The instrument first brushes the specimen to free fiber ends on the fabric surface, then rubs two specimens together in a circular motion to form pills.

BUBBLE-JET PRINTING: A fabric printing system, similar to ink-jet printing of paper, in which minute droplets of a low-viscosity print paste are sprayed onto the substrate.

BUCKET SPINNING: See POT SPINNING.

BUCKRAM: A scrim fabric with a stiff finish, often used as interlining.

BUILDUP: 1. A term applied to substantivity of dye for a textile material. It refers to the ability of a dye to produce deep shades. **2.** An unintentional accumulation of material on a textile or other surface (such as a processing roll).

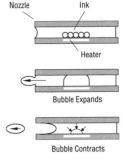

Sequence of Bubble-Jet Printing

BULK DEVELOPMENT: Any of various relaxation treatments to produce maximum bulk in textured or latent crimp yarns or in fabrics made from them. The essential conditions are heat, lubrication, movement, and the absence of tension. Bulk development may be accomplished during wet processing or may be a separate operation such as hot-air tumbling, steam-injection tumbling, or dry cleaning.

BULKED CONTINUOUS FILAMENT YARN: See BCF YARN.

BULKED YARN: See TEXTURED YARNS, 1.

BULK UNIFORMITY: A term used to describe the relative consistency in the density of individual textured yarns processed under similar conditions.

BUNTING: A soft, flimsy, loose-textured, plain-weave cloth most frequently used in flags. Bunting was originally made from cotton or worsted yarns, but today's flags are made primarily from nylon or acrylic fibers.

BURL: A small knot or slub in a yarn or fabric. (Also see NEP.)

BURLAP: A coarse, heavy, plain-weave fabric constructed from singles yarn of jute. Used for bags, upholstery lining, curtains, and draperies.

BURLING: 1. The process of removing loose threads and knots from fabrics with a type of tweezers called a burling iron. **2.** The process of correcting loose tufts and replacing missing tufts following carpet construction.

BURNING RATE: The speed at which a fabric burns. It can be expressed as the amount of fabric affected per unit time, in terms of distance or area travelled by the flame, afterglow, or char.

BURN-OUT PRINTING: See PRINTING, 1.

BURR: A device that assists in loop formation on circular-knitting machines equipped with spring needles.

BURSTING STRENGTH: 1. The ability of a material to resist rupture by pressure. **2.** The force required to rupture a fabric by distending it with a force applied at right angles to the plane of the fabric under specified conditions. Bursting strength is a measure widely used for knit fabrics, nonwoven fabrics, and felts where the constructions do not lend themselves to tensile tests. The two basic types of bursting tests are the inflated diaphragm method and the ball-burst method.

BUTCHER'S LINEN: A plain-weave, stiff fabric with thick-and-thin yarns in both the warp and the filling. The fabric was originally made of linen but is now duplicated in 100% polyester or a variety of blends such as polyester/rayon or polyester/cotton.

C

CABINET: A basic part of the manufactured-fiber spinning machine where, in dry spinning, the filaments become solidified by solvent evaporation and, in melt spinning, the filaments are solidified by cooling.

CABLED YARN: A yarn formed by twisting together two or more plied yarns.

CABLE-LAID ROPE: See HAWSER.

CABLE STITCH: A knit effect produced by crossing a group of stitches over a neighboring stitch group.

CABLE TWIST: A construction of thread, yarn, cord, or rope in which each successive twist is in the direction opposite to the preceding twists; i.e., an S/Z/S or Z/S/Z construction.

CAD: Acronym for COMPUTER-AIDED DESIGN.

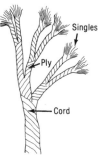

Cable Twist

CAKE: In the viscose rayon process, the cylindrical package that is formed when the spun filament yarn is thrown by centrifugal force into a "pot" where it is collected before it is washed, dried, and rewound onto packages for shipment.

CAKE DYEING: See DYEING.

CALENDER: A machine used in finishing to impart a variety of surface effects to fabrics. A calender essentially consists of two or more heavy rollers, sometimes heated, through which the fabric passes under heavy pressure.

CALENDER BONDING: A method of thermally bonding nonwoven structures using heated calender rolls to fuse low-temperature melting fibers in the web. Sometimes a patterned roll is used to bond the web only at specific points.

CALENDER COATING: See COATING.

CALENDERING: A mechanical finishing process for fabrics to produce special effects, such as high luster, glazing, moiré, and embossed effects. In this operation, the fabric is passed between heated rolls under pressure.

Normal Fabric

Calendered Fabric

Effect of Calendering

CALENDER ROLLS: 1. The main cylinders on a calender. **2.** Smooth or fluted rolls used on various fiber-processing machines such as pickers and cards to compress the lap or sliver as it passes between them.

CALICO: A plain, closely woven, inexpensive cloth, usually cotton or a cotton/manufactured fiber blend, characteristically having figured patterns on a white or contrasting background. Calico is typically used for aprons, dresses, and quilts.

CALORIMETRY: The process of measuring quantities of absorbed or evolved heat, often used to determine specific heat.

CAM: 1. A rotating or sliding piece or projection used to impart timed or periodic motion to other parts of a machine. It is used chiefly as a controlling or timing element in machines rather than as part of a power transmission mechanism. Cams are particularly important in both knitting and weaving machinery. **2.** Acronym for COMPUTER-AIDED MANUFACTURING.

CAMBRIC: A soft, white, closely woven, cotton or cotton blend fabric that has been calendered on the right side to give it a slight gloss. Cambric is used extensively for handkerchiefs.

CAN: 1. A cylindrical container, about 3 feet high and 10–12 inches in diameter, that is used to collect sliver delivered by a card, drawing frame, etc. **2.** See DRYING CYLINDERS.

CANDLE FILTER: A small filter interposed between the spinning pump and spinning jet to effect final filtration of the spinning solution prior to extrusion.

CANDLE WATER TEMPERATURE: The temperature of the water surrounding the candle filter or within the heating jacket during fiber extrusion.

CANDLEWICK FABRIC: An unbleached muslin base fabric used to produce a chenille-like fabric by applying candlewick (heavy-plied yarn) loops and cutting the loops to give a fuzzy effect.

CANTON FLANNEL: A heavy cotton or cotton blend material with a twilled face and a napped back. The fabric's strength, warmth, and absorbance make it ideal for interlinings and sleeping garments.

CANVAS: See DUCK.

CAPACITANCE: The measure of the ability of a nonconductor to store electrical energy by means of the potential difference across the surfaces of the nonconductor.

CAPROLACTAM: A white, crystalline, cyclic amide ($C_6H_{11}NO$) which yields ε-amino-caproic acid on hydrolysis and is used as a raw material in the manufacture of nylon 6.

CAP SPINNING: A system of spinning employing a stationary, highly polished metal cap just large enough to fit over the take-up bobbin, which revolves at a high rate of speed. The cap controls the build and imparts sufficient tension to the yarn for winding. The yarn is twisted and wound onto packages simultaneously.

CAPSTAN: A post or guide around which moving yarn is wrapped to control tension.

CARBON-ARC LAMP: A type of fading lamp which utilizes an arc between two carbon electrodes as the source of radiation.

CARBON FIBER: High-tensile fiber or WHISKERS made by heating rayon or polyacrylonitrile fibers or petroleum residues to appropriate temperatures. Fibers may be 7–8 microns in diameter and are more than 90% carbonized.

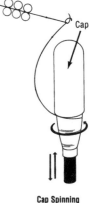

Cap Spinning

CARBONIZING: A chemical process for eliminating cellulosic material from wool or other animal fibers. The material is reacted with sulfuric acid or hydrogen chloride gas followed by heating. When the material is dry, the carbonized cellulose material is dust-like and can be removed.

CARBOXYL END GROUP: The chain-terminating (–COOH) group found in polyamide and polyester polymers.

CARBOXYMETHYL CELLULOSE: An acid ether derivative of cellulose formed by the reaction of alkali cellulose with chloroacetic acid. The sodium salt of this compound is commonly used as a stabilizer or an emulsifier.

CARD: A machine used in the manufacture of staple yarns. Its functions are to separate, align, and deliver the fibers in a sliver form and to remove impurities. The machine consists of a series of rolls, the surfaces of which are covered with many projecting wires or metal teeth. Short staple systems employ flat strips covered with card clothing rather than small rolls. (Also see FLAT CARD.)

CARD CHOKING: See CYLINDER LOADING.

CARD CLOTHING: The material used to cover the working surfaces of the card, i.e., cylinder and rolls or flats. The clothing consists of either wire teeth set in a foundation fabric or rubber, or narrow serrated metal flutes which are spirally arranged around the roll. The metallic wire has the appearance of a band-saw blade.

CARD CONVERSION EFFICIENCY: The efficiency of the carding process, expressed as a percentage obtained from the ratio of sliver output to staple input.

CARDED WEB: The thin sheet of staple fibers produced by a card. It may be collected flat for combining with other webs to make dry-laid nonwoven fabrics, or condensed into a sliver which is drawn and twisted to make spun yarn.

CARDED YARN: A cotton yarn that has been carded but not combed. Carded yarns contain a wider range of fiber lengths and, as a result, are not as uniform or as strong as combed yarns. They are considerably cheaper and are used in medium and coarse counts.

CARDIGAN: 1. A modification of the rib-knitting stitch to allow tucking on one (half cardigan) or both (full cardigan) sets of needles. **2.** A sweater that buttons down the front.

CARDING: A process in the manufacture of spun yarns whereby staple fiber is opened, cleaned, aligned, and formed into a continuous web which may be either condensed to form SLIVER or collected as a flat web for making nonwoven fabric.

CARDING MACHINE: See CARD.

CARDING WOOL: Fine wool 1¼-inches in length and coarse wool 2 inches in length can be carded. The term signifies that the stock is suitable only for woolen yarn manufacture.

CARD SLIVER: The thick, ropelike strand of untwisted fibers delivered by a card.

CARE LABEL: A permanently attached label on most types of textile consumer goods that gives directions for maintaining the product (cleaning, ironing, etc.). Such labeling is mandated by the Federal Trade Commission rule of July 3, 1972.

CARPET BACKING: A primary backing through which the carpet tufts are inserted is always required for tufted carpets. The backing is usually made of woven jute or nonwoven manufactured fiber fabrics. A secondary backing, again made of jute or manufactured fibers, is normally added at the latex backcoating stage. Carpet backings are an important end use for nonwoven fabrics.

CARPETS: Heavy functional and ornamental floor coverings consisting of pile yarns or fibers and a backing system. They may be tufted or woven. (Also see TUFTED CARPET.)

CARPET TILES: Loose-laid or self-adhesive-backed squares of carpet.

CARPET UNDERLAY: A separate fabric which is used to provide cushioning for carpet. Carpet underlays are made of hair and jute, sponge rubber, bonded urethane or foamed urethane.

CARPET WEAR TESTER: An instrument for testing the wear of textile floor coverings due to friction and pressure by measuring loss of thickness.

CARRIER: 1. A product added to a dyebath to promote the dyeing of hydrophobic manufactured fibers and characterized by affinity for, and ability to swell, the fiber. **2.** A moving holder for a package of yarn used on a braiding machine. **3.** A term sometimes used to describe the tube or bobbin on which yarn is wound.

CARRIERLESS DYEING VARIANTS: Polymers that have been modified to increase their dyeability. Fibers and fabrics made from these polymers can be dyed at the boil without the use of carriers.

CARRIER YARN: A yarn used to support another yarn as an aid to further processing.

CARVED PILE: In carpets, pile that has been sheared at different levels to form a three dimensional pattern. (Also see SCULPTURED.)

CASEIN FIBER: A protein fiber made by dissolving precipitated milk protein in an alkaline solution. The solution is extruded through spinnerets into an acid bath. (Also see AZLON FIBER.)

CASEMENT CLOTH: A general term applied to lightweight, sheer fabrics used for curtains and for screening purposes and as a backing for heavy drapery fabrics of the decorative type. This type of fabric is sometimes made in small fancy weaves for dresswear.

CASHMERE: The extremely soft hair of the cashmere goat. Cashmere is often blended with sheep's wool in fabrics.

CAST COATING: See COATING.

CATALYST: A chemical that accelerates a reaction. The catalyst is not part of the reaction but increases the rate at which it takes place.

CATERPILLAR: A large slub formed in a combination or plied yarn as a result of one of the ends breaking and sliding or skinning back along the other yarn.

CAT EYE: See PINHOLE.

CATION: A positively charged ion.

CATIONIC DYEABLE VARIANTS: Polymers modified chemically to make them receptive to cationic dyes.

CATIONIC DYES: See DYES, BASIC DYES.

CAUSTIC SODA: The common name for sodium hydroxide.

CAVALRY TWILL: A pronounced, raised cord on a 63° twill weave characterizes this rugged cloth usually made from wool or wool blend yarns.

CCI: Acronym for the Cotton Council International.

CELLOPHANE: A generic term for regenerated cellulose film, which is used primarily for packaging. The film is transparent and may be dyed in many colors or coated to render it moistureproof or heat-sealable.

CELLULASE TREATMENT: See ENZYME FINISHING.

CELLULOSE: A carbohydrate which is the chief component of the cell walls of plants. Cellulose is found in wood and in cotton, linen, jute, hemp, and all of the bast, leaf, and stem fibers. It is a basic raw material in the manufacture of rayon, acetate, and triacetate fibers.

CELLULOSE ACETATE: See ACETATE FIBER.

CELLULOSIC FIBER: A fiber composed of, or derived from, cellulose. Examples are cotton (cellulose), rayon (regenerated cellulose), acetate (cellulose acetate), and triacetate (cellulose triacetate).

CENTERING MARK: See CLIP MARK.

CENTER LOOP: See KINK, 1.

CENTRIFUGAL POT: See POT SPINNING.

CENTRIFUGE: A machine that employs centrifugal force to remove excess liquid from fabrics. In general, centrifuges are also used to separate materials of different densities.

CERAMIC FIBER: An aluminum silicate fiber made by heating aluminum fluoride at 1000–1200°C with silica and water vapor. The crystals, or WHISKERS, obtained are up to 1 cm long and have high strength. Ceramic fibers are used in reinforced plastics.

CHAFED END: A warp end that has been abraded during processing. It generally appears as a dull yarn often containing broken filaments.

CHAFE MARK: See ABRASION MARK.

CHAFER FABRIC: A fabric, coated with unvulcanized rubber, that is wrapped around the bead section of a tire before vulcanization of the complete tire. The purpose of the chafer fabric is to maintain an abrasion-resistant layer of rubber in contact with the wheel on which the tire is mounted.

CHAIN BINDERS: Yarns running in the warp direction on the back of a woven carpet which hold construction yarns together.

CHAIN DYEING: See DYEING.

CHALKINESS: 1. A dull, whitened appearance sometimes associated with certain extra-dull colors. **2.** A fillingwise fabric defect observed as bands varying in luster or sheen.

CHALLIS: A very soft, lightweight, plain-weave fabric, usually printed with a delicate floral pattern. The name is derived from the Anglo-Indian term "shalee" meaning soft.

CHAMBRAY: 1. A plain-woven spun fabric, almost square (i.e., 80 x 76), with a colored warp and a white filling. Lightweight chambrays are used for shirts, dresses, and children's clothes. **2.** A similar but heavier fabric of carded yarn, used for work clothing.

CHAMELEON: A variable multicolored effect achieved by using warp yarns of one color and two filling yarns of different colors in each shed. It is sometimes used in taffeta, faille, or poplin made from silk or manufactured filament yarns.

CHANGE IN FILLING: See MIXED END OR FILLING.

CHANGE IN LENGTH ON UNTWISTING: The increase or decrease in length measured when a specimen is untwisted. The change is expressed as the percentage extension or contraction of the nominal gauge length of the specimen, i.e., specimen length prior to untwisting.

CHARGED SYSTEM: A method of dry cleaning of textile materials in which water is dispersed in the solvent by means of a surfactant additive to help remove water-soluble soil.

CHAR LENGTH: In flammability testing, the distance from the edge of the sample exposed to the flame to the upper edge of the charred or void area.

CHEESE: A cylindrical package of yarn wound on a flangeless tube.

CHEESECLOTH: A low-count, plain-weave, soft cotton or cotton blend cloth also known as gauze.

CHELATING AGENT: A compound that will inactivate a metallic ion by making it an integral part of an inner ring structure. The metal is attached by coordinate links to two or more nonmetal atoms in the same molecule.

CHEMICAL CRIMPING: A crinkled or puckered effect in fabric obtained by printing sodium hydroxide onto the goods in a planned design. When the material is washed, the part to which the paste has been applied will shrink and cause untreated areas to pucker. The same effect is obtained with a caustic resist print and a sodium hydroxide bath.

CHEMICAL FIBER: See MANUFACTURED FIBER.

CHEMICAL FINISHING: Processes in which additives are applied to change the aesthetic and functional properties of a material. Examples are the application of antioxidants, flame retardants, wetting agents, and stain and water repellents.

CHEMICAL STABILITY: Degree of resistance of a material to chemicals, such as acids, bases, solvents, oils, and oxidizing agents, and to chemical reactions, including those catalyzed by light.

CHENILLE: 1. A yarn with a fuzzy pile protruding from all sides, cut from a woven chenille weft fabric. Chenille yarns are made from all fibers, and they are used as filling in fabrics and for embroidery, fringes, and tassels. **2.** Fabric woven with chenille yarns. (Also see TUFTED FABRIC.)

CHEVIOT: A rugged tweed made from uneven yarn, this fabric usually has a rather harsh hand.

CHEVRON: A broad term applied to prints in zigzag stripes or to herringbone weaves.

CHIFFON: A plain-weave, lightweight, sheer, transparent fabric made from fine, highly twisted yarns. It is usually a square fabric, i.e., having approximately the same number of ends and picks and the same count in both warp and filling.

CHINA SILK: A very soft, lustrous, plain-woven fabric made from silk produced in China or Japan.

CHINCHILLA CLOTH: A heavy, twill-weave, filling-pile fabric with a napped surface that is rolled into little tufts or nubs. The material is frequently double faced with a knitted or woven, plain or fancy back. Chinchilla cloth is used primarily in coats. The term is also used to refer to a knitted woolen fabric having a napped surface.

CHINO: A cotton or cotton blend twill used by armies throughout the world for summer-weight uniforms. Chino is frequently dyed khaki.

CHINTZ: A glazed fabric produced by friction calendering. Unglazed chintz is called cretonne.

CHIP: 1. The form of polymer feedstock used in fiber production. (Also see FLAKE.) **2.** The feedstock for a pulp digestor. **3.** A defect in a nonwoven fabric.

CHLORINATED WOOL: Wool that has been treated with chlorine by any of several methods to impart felting resistance by partial removal of the natural scales on the surface of the fibers.

CHLORINE BLEACH: Any chlorine-based oxidizing agent for whitening some textile fibers. The most common type is a water solution of sodium hypochlorite.

CHLORINE RETENTION: A characteristic of several resins and textile finishes whereby they retain some of the chlorine from bleach. On heating of the goods, the chlorine forms hydrochloric acid, causing tendering of the cloth. This is especially true of certain wrinkle resistant finishes for cotton and rayon.

CHOKED COILER: A condition in carding or drawing in which sliver is either puffy, badly condensed, or very uneven, leading to overloading of the coiler trumpets and causing work stoppage.

CHOKED FLYERS: A situation in which roving will not pass through the flyer channels because of heavy or cockled conditions caused by such factors as uneven drafting, waste, overcut fibers, and improper finish.

CHROMATICITY: The quality of color expressed as a function of wavelength and purity.

CHROMATOGRAPHY: The generic name of a group of processes for separating and analyzing mixtures of chemical compounds. The separation depends on the redistribution of molecules of the mixture between phases, one of which is thin, often reaching molecular dimensions. For this reason, molecular size and shape are important in the separation, and extremely subtle separations are possible. Gas chromatography and thin-layer chromatography are widely used methods for analysis of textiles.

CHROME DYES: See DYES.

CHUTE-FEED SYSTEM: Pneumatic fiber transport system used in linking textile processing equipment or operations, especially opening, blending, and carding.

CI: 1. Acronym for Colour Index. **2.** Acronym for Cotton, Incorporated.

CIE: A color classification system developed by the Commission Internationale de l'Éclairage.

CIM: Acronym for COMPUTER-INTEGRATED MANUFACTURING.

CIRCULAR-KNIT FABRIC: A tubular weft-knit fabric made on a circular-knitting machine.

CIRCULAR KNITTING: See KNITTING, 2.

CIRÉ: A brilliant patent leather effect produced by application of wax, heat, and pressure.

CIRFS: Acronym for Committee International de Rayon et Fibres Synthetique.

CLAMPS: The parts of a testing machine that are used to hold a specimen while it is subjected to force. (Also called JAWS.)

CLARITY: 1. In general, the optical property of being clear. **2.** In acetate manufacture, a measure of the appearance of dope solutions, indicating the quality of the acetylation mixture. **3.** In printing, the sharpness or definition of a print pattern.

CLEARING: The treatment of printed fabrics with a chemical solution to improve the appearance of the whites. In many cases, the treatment also brightens the printed areas. (Also see REDUCTION CLEARING.)

CLIP MARK: Visible deformation of selvage due to pressure from a tenter clip.

CLO: A unit of thermal resistance. The insulation needed to keep an individual producing heat at the rate of 58 W/m^2 comfortable at 21°C air temperature with air movement of 0.1 m/s. One clo is roughly equal to the insulation value of typical indoor clothing.

CLOQUÉ FABRIC: From the French term for blistered, it refers to any fabric whose surface exhibits an irregularly raised blister effect.

CLOSED LOOP: In warp knitting, a loop at the base of which the yarn crosses over itself.

CLOSED SHEDDING: A weaving method in which all warp yarns are raised to the same level after insertion of each pick.

CLOTH: A generic term embracing all textile fabrics and felts. Cloth may be formed of any textile fiber, wire, or other material, and it includes any pliant fabric woven, knit, felted, needled, sewn, or otherwise formed.

Closed Loop

CLOTH ROLL: The roll at the front of a loom onto which the fabric is wound.

CLOUDY WEB: An uneven or irregular web from the doffer of a card.

CLUMPS: In nonwoven fabrics, an irregularly shaped grouping of fibers caused by insufficient fiber separation.

COACERVATION: The collection of colloidal particles into droplets held together by electrostatic attraction. This term for the equilibrium state of colloidal systems was introduced in 1929.

COAGULATION: The precipitation of particles from a suspension in a liquid, usually resulting in formation of a gel.

COAGULATION BATH: A liquid bath that serves to harden viscous polymer strands into solid fibers after extrusion through a spinneret. Used in wet-spinning processes such as in rayon or acrylic fiber manufacture.

COALESCED FILAMENTS: Filaments stuck together by design or accident during the extrusion process.

COALESCENCE: Merging of two or more substances into a larger substance, i.e., COALESCED FILAMENTS.

COARSE END: See COARSE THREAD.

COARSE FILLING: See COARSE THREAD.

COARSE PICK: See COARSE THREAD.

COARSE THREAD: A yarn larger in diameter than other yarns being used in the fabric.

COATED FABRIC: A fabric to which a material such as plastic, resin, or rubber has been applied in firmly adhering layers to provide certain properties, such as water impermeability.

COATING: The application of a semi-liquid material such as rubber, polyvinyl chloride, or polyurethane to one or both sides of a textile material. Once the coating has been dried (and cured, if necessary), it forms a bond with the fabric.

Blade-in-Air Coating: In this direct coating method, the moving fabric substrate has no mechanical support but is held in position by accurate tension control. The angle of the blade controls the amount of coating applied.

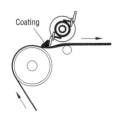

Blade-in-Air Coating

Calender Coating: A type of roller coating that is actually a laminating operation. The coating is formed into a sheet, then joined with the fabric.

Cast Coating: A method by which resinous materials such as vinyl are coated onto a fabric and cured by heated casting drums.

Dip Coating: The process of passing a fabric through a solution of resin or elastomer, then through squeeze rolls to remove excess and leave a thin surface layer on the base fabric. In this process, both sides can be coated in one pass. (Also see DIP TREATING.)

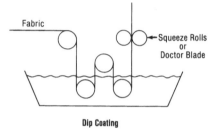

Dip Coating

Direct Coating: The simplest method of coating, this procedure involves spreading the coating with a knife. The moving fabric substrate is usually supported by a roller or a sleeve. The gap between the knife and the fabric determines coating thickness.

Roller Coating: In this method, a roller is used to apply the coating to the moving substrate fabric. Various roll configurations can be used.

Direct Coating

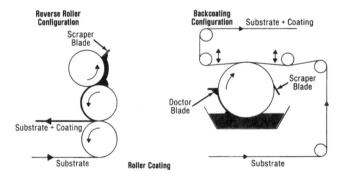

Roller Coating

Transfer Coating: This method involves applying the coating to a temporary substrate and then adding an adhesive coating (tie coat) to allow transfer by roller of the coating to the desired substrate. (See diagram on the next page.)

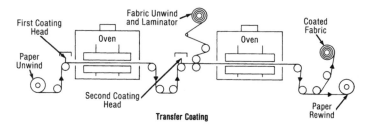

Transfer Coating

COCKLED YARN: 1. A defective spun yarn in which some fibers do not lie parallel to the other fibers but instead are curled and kinked, forming a rough and uneven surface on the yarn. The general cause is fiber overcut to the extent that the drafting rolls catch and hold both ends of the fiber at the same time while attempting to draft, resulting in slippage or breakage. (Also see OVERCUT.) **2.** A term to describe a defective spun yarn containing slubs.

COCKLING: A crimpiness or pucker in yarn or fabric usually caused by lack of uniform quality in the raw material used, improper tension on yarn in weaving, or weaving together yarns of different numbers.

COFORMING: Forming a nonwoven web through the concurrent use of elements from at least two different web-forming technologies.

COHESION: The force that holds fibers together during yarn manufacturing or processing. It is usually a function of lubricant (type and amount) and fiber crimp.

COILING: The depositing of sliver into cylindrical cans in helical loops. This arrangement permits easy removal for further processing.

COIL YARN: See TEXTURED YARNS, 2.

COLD DRAWING: A process for stretching manufactured fibers under cold conditions to improve their properties. Only certain types of fibers can be cold drawn. (Also see DRAWING, 2. and HOT DRAWING.)

COLD-PAD-BATCH DYEING: See DYEING.

COLLAPSED BALLOON SPINNING: A type of ring spinning process used for coarse semiworsted and wool carpet yarns. The balloon size is greatly reduced by contact with the top of the spindle to allow the use of a larger package size or higher spindle speed.

COLOR ABRASION: Color changes in localized areas of a garment resulting from differential wear.

COLORFASTNESS: Resistance to fading; i.e., the property of a dye to retain its color when the dyed (or printed) textile material is exposed to conditions or agents such as light, perspiration, atmospheric gases, or washing that can remove or destroy the color. A dye may be reasonably fast to one agent and only moderately fast to another. Degree of fastness of color is tested by standard procedures. Textile materials often must meet certain fastness specifications for a particular use.

COLORIMETER: 1. A device that specifies color by measuring the intensities of the three primary colors that compose the color under study. **2.** An instrument for measuring the concentration of a known substance in solution by comparing the liquid's color with standard colors.

COLORIMETRY: Any technique for evaluating a given color in terms of standard colors.

COLOR MEASUREMENT: A system of quantitative specification of color based on colorimetric or spectrophotometric data.

COLOR STRIPPER: A chemical used to remove some or all of the dyestuffs from a fiber, yarn, or fabric so that a dyeing defect can be corrected, a shade lightened, or another color applied.

COLOR VALUE: The yield of a colorant compared with a standard of equal cost.

COLOR YIELD: The depth of color obtained when a standard weight of colorant is applied under standard conditions.

COLOUR INDEX (CI): A listing of dyes and chemical structures published by the Society of Dyers and Colourists. Each structure is assigned a name according to chemical composition. Each dye is assigned a number according to its class and shade. A correlating structure number is given when available.

COMBED SLIVER: A continuous band of untwisted fiber, relatively free of short fibers and trash, produced by combing card sliver.

COMBED YARN: A yarn produced from combed sliver. (Also see COMBING.)

COMBINATION FABRIC: A fabric containing: (1) different fibers in the warp and filling (e.g., a cotton warp and a rayon filling), (2) ends of two or more fibers in the warp and/or filling, (3) combination yarns, (4) both filament yarn and spun yarn of the same or different fibers, or (5) filament yarns of two or more generic fiber types. Combination fabrics may be either knit or woven. They should not be confused with BLEND FABRICS. Although blend fabrics also contain more than one fiber, the same intimately blended spun yarn is present in both warp and filling.

COMBINATION YARN: A plied yarn containing two or more yarns that vary in fiber composition, content, and/or twist level; or a plied yarn composed of both filament yarn and spun yarn.

COMBINED YARN: See COMBINATION YARN.

COMBING: A step subsequent to carding in cotton and worsted system processing which straightens the fibers and extracts neps, foreign matter, and short fibers. Combing produces a stronger, more even, more compact, finer, smoother yarn.

COMBING WOOL: Wool fibers 1½–6 inches in length used in worsted yarn manufacture.

COMFORT: Performance parameter of apparel referring to wearability. Encompasses such properties as wicking, stretch, hand, etc.

COMFORT STRETCH: A term used to describe fabrics with about 10%–15% stretch that are used mostly in garments requiring a moderate amount of elasticity. (Contrast with POWER STRETCH.)

COMMERCIAL ALLOWANCE: The commercial moisture regain plus a specific allowance for finish used in calculating the commercial or legal weight of a fiber shipment.

COMMERCIAL MOISTURE REGAIN: An arbitrary value adopted as the moisture regain to be used in calculating the commercial or legal weight of a fiber shipment.

COMMERCIAL WEIGHT: 1. In natural fibers, the dry weight of fibers or yarns plus the commercial moisture regain. **2.** In manufactured fibers, the dry weight of staple spun yarns or filament yarns after scouring by prescribed methods, plus the commercial moisture regain.

COMMINGLED YARN: In aerospace textiles, two or more continuous multifilament yarns, the filaments of which have been intermixed with each other without adding twist or otherwise disturbing the parallel relationship of the combined filaments. Usually consists of a reinforcing yarn, such as graphite or glass, and a thermoplastic matrix yarn.

End View

Commingled Yarn

COMPACTED YARN: Air jet interlaced yarn. Since the entanglement serves only as a substitute for twist, the degree of interlace or tangle is not as great as in air jet bulked yarn.

COMPACTION: See INTERMINGLING.

COMPACTOR: A machine developed by Fabric Research Laboratories which is used to compact fabrics or to produce warp-stretch fabrics by means of forced crimp and/or shrinkage of the warp yarn.

COMPACT SPINNING PROCESS: A term generally referring to a spinning process carried out using any one of the several small spinning machines of compact design offered by equipment vendors as "packaged" units in which spinning and subsequent processing (drawing, crimping, cutting, etc.) are linked.

COMPATIBLE SHRINKAGE: A term used for bonded fabrics to indicate that the face fabric and lining have similar shrinkage. This is necessary to avoid puckering.

COMPLIANCE: The ability of a fiber to yield under stress; the ratio of the change in strain to the change in stress that produces it; the reciprocal of the textile modulus.

COMPOSITE: 1. An article or substance of two or more constituents, generally, with reinforcing elements dispersed in a matrix or continuous phase. **2.** Hard or soft constructions in which the fibers themselves are consolidated to form structures rather than being formed into yarns. Rigidity of these constructions is controlled by the density, the modulus of the load-bearing fibers, and the fraction of fusible fibers. Strength is controlled by adhesion and shear-yield

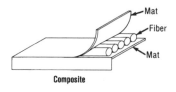

Composite

strength of the matrix unless fibers are bonded in a load-transferring matrix. **3.** A structure made by laminating a nonwoven fabric with another nonwoven, with other materials, or by impregnating a nonwoven fabric with resins.

COMPOSITE FIBERS: Fibers composed of two or more polymer types in a sheath-core or side-by-side relation. (Also see BICOMPONENT FIBER.)

COMPOSITE NONWOVEN: A fabric made by integrating two or more basic nonwoven web formation methods to produce the web.

COMPOSITE YARN: A yarn constructed of two or more components, staple fiber and/or filament, that are combined in the spinning process. (Also see COMBINATION YARN and CORE-SPUN YARN.)

COMPOUND FABRIC: A woven fabric with separate plies, each with its own warp and filling, that are produced simultaneously and joined in one weaving process.

COMPRESSIBILITY: Refers to the ease of reducing the bulk of fabric, carpet, batting, or other material. May be high or low, soft or hard.

COMPRESSION SET: The degree to which a textile material fails to return to its original thickness after compression.

COMPRESSIVE SHRINKAGE: A preshrinking process for fabric. The damp fabric is pressed between a heated cylinder and a thick felt or rubber blanket which causes lengthwise compression. (Also see SANFORIZED®).

COMPUTER-AIDED DESIGN: Design implemented by the use of a computer instead of manually. The computer performs many of the detailed tasks, freeing the designer for the creative process. Designs for fabrics and printing can be seen on screen, making alterations faster and easier and reducing error.

COMPUTER-AIDED MANUFACTURING: Production processes in which product characteristics are monitored and controlled by computer.

COMPUTER-INTEGRATED MANUFACTURING: Managing multistage manufacturing processes with a series of coordinated computers that monitor and regulate the sequential operations.

COMPUTERIZED COLOR VISUALIZATION: Various COMPUTER-AIDED DESIGN (CAD) systems for specifying and communicating color accurately.

CONDENSATION POLYMERIZATION: A polymerization process yielding a product in which the repeating unit has fewer atoms than the monomer or monomers. Generally, the separation of water or some other simple substance occurs as a result of the reaction, e.g., ethylene glycol in polyester production.

41

CONDITIONING: A process of allowing textile materials (staple, tow, yarns, and fabrics) to reach hygroscopic equilibrium with the surrounding atmosphere. Materials may be conditioned in a standard atmosphere (65% RH, 70°F) for testing purposes or in arbitrary conditions existing in manufacturing or processing areas.

CONE: A conical package of yarn, usually wound on a disposable paper core.

CONFIDENCE INTERVAL: The range within which a value can be expected to fall with a given probability.

CONING: The transfer of yarn from skeins or bobbins or other types of packages to cones.

CONJUGATE FIBER: A side-by-side bicomponent fiber with the ability to produce helical crimp on exposure to heat or hot-wet conditions because of differential shrinkage of the components. (Also see BICOMPONENT FIBER, SIDE-BY-SIDE BICOMPONENT FIBER.)

CONJUGATE YARN: A yarn made from conjugate filaments.

CONSOLIDATION: Application of heat and pressure to form composite structures.

CONSTANT-RATE-OF-EXTENSION TENSILE TESTER: A tensile testing machine in which the rate of increase of specimen length is uniform with time (ASTM).

CONSTANT-RATE-OF-LOAD TENSILE TESTER: A testing machine in which the rate of increase of the load being applied to the specimen is uniform with time after the first 3 seconds (ASTM).

CONSTANT-RATE-OF-TRAVERSE TENSILE TESTER: A testing machine in which the pulling clamp moves at a uniform rate and the load is applied through the other clamp which moves appreciably to actuate a weighing mechanism, so that the rate of increase of load or elongation is dependent upon the extension characteristics of the specimen (ASTM).

CONSTRUCTION: A term used in identifying the structure of a yarn, fabric, or other textile material. For example, details such as denier (decitex), filament count, twist level and direction, and number of plies for a filament yarn; and type of weave, end and pick count, width, and number of yards per pound for a woven fabric.

CONTACT ANGLE: The angle between the surface of a liquid and the surface of a partially submerged object or the container at the line of contact. The smaller the contact angle, the greater the wettability of the solid.

CONTINUOUS DYEING: See DYEING.

CONTINUOUS FILAMENT: See FILAMENT.

CONTINUOUS FILAMENT YARN: See FILAMENT YARN.

CONTINUOUS POLYMERIZATION:
In polymer manufacture, linkage of the various stages of polymerization so that materials flow without interruption from the addition of raw materials to delivery of the finished polymer from the system. Extrusion as film, chip or fiber may be linked to a continuous polymerization line. Because there is no break in the process while the transition from low molecular weight to high occurs, multiple stage reaction vessels may be required and accurate process control is critical.

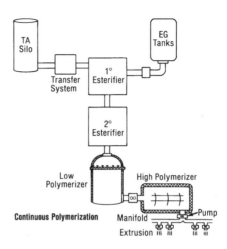

Continuous Polymerization

CONTINUOUS PROCESS: A general term for any process that is accomplished continuously, providing a continuous output, instead of in batches.

CONTRACTION: See TAKE-UP (TWIST) and TAKE-UP (YARN IN FABRIC).

CONVERTED FABRIC: A finished fabric as distinguished from greige fabric.

CONVERTER: An individual or organization which buys greige fabrics and sells them as a finished product to cutters, wholesalers, retailers, and others. The converter arranges for the finishing of the fabric, namely bleaching, mercerizing, dyeing, printing, etc., to the buyers' specifications.

CONVOLUTION: 1. An irregular spiral or twisted condition characteristic of mature cotton fiber. It is visible under a microscope. The finer fibers are generally more twisted than the coarser fibers. **2.** Coil and curl in certain types of textured yarns which provide bulkiness to the yarn.

COP: 1. A headless tube upon which yarn or thread is wound. **2.** Thread or yarn wound into the shape of a hollow cylinder with tapered ends. **3.** Filling yarn wound upon a tapered tube (generally paper).

COPOLYMER: A polymer composed of a combination of more than one monomer (usually two). Copolymers are the basis of some manufactured fibers.

CORD: 1. The product formed by twisting together two or more plied yarns. **2.** A rib on the surface of a fabric (e.g., corduroy and whipcord).

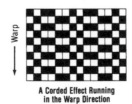

A Corded Effect Running in the Warp Direction

A Corded Effect Running in the Filling Direction

CORDAGE: A general term for all types of cord, rope, cable, and twine.

CORDED FABRIC: See CORD, 2.

CORDED SELVAGE: See LOOPY SELVAGE.

CORD FABRIC: See TIRE FABRIC.

CORDONNET: 1. A heavy yarn used to outline design patterns in textiles, especially laces and trim materials. **2.** A plied silk yarn used for hand knitting, crocheting, and embroidering.

CORDUROY: A filling-pile fabric with ridges of pile (cords) running lengthwise parallel to the selvage.

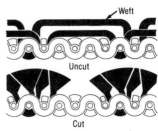

Corduroy: Section Through Warp

CORE-BULKED YARN: See TEXTURED YARNS, 3.

CORE SPINNING: The process of making a core-spun yarn. It consists of feeding the core yarn (an elastomeric filament yarn, a regular filament yarn, a textured yarn, or a previously spun yarn) into the front delivery roll of the spinning frame and of covering the core yarn with a sheath of fibers during the spinning operation.

CORE-SPUN YARN: A yarn made by twisting fibers around a filament or a previously spun yarn, thus concealing the core. Core yarns are used in sewing thread, blankets, and socks and also to obtain novelty effects in fabrics.

CORKSCREW TWIST: A place in yarn or cord where uneven twist produces a corkscrew-like appearance.

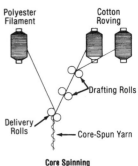

Core Spinning

CORRUGATION MARK: A fabric defect consisting of a crimped, rippled, wavy, pebbled, or cockled area in the fabric spoiling the uniformity of the texture.

CORTEX: The inner layer of wool and other animal fibers. It is composed of spindle-shaped cells and comprises the major portion of the fiber structure.

COT: The covering material used on various fiber-processing rolls, especially drawing rolls. Leather, cork, rubber, and synthetic materials are frequently employed.

COTTAGE STEAMER: A chamber used for batch steaming of printed or dyed textiles. Cloth is looped on "poles" on a special cart which fits into the steamer for processing.

COTTON COUNT: The yarn numbering system based on length and weight originally used for cotton yarns and now employed for most staple yarns spun on the cotton, or short-staple, system. It is based on a unit length of 840 yards, and the count of the yarn is equal to the number of 840-yard skeins required to weigh 1 pound. Under this system, the higher the number, the finer the yarn. (Also see YARN NUMBER.)

COTTON FIBER: A unicellular, natural staple fiber which is the seed hair of plants of the genus *Gossypium*. It is almost pure cellulose and a distinguishing characteristic is its irregular spiral configuration. The fiber is fine and its length varies from less than 1/2 inch to over 2 inches. The quality and color of cotton fiber, normally creamy white but sometimes much darker, is determined by the plant variety as well as the location, soil and climatic conditions under which it is cultivated. The largest cotton producers by far today are China, the U.S., and Russia. Other growers with high output are India, Pakistan, Brazil, Turkey, and several South American and African countries.

CHARACTERISTICS: For marketing, cotton fibers are graded and classed for length, fineness, strength, and color. It is a highly versatile fiber with high strength and a high moisture regain of 8%, which contributes to its comfort.

END USES: Cotton is the most widely used natural fiber. Because of its versatility and comfort, cotton is widely used throughout the world in a very broad range of textile materials. Today cotton is often blended with other staple fibers, especially polyester, to take advantage of the characteristics of both fibers.

COTTON LINTERS: See LINTERS.

COTTON SYSTEM: A process originally used for manufacturing cotton fiber into yarn, and now also used extensively for producing spun yarns of manufactured fibers, including blends. Processing on the cotton system includes the general operations of opening, picking, carding, drawing, roving, and ring or mule spinning in the production of carded yarns. For combed yarns, three steps, culminating in combing, are included after the carding operation. There have been many modifications of this process, especially for the so-called "long draft," or "Casablancas," system. The cotton system is also proving to be the basis of many hybrid systems for handling wool yarns and for manufacturing other long-staple yarns.

COUNT: 1. A numerical designation of yarn size indicating the relationship of length to weight. (Also see YARN NUMBER.) **2.** The number of warp yarns (ends) and filling yarns (picks) per inch in a woven fabric, or the number of wales and courses per inch in a knit fabric. For example, a fabric count of 68 x 52 indicates 68 ends per inch in the warp and 52 picks per inch in the filling.

COUPLING: Combining an organic compound, usually a phenol or arylamine, with a diazonium salt to form an azo compound. In textile dyeing, the fiber or fabric is first treated with a coupling component, followed by treatment with a solution of the diazonium salt to form an insoluble dye inside the fiber. (Also see DYES, NAPHTHOL DYES.)

COURSE: The row of loops or stitches running across a knit fabric, corresponding to the filling in woven fabrics.

COVER: 1. The degree of evenness of thread spacing. **2.** The degree to which underlying structure is concealed by the surface material, as in carpets, the degree to which pile covers backing. **3.** The ability of a dye to conceal defects in fabric.

COVERED YARN: A type of composite yarn made by wrapping a spun or filament yarn around a core of bundled fibers (see FASCIATED YARN) or another yarn. The core may also be an elastic yarn such as spandex.

COVER FACTOR: The fraction of the surface area that is covered by yarns assuming round yarn shape.

COVERING: A process for producing a COVERED YARN.

COVERSTOCK: A lightweight nonwoven material used to contain and conceal an underlying core material. Examples are the facing materials that cover the absorbent cores of diapers, sanitary napkins, and adult incontinence products.

COVERT: A closely woven fabric with a warp face of woolen or worsted yarn. Its characteristically flecked appearance is obtained by using two-ply yarn with one dark thread alternating with a light thread. Covert is used for topcoats, suits and sportswear.

COWOVEN FABRIC: In aerospace textiles, a fabric in which a reinforcing fiber and a matrix fiber are adjacent to each other as one end in the warp and/or filling direction.

End View

Cowoven Yarn

CPI: Acronym for CRYSTALLINE PERFECTION INDEX or crimps per inch.

CRAB: A hand device used to stretch carpets in a small area.

CRABBING: The process of heating wool or hair fabrics, under tension, in a hot or boiling liquid, then cooling under tension, to provide the fabric with dimensional stability for further wet processing.

CRACK: A defect in a woven fabric consisting of an open fillingwise streak extending partly or entirely across the fabric.

CRACK MARK: A sharp break or crease in the surface of a coated or laminated fabric.

CRASH: A coarse fabric with a rough, irregular surface made from thick, uneven yarns.

CRE: Acronym for constant rate of extension. See CONSTANT-RATE-OF-EXTENSION TENSILE TESTER.

CREASE: A break or line in a fabric generally caused by a sharp fold. Creases may be either desirable or undesirable, depending upon the situation. A crease may be intentionally pressed into a fabric by application of pressure and heat and sometimes moisture.

CREASE RECOVERY: See WRINKLE RECOVERY.

CREASE-RESISTANT: A term used to describe a fabric treated chemically to improve its resistance to and recovery from wrinkling.

CREASE RETENTION: The ability of a fabric to maintain an inserted crease. Crease retention can be measured subjectively or by the relation of a crease in a subsequent state to the crease in the initial state. Crease retention may be strongly dependent on the conditions of use, e.g., normal wear, washing, or tumble drying.

CREEL: 1. A framework arranged to hold slivers, rovings, or yarns so that many ends can be withdrawn smoothly and evenly without tangling. **2.** A similar device used to aggregate sub-tows to tows in manufactured staple processing, especially polyester.

CREELING: The mounting of supply packages in a creel to feed fiber to a process, i.e., beaming or warping.

CREEP: See DELAYED DEFORMATION.

CRENULAR CROSS SECTION: See CROSS SECTION.

CREPE: A lightweight fabric characterized by a crinkling surface obtained by the use of: (1) hard-twist filling yarns, (2) chemical treatment, (3) crepe weaves, and (4) embossing.

CRETONNE: See CHINTZ.

CREWEL YARN: A loosely constructed, two-ply worsted yarn used for crewel embroidery.

CRIMP: 1. The waviness of a fiber expressed as crimps per unit length. **2.** The difference in distance between two points on an unstretched fiber and the same two points when the fiber is straightened under specified tension. Crimp is expressed as a percentage of the unstretched length. **3.** The difference in distance between two points on a yarn as it lies in a fabric and the same two points when the yarn has been removed from the fabric and straightened under specified tension, expressed as a percentage of the distance between the two points as the yarn lies in the fabric.

CRIMP AMPLITUDE: The height of displacement of the fiber from its uncrimped condition.

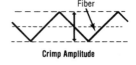

Crimp Amplitude

CRIMP DEREGISTERING: The process of opening a tow band by causing the peaks and valleys of the crimp to lay randomly rather than uniformly.

CRIMPED YARN: See TEXTURED YARNS, 4.

CRIMP ENERGY: The amount of work required to uncrimp a fiber.

CRIMP FREQUENCY: The crimp level, or number of crimps per inch in yarn or tow.

CRIMPING: The process of imparting crimp to tow or filament yarn.

CRIMP SETTING: An aftertreatment to set the crimp in yarn or fiber. Usually heat and steam are used, although the treatment may be chemical in nature.

CRINKLE: 1. A wrinkled or puckered effect in fabric. It may be obtained either in the construction or in the finishing of the fabric. **2.** The term is sometimes incorrectly used to describe the crimp of staple fiber.

CRINKLE YARN: See TEXTURED YARNS, 4.

CRINOLINE: A stiff, heavily sized fabric used as an interlining or to support areas such as the edge of a hem.

CRITICAL APPLICATION VALUE: In applying wet finishes on fabric, the minimum pickup that will provide a uniform distribution of solids after drying and curing.

CRITICAL LENGTH: See BREAKING LENGTH.

CRL: Acronym for constant rate of load. See CONSTANT-RATE-OF-LOAD TENSILE TESTER.

CROCHETING: The interlocking of loops from a single thread with a hooked needle. Crocheting can be done either by hand or by machine.

CROCKING: The rubbing-off of dye from a fabric as a result of insufficient dye penetration or fixation, the use of improper dyes or dyeing methods, or insufficient washing and treatment after the dyeing operation. Crocking can occur under dry or wet conditions.

CROCKMETER: Laboratory instrument for testing the fastness of dyed or printed textiles to rubbing.

CROOKED CLOTH: See BAGGY CLOTH.

CROSS DIRECTION: The width dimension, within the plane of the fabric, that is perpendicular to the direction in which the fabric is being produced by the machine.

CROSS DYEING: See DYEING.

CROSS-FLOW QUENCH: In cooling extruded polymer filaments, refers to cooling air directed from one side across the path of the filaments. There may be some type of suction on the opposite side to remove the heated air.

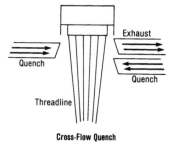

Cross-Flow Quench

CROSSLAPPER: A machine used to fold or layer fiber webs across their width. Crosslapping is used to produce both machine and cross-machine fiber orientation, to change web width, and to change web weight.

CROSS-LINKING: The stabilization of cellulosic or manufactured fibers through chemical reaction with certain compounds in such a way that the cellulose or manufactured polymer chains are bridged across or "cross-linked." Cross-linking improves such mechanical factors as wrinkle resistance.

Random cross-linking in manufactured polymers is undesirable and leads to brittleness and loss of tensile strength.

CROSS SECTION: The shape of an individual filament when cut at right angles to its axis. Normal shapes for manufactured fibers vary, e.g., round (nylon, polyester, polypropylene, and some acrylics), serrated or crenular (viscose rayon, acetate, and triacetate), bean-shaped (some acrylics and modacrylics). The shapes of manufactured fibers can be modified by changing the shape of the holes in the spinneret. Cross sectional variants are produced intentionally in a wide variety of shapes for different physical effects such as change in luster or hand, improved resistance to soiling, etc. Examples are trilobal (T and Y) and other multilobal shapes (cruciform, K, X, pentalobal, star, etc.), I-beam, ribbon, square, triangular, elliptical, hollow, and many others.

Cross Sections

CROSS-STITCH: See PINHOLE.

CROWSFEET: A fabric defect consisting of breaks or wrinkles of varying degrees of intensity and size, resembling bird's footprints in shape, and occurring during wet processing of fabrics.

CRT: Acronym for constant rate of traverse. See CONSTANT-RATE-OF-TRAVERSE TENSILE TESTER.

CRYSTALLINE: Made up of crystals. The term crystalline applies to sections of all chemical fibers, which consist of alternate crystalline and amorphous (noncrystalline) regions. These regions are influenced by manufacturing conditions and to some extent can be controlled. The degree of crystallinity influences the physical properties of fibers.

CRYSTALLINE GROWTH: 1. The expansion and development of a crystal. The process involves diffusion of the crystallizing material to special sites on the surface of the crystal, incorporation of the molecules into the surface at these sites, and diffusion of heat away from the surface of the crystal. **2.** The transformation of disoriented molecules, usually of the same substance, to a higher state of order. This process generally occurs rapidly for small molecules; however, the process is slow for polymer molecules and is arrested at temperatures below the glass transition temperature.

CRYSTALLINE PERFECTION INDEX: A measure of the crystallinity of a fiber. In general, higher levels of CPI indicate higher levels of temperature exposure.

CRYSTALLINITY: 1. The state or quality of being crystalline. **2.** The extent to which a polymer exists in a lattice structure.

CRYSTALLIZATION: The formation of highly-ordered substances (crystals) from solutions or melts. In polymers, crystalline areas are interspersed with amorphous areas in a lattice-like network. (Also see MACROLATTICE.)

CUPIONI: A type of specialty or novelty yarn having slubs or enlarged sections of varying length.

CUPRAMMONIUM RAYON: Filaments produced by precipitating cellulose dissolved in a solution of copper oxide in ammonia. (Also see RAYON FIBER.)

CURING: 1. In finishing fabrics, the process by which resins or plastics are set in or on textile materials, usually by heating. **2.** In rubber processing, vulcanization. It is accomplished either by heat treatment or by treatment in cold sulfuryl chloride solution.

CURL: See KINK.

CUSHION-BACKED CARPET: A carpet with padding made as an integral part of the backing.

CUSTOM TUFTED: A term used to describe carpet or rugs that have been manually tufted with a hand machine through the back.

CUT: 1. A unit of yarn number. The number of 100-yard lengths per pound avoirdupois of asbestos yarn or glass yarn, or the number of 300-yard lengths per pound avoirdupois of woolen yarn. **2.** A length of woven cloth. **3.** The number of needles per inch on a circular-knitting machine. A machine with 34 needles per inch is a 34-cut machine, and a fabric produced on it is called a 34-cut fabric.

CUTICLE: The surface layer of wool and other animal fibers, consisting of overlapping scales. (Also see CORTEX.)

CUT PILE: A pile surface obtained by cutting the loops of yarn in a tufted or woven carpet.

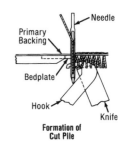

Formation of
Cut Pile

CUT SELVAGE: A cut or break occurring only in the selvage. A cut selvage is caused by incorrect loom adjustment during weaving or improper edge construction. The term also refers to loose edges cut during shearing of the fabric.

CUT STAPLE: 1. An inferior cotton fiber that was accidently cut because it was too damp during ginning. **2.** A term sometimes used to denote staple of manufactured fibers.

CUT TAPE: See SLIT TAPE.

CUTTER: 1. A mechanical device used to cut tow into staple. **2.** A firm engaged in making up garments from finished fabrics. **3.** A person employed in the wholesale garment industry whose specific work is to cut layers of fabric to be formed into garments.

CUT VELVET: See BEADED VELVET.

CUT YARN: A defective yarn, i.e., cut partially or completely through, resulting from malprocessing.

CYCLIC STRESS-STRAIN: Repeated loading of a yarn on a tensile testing machine and the determination of the physical properties of the yarn during these cycles.

CYCLIC TRIMER: Strictly, a polymer, in cyclic form, that contains three repeating groups. Cyclic trimer is a by-product found in all commercial polyester and results in deposit buildup in package-dyeing equipment.

CYLINDER: 1. In carding, a large cast iron shell, with an outer diameter of 40–45 inches, completely covered with card clothing on the surface. The shell is mounted rigidly on a shaft which projects at each end to rest in bearings. The cylinder must be accurately balanced since it rotates at speeds of 160 revolutions per minute and higher. **2.** The main roll, or pressure bowl, on roller printing machines. The engraved rolls that apply color are arranged around the

Circular-Knitting Machine Cylinder

cylinder. (Also see PRINTING, ROLLER PRINTING.) **3.** A slotted cylindrical housing for the needles in a circular-knitting machine. The number of slots per inch in the cylinder determines the cut of the machine. **4.** See DRYING CYLINDERS.

CYLINDER LOADING: Fibers imbedded so deeply in the wire clothing on a card cylinder that they resist transfer to the doffer cylinder according to the normal fiber path through the card. Causes include improper finish, excess moisture, or static on the fiber. The fiber builds up to such an extent that the carding operation is adversely affected. In extreme cases, the card will be slowed or stopped.

CYMATIC PRINTING: This proprietary process owned by KBC is a method in which the oscillations of a musical chord are "caught" on a quartz plate and the vibration patterns photographed. The patterns thus obtained are used in making unique print fabrics of unusual variety and originality.

D

DAMAGED SELVAGE: See CUT SELVAGE.

DAMASK: A firm, glossy, jacquard-patterned fabric that may be made from linen, cotton, rayon, silk, or a combination of these with various manufactured fibers. Similar to brocade, but flatter and reversible, damask is used for napkins, tablecloths, draperies, and upholstery.

DAMPENING: In tire cord, the relative ability to absorb energy and deaden oscillation after excitation.

DEAERATION: 1. Removal of undissolved and dissolved gases or air from polymer solutions before the extrusion process. **2.** In beam dyeing, a technique to remove air from the fabric wound on the perforated beam.

DECATING: See DECATIZING.

DECATING MARK: A crease mark or impression extending fillingwise across the fabric near the beginning or end of the piece.

DECATIZING: A finishing process in which fabric, wound tightly on a perforated roller, either has hot water circulated through it (wet decatizing), or has steam blown through it (dry decatizing). The process is aimed chiefly at improving the hand and removing wrinkles.

DECITEX: One tenth of a TEX.

DECORTICATING: A mechanical process for separating the woody matter from the bast fiber of such plants as ramie and hemp.

DEEP-DYEING VARIANTS: Polymers that have been chemically modified to increase their dyeability. Fibers and fabrics made from them can be dyed to very heavy depth.

DEFECTS: A general term that refers to some flaw in a textile product that detracts from either performance or appearance properties.

DEFLECTED NEEDLES: See BENT NEEDLE(S), 1.

DEFORMATION: A change in the shape of a specimen, e.g., an increase in length produced as the result of the application of a tensile load or force. Deformation may be immediate or delayed, and the latter may be recoverable or nonrecoverable.

DEGRADATION: The loss of desirable physical properties by a textile material as a result of some process or physical/chemical phenomenon.

DEGREASING: 1. Any process to remove the natural oils and grease from wool by means of a solvent or an aqueous treatment. **2.** The removal of fats, oils, grease, waxes and soil from any textile material using an organic solvent.

DEGREE OF ESTERIFICATION: The extent to which the acid groups of terephthalic and/or other acids have reacted with diols to form ester groups in polyester polymer production.

DEGREE OF POLYMERIZATION: Refers to the number of monomer units in an average polymer. It can be controlled during processing and affects the properties of the end product.

DEGUMMING: The removal of gum from silk by boiling in a mildly alkaline solution. Usually accomplished on the knit or woven fabric.

DELAMINATION: A defect of tufted carpet in which the primary backing and its tufted face yarns separate from the secondary backing.

DELAYED DEFORMATION: Deformation that is time-dependent and is exhibited by material subjected to a continuing load; creep. Delayed deformation may be recoverable or nonrecoverable following removal of the applied load.

DELUSTERING: Subduing or dulling the natural luster of a textile material by chemical or physical means. The term often refers to the use of titanium dioxide or other white pigments as delustrants in textile materials.

DELUSTRANT: A substance that can be used to dull the luster of a manufactured fiber. Often a pigment such as titanium dioxide.

DENIER: A weight-per-unit-length measure of any linear material. Officially, it is the number of unit weights of 0.05 grams per 450-meter length. This is numerically equal to the weight in grams of 9,000 meters of the material. Denier is a direct numbering system in which the lower numbers represent the finer sizes and the higher numbers the coarser sizes. In the U.S., the denier system is used for numbering filament yarns (except glass), manufactured fiber staple (but not spun yarns), and tow. In most countries outside the U.S., the denier system has been replaced by the TEX system. The following denier terms are in use:

Denier per Filament (dpf): The denier of an individual continuous filament or an individual staple fiber if it were continuous. In filament yarns, it is the yarn denier divided by the number of filaments.

Yarn Denier: The denier of a filament yarn. It is the product of the denier per filament and the number of filaments in the yarn.

Total Denier: The denier of a tow before it is crimped. It is the product of the denier per filament and the number of filaments in the tow. The total denier after crimping (called crimped total denier) is higher because of the resultant increase in weight per unit length.

DENIER VARIATION: Usually variation in diameter, or other cross-sectional dimension, along the length of a filament or bundle of filaments. It is caused by malfunction or lack of process control in fiber manufacturing and degrades resulting fabric appearance or performance.

DENIM: A firm 2 x 1 or 3 x 1 twill-weave fabric, often having a whitish tinge, obtained by using white filling yarns with colored warp yarns. Heavier weight denims, usually blue or brown, are used for dungarees, work clothes, and men's and women's sportswear. Lighter weight denims with a softer finish are made in a variety of colors and patterns and are used for sportswear and draperies.

DENSITY: The mass per unit volume (usually expressed as grams per cubic centimeter). (Also see SPECIFIC GRAVITY.)

DENSITY HEIGHT: In carpets, the square of the density multiplied by the pile height. It is a criterion by which the potential wear life of different carpet grades can be compared theoretically if all other factors are constant.

DENT: On a loom, the space between the wires of a reed.

DEREGISTERING (CRIMP): Process of disordering or disaligning the crimp in a tow band to produce bulk. (Also see THREADED-ROLL PROCESS.)

DESIZING: A wet process for removing yarn size from greige fabrics by converting it to a soluble form that can be scoured out of the fabric.

DESORPTION: The release of an absorbed or adsorbed substance from a material.

DESULFURIZING: An aftertreatment to remove sulfur from newly spun viscose rayon by passing the yarn through a sodium sulfide solution.

DETERGENT: A synthetic cleaning agent containing surfactants that do not precipitate in hard water and have the ability to emulsify oil and suspend dirt.

DETWISTER: A device for opening fabric in rope form to its full width.

DEVELOPED DYES: See DYES.

DEVELOPING: A stage in dyeing or printing in which leuco compounds, dyes, or dye intermediates are converted to the final, stable state or shade.

DEWPOINT: The temperature at which a gas begins to condense as a liquid at a given pressure. Thus in air, it is the temperature at which the air becomes saturated when cooled with no further addition of moisture or change in pressure.

DHMEU: Acronym for DIMETHYLOLDIHYDROXYETHYLENEUREA. (Also see GLYOXAL RESINS.)

DIAGONAL (45°) FLAME TEST: See FLAMMABILITY TESTS.

DIAGONAL WEAVE: A weave that produces a distinct diagonal line in the fabric, especially twill weaves.

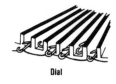

Dial

DIAL: In a circular-knitting machine, a circular steel plate with radially arranged slots for needles. A knitting machine equipped with both a dial and a CYLINDER can produce double-knit fabrics.

DIAMINE: A compound with two amino groups. Hexamethylenediamine, one of the intermediates in the manufacture of nylon 66 salt, is an example of this chemical type.

DIAMOND BARRING: A defect in woven or flat-knitted fabrics characterized by a diamond pattern and caused by periodic variation in the size, twist level, tension, crimp, etc., of the weft yarn.

DIAZOTIZATION: In dyeing, the chemical conversion of an aromatic amine group ($-NH_2$) on a dye or dyeing auxiliary to a diazonium group ($-N=N^+Cl^-$) using nitrous acid.

DIELECTRIC BREAKDOWN VOLTAGE: In an electrical insulating material, the voltage at which electrical breakdown occurs, i.e., the voltage at which current will flow and/or the material melts.

DIELECTRIC CONSTANT: Measure of the ability of a dielectric material to store electrical potential energy under the influence of an electric field, measured by the ratio of the capacitance of a condenser with the material as the dielectric to its capacitance with a vacuum as the dielectric.

DIELECTRIC STRENGTH: The average voltage gradient at which electrical failure or breakdown occurs. Expressed in volts per mil.

DIE SWELL: In melt or solution spinning of manufactured fibers, the maximum diameter of the polymer extrudate as it emerges from the spinneret orifice compared with the diameter of the orifice.

DIFFERENTIAL DYEING: See DYEING.

DIFFERENTIAL THERMAL ANALYSIS: A method of determining the temperature at which thermal events occur in a material undergoing continuous heating.

DIFFUSION: 1. A more or less gradual movement of molecules or ions through a solution or fiber as a result of the existence of a concentration gradient or repulsive or attractive forces. **2.** The random movement of gas molecules.

DIMENSIONAL RESTORABILITY: The ability of a fabric to be returned to its original dimensions after laundering or dry cleaning, expressed in percent. For example, 2% dimensional restorability means that although a fabric may shrink more than this in washing, it can be restored to within 2% of its original dimensions by ordinary home pressing methods.

DIMENSIONAL STABILITY: The ability of textile material to maintain or return to its original geometric configuration.

DIMETHYLOLDIHYDROXYETHYLENEUREA: A low-formaldehyde chemical finishing agent for crosslinking cotton and other cellulose fibers.

DIMETHYLOLETHYLENEUREA: A low-formaldehyde chemical finishing agent for crosslinking cotton and other cellulose fibers.

DIMETHYL TEREPHTHALATE: [p-C$_6$H$_4$(COOCH$_3$)$_2$], an intermediate used in the production of polyethylene terephthalate, the polymer from which polyester fibers and resins are made.

DIMITY: A sheer, thin, spun cloth that sometimes has cords or stripes woven in. It is used for aprons, pinafores, and many types of dress goods.

DIN: Acronym for Deutsches Institut für Normung e.V.

DIP: 1. Immersion of a textile material in some processing liquid. The term is usually used in connection with a padding or slashing process. **2.** The rubber compound with which tire cords and other in-rubber textiles are treated to give improved adhesion to rubber.

DIP DYEING: See DYEING.

DIP PENETRATION: The degree of saturation through a tire cord after impregnation with an adhesive.

DIP PICKUP: The amount of adhesive applied to a tire cord by dipping, expressed as a percentage of the weight of the cord before dipping.

DIP TREATING: The process of passing fiber, cord, or fabric through an adhesive bath, followed by drying and heat-treating of the adhesive-coated fiber to obtain better adhesion.

DIRECT CABLING: A method of producing a balanced plied yarn from balanced singles yarns on a TWO-FOR-ONE TWISTER.

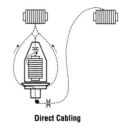

Direct Cabling

DIRECT DYES: See DYES.

DIRECT ESTERIFICATION: In the production of polyethylene terephthalate, the process in which ethylene glycol is reacted with terephthalic acid to form bis-β-hydroxyethyl terephthalate monomer with the generation of water as a by-product.

DIRECTIONALLY ORIENTED FABRICS: Rigid fabric constructions containing inlaid warp or fill yarns held in place by a warp-knit structure. Used in geotextiles, coated fabrics, composites, etc.

DIRECTION OF TWIST: See TWIST, DIRECTION OF.

DIRECT PRINTING: See PRINTING, 1.

DIRECT SPINNING: 1. A process for the production of manufactured fiber in which polymerization is followed directly by extrusion. **2.** A variation of the COTTON SPINNING SYSTEM in which yarn is spun directly from card sliver.

DIRECT WARPING: A method of winding warp yarns in preparation for weaving in which the yarn is wound from packages on a creel directly onto a beam. (Contrast with SECTION WARPING.)

DIRECT YARN NUMBER: A designation for yarn size using a system such as DENIER or TEX in which the higher numbers identify coarser yarns. In indirect numbering systems such as the cotton count, the number is the reciprocal of linear density; thus the lower the number, the coarser the yarn.

DISCHARGE PRINTING: See PRINTING, 1.

DISCHARGING: 1. See PRINTING, 1. DISCHARGE PRINTING. **2.** See DEGUMMING.

DISCOLORED PICK: See MIXED END OR FILLING.

DISC TEST: An in-rubber test used to predict the fatigue resistance of tire cords and other industrial yarns.

DISPERSANT: A dispersing agent, often of a surface active chemical, that promotes formation of a dispersion or maintains a state of dispersion by preventing settling or aggregation.

DISPERSE DYES: See DYES.

DISPERSION: 1. A system consisting of finely divided particles and the medium in which they are distributed. **2.** Separation of light into colors by diffraction or refraction. **3.** A qualitative estimation of the separation and uniform distribution of fibers in the liquid during the production of a wet-formed nonwoven fabric.

DISPERSION SPINNING: A process for extrusion of fibers from polymers that will not melt or form solutions for the spinning process. Fine polymer particles are dispersed in a carrier such as a gum solution for extrusion, after which the polymer is fused to form fibers and the carrier is removed.

DISTRIBUTION LENGTH: In fibers, a graphic or tabular presentation of the proportion or percentage (by number or by weight) of fibers having different lengths.

DIVIDED THREADLINE EXTRUSION: Spinning of two separate threadlines from one spinneret.

DMEU: Acronym for DIMETHYLOLETHYLENEUREA. (Also see GLYOXAL RESINS.)

DOBBY: 1. A mechanical attachment on a loom. A dobby controls the harnesses to permit the weaving of geometric figures. **2.** A loom equipped with a dobby. **3.** A fabric woven on a dobby loom.

DOCTOR BLADE: 1. A metal knife that cleans or scrapes the excess dye from engraved printing rollers, leaving dye paste only in the valleys of engraved areas. Also used to describe other blades that are used to apply materials evenly to rollers or fabrics. **2.** In coating fabrics, a metal knife that spreads the coating material as it is applied to the moving fabric, thereby achieving an even application while removing the excess coating.

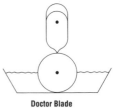

Doctor Blade

DOCTOR STREAK: A defect in printed fabrics consisting of a wavy white or colored streak in the warp direction. It is caused by a damaged or improperly set doctor blade on the printing machine.

DOESKIN FINISH: A soft low nap that is brushed in one direction. Cloth with this type of finish is used on billiard tables and in menswear.

DOFF: A set of full bobbins produced by one machine (a roving frame, a spinning frame, or a manufactured filament-yarn extrusion machine).

DOFFER: 1. The last or delivery cylinder of the card from which the sheet of fibers is removed by the doffer comb. **2.** An operator who removes full bobbins, spools, containers, or other packages from a machine and replaces them with empty ones.

DOFFER COMB: A reciprocating comb, the teeth of which oscillate close to the card clothing of the doffer to strip the web of fibers from the card.

DOFFER LOADING: Fibers imbedded so deeply into the doffer wire clothing that the doffer comb cannot dislodge them to form a traveling web.

DOFFING: The operation of removing full packages, bobbins, spools, roving cans, caps, etc., from a machine and replacing them with empty ones.

DONEGAL: A tweed fabric with colorful slubs woven in, donegal is used for suits and coats.

DOPE: See SPINNING SOLUTION.

DOPE-DYED: See DYEING, SOLUTION-DYEING.

DOTTED SWISS: A sheer cotton or cotton blend fabric with small dot motif, dotted swiss is used for dress goods, curtains, baby clothes, etc.

DOUBLE BACK: A secondary backing glued to the back of a carpet, usually to increase dimensional stability.

DOUBLE-CLOTH CONSTRUCTION: Two fabrics are woven in the loom at the same time, one fabric on top of the other, with binder threads holding the two fabrics together. The weave on the two fabrics can be different.

DOUBLED YARN: See PLIED YARN.

DOUBLE END: Two ends woven as one in a fabric. A double end may be intentional for fabric styling, or accidental, in which case a fabric defect results.

DOUBLE-KNIT FABRIC: A weft-knit fabric produced on a dial-and-cylinder knitting machine, which is equipped with two sets of latch needles situated at right angles to each other. The double construction that results is heavier and more stable than a single-knit construction. (Also see JACQUARD KNIT FABRIC.)

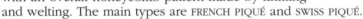

DOUBLE PICK: See MISPICK.

DOUBLE PIQUÉ: A non-jacquard double-knit fabric with an overall honeycomb pattern made by knitting and welting. The main types are FRENCH PIQUÉ and SWISS PIQUÉ.

Double-Knit Fabric
Construction

DOUBLE SELVAGE: See ROLLED SELVAGE.

DOUBLE WEAVE: A fabric woven with two systems of warp or filling threads so combined that only one is visible on either side. Cutting the yarns that hold the two cloths together yields two separate cut-pile fabrics.

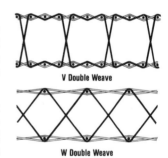

V Double Weave

W Double Weave

DOUBLE-WOVEN PILE FABRIC: A pile fabric produced by weaving two separate woven fabrics face to face with float yarns interlaced between the two. An automatic knife on the loom moves between the two fabrics severing the floats, which become the cut pile.

DOUBLING: 1. A process for combining several strands of sliver, roving, or yarn in yarn manufacturing. **2.** The process of twisting together two or more singles or plied yarns, i.e., plying. **3.** A British term for twisting. **4.** The term doubling is sometimes used in a sense opposite to singling. This is unintentional plying. **5.** A yarn, considerably heavier than normal, produced by a broken end becoming attached to and twisting into another end.

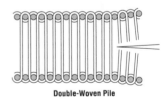

Double-Woven Pile

DOUPPIONI: A rough or irregular yarn made of silk reeled from double or triple cocoons. Fabrics of douppioni have an irregular appearance with long, thin slubs. Douppioni-like yarns are now being spun from polyester and/or rayon staple.

DOUP WEAVE: See LENO WEAVE.

DOWNDRAFT METIER: A dry-spinning machine in which the air flow within the drying cabinet is in the same direction as the yarn path (downward).

DOWN-GRADE: In quality control, the lowering of the grade and/or value of a product due to the presence of defects.

DOWNTWISTER: A cap, ring, or flyer twisting frame.

DOWNTWISTING: A process for inserting twist into yarn in which the yarn passes downward from the supply package (a bobbin, cheese, or cone) to the revolving spindle. The package or packages of yarn to be twisted are positioned on the creel, and the ends of yarn are led downward through individual guides and stop motions to the positively driven feed roll and from there to the revolving take-up package or bobbin, which inserts twist.

DOWTHERM®: Trademark of Dow Chemical Company for a series of heat-transfer media. Dowtherm jackets are used around molten polymer processing lines.

DPF: Acronym for denier per filament and decitex per filament.

DRAFT: In weaving, a pattern or plan for drawing-in.

DRAFTING: See DRAWING, 1.

DRAFTING APRON: See APRON.

DRAFTING ROLLS: Sequential sets of rolls on drawframes and roving, combing and spinning machines. Each set of rolls rotates faster than the preceding set, which attenuates the sliver or roving in the drawing process.

DRAFTING ZONE: The space between two sets of drafting rolls.

DRAFT RATIO: The ratio between the weight or length of fiber fed into various machines and that delivered from the machines in spun yarn manufacture. It represents the reduction in bulk and weight of stock, one of the most important principles in the production of yarn from staple fibers.

DRAGGED-IN FILLING: See PULLED-IN FILLING.

DRAINAGE FABRICS: See GEOTEXTILES.

DRAPE: A term to describe the way a fabric falls while it hangs; the suppleness and ability of a fabric to form graceful configurations.

DRAW-BACK: A crossed end; an end broken during warping that when repaired was not free or was tied in with an adjacent end or ends overlapping the broken end. The end draws or pulls back when unwound on the slasher. (Also see STICKER, 1.)

DRAW-CRIMPING: See DRAW-TEXTURING.

DRAW-DOWN: See DRAW RATIO.

DRAWFRAME BLENDS: Blends of fibers made at the drawframe by feeding in ends of appropriate card sliver. This method is used when blend uniformity is not a critical factor.

DRAWING: 1. The process of attenuating or increasing the length per unit weight of laps, slivers, slubbings, or rovings. **2.** The hot or cold stretching of continuous filament yarn or tow to align and arrange the crystalline structure of the molecules along the fiber axis to achieve improved tensile properties.

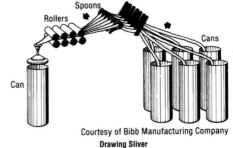

Courtesy of Bibb Manufacturing Company
Drawing Sliver

DRAWING-IN: In weaving, the process of threading warp ends through the eyes of the heddles and the dents of the reed.

DRAWN TOW: A zero-twist bundle of continuous filaments that has been stretched to achieve molecular orientation. (Tows for staple and spun-yarn applications are usually crimped.)

DRAW RATIO: The ratio of linear density or cross-sectional area of filaments before and after they are stretched following extrusion.

DRAW-SIZING: A system linking draw-warping and sizing in a continuous process. A typical system includes the following elements: (1) creel, (2) eyelet board, (3) warp-draw machine, (4) intermingler, (5) tension compensator and break monitor, (6) sizing bath, (7) dryers, (8) waxing and winding units.

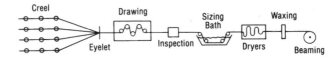

Draw-Sizing

DRAW-SPINNING: See SPIN-DRAWING.

DRAW-TEXTURING: In the manufacture of thermoplastic fibers, the simultaneous process of drawing to increase molecular orientation and imparting crimp to increase bulk.

DRAW-TWISTING: The operation of stretching continuous filament yarn to align and order the molecular and crystalline structure in which the yarn is taken up by means of a ring-and-traveler device that inserts a small amount of twist (usually $\frac{1}{4}$–$\frac{1}{2}$ turn per inch) into the drawn yarn.

DRAW-WARPING: A process in which a number of threadlines, usually 800–2000 ends of POY feedstock, are oriented under essentially equal mechanical and thermal conditions by a stretching stage using variable speed rolls, then directly wound onto the beam. This process gives uniform end-to-end properties.

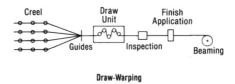

Draw-Warping

DRAW-WINDING: The operation of stretching continuous filament yarn to align or order molecular and crystalline structure. The drawn yarn is taken up on a parallel tube or cheese, resulting in a zero-twist yarn.

DREF PROCESS: See FRICTION SPINNING.

DRILL: A strong denim-like material with a diagonal 2 x 1 weave running toward the left selvage. Drill is often called khaki when it is dyed that color.

DROPPED STITCHES: A defect in knit cloth characterized by recurrent cuts in one or more wales of a length of cloth.

DROP STITCH: 1. An open design made in knitting by removing some of the needles at set intervals. **2.** A defect in knit fabric.

DROP WIRES: A stop-motion device utilizing metal wires suspended from warp or creeled yarns. When a yarn breaks, the wire drops, activating the switch that stops the machine.

DRY CLEANING: Removing dirt and stains from fabrics or garments by processing in organic solvents (chlorinated hydrocarbons or mineral spirits).

DRYER FABRIC: See PAPERMAKER'S FELT.

DRY FILLING: The application of finishing chemicals to dry fabric, usually by padding.

DRYING CYLINDERS: Any of a number of heated revolving cylinders for drying fabric or yarn. They are arranged either vertically or horizontally in sets, with the number varying according to the material to be dried. They are often internally heated with steam and Teflon-coated to prevent sticking.

DRY-LAID NONWOVEN: Nonwoven web made from dry fiber. Usually refers to fabrics from carded webs versus air-laid nonwovens which are formed from random webs.

DRY-LAID PULP: A nonwoven fabric formed in the dry state primarily from wood pulp.

DRY LAYING: The production of fiber webs by methods that do not use water or other liquids, i.e., air-laying or carding.

DRY SPINNING: See SPINNING, 2.

DUCK: A compact, firm, heavy, plain-weave fabric with a weight of 6–50 ounces per square yard. Plied yarn duck has plied yarns in both warp and filling. Flat duck has a warp of two singles yarns woven as one and a filling of either singles or plied yarn.

DUCK EYE: See PINHOLE.

DULL: A term applied to manufactured fibers that have been chemically or physically modified to reduce their normal luster. Matte; opposite of bright; low in luster.

DUMBBELLS: A defect frequently seen in wet-formed nonwoven fabrics; an unusually long fiber will become entangled with groups of regular-length fibers at each end, thus producing a dumbbell-shaped clump.

DUNGAREE: A term describing a coarse denim-type fabric, usually dyed blue, that is used for work overalls.

DUPLEX PRINTING: See PRINTING, 1.

DURABILITY: A relative term for the resistance of a material to loss of physical properties or appearance as a result of wear or dynamic operation.

DURABLE PRESS: A term describing a garment that has been treated so that it retains its smooth appearance, shape, and creases or pleats in laundering. In such garments no ironing is required, particularly if the garment is tumble dried. Durable-press finishing is accomplished by several methods; two of the most common are the following: (1) A fabric that contains a thermoplastic fiber and cotton or rayon may be treated with a special resin that, when cured, imparts the permanent shape to the cotton or rayon component of the fabric. The resin-treated fabric may be precured (cured in finishing and subsequently pressed in garment form at a higher temperature to achieve the permanent shape) or postcured (not cured until the finished garment has been sewn and pressed into shape). In both cases, the thermoplastic fiber in the garment is set in the final heat treatment. This fiber, when heat-set, also contributes to the permanence of the garment shape, but the thermoplastic component of the blend is needed for strength since the cotton or rayon component is somewhat degraded by the durable-press treatment. (2) Garments of a fabric containing a sufficient amount of a thermoplastic fiber, such as polyester, nylon, or acrylic, may be pressed with sufficient pressure and time to achieve a permanent garment shape. (Also see EASY-CARE and PERMANENT FINISH.)

DUST-RESISTANT: A term applied to a fabric that has been tightly woven so that it resists dust penetration.

DWELL TIME: The time during a process in which a particular substance remains in one location (e.g., the time during which molten polymer remains in a spinning pack).

DYEABILITY: A term used to describe the ability of fibers to accept dyes. (Also see AFFINITY and SUBSTANTIVITY.)

DYEBATH: A solution or dispersion containing dyes and dyeing auxiliaries for the dyeing process. Water is usually the application medium. (Also see DYEING, SOLVENT DYEING.)

DYE CAPACITY: The amount of dye a fiber can hold.

DYE CARRIER: See CARRIER, 1.

DYE FIXATION: See FIXATION.

DYE FLECK: 1. An imperfection in fabric caused by residual undissolved dye. **2.** A defect caused by small sections of undrawn thermoplastic yarn that dye deeper than the drawn yarn.

DYEING: A process of coloring fibers, yarns, or fabrics with either natural or synthetic dyes. Some of the major dyeing processes are described below:

Alkaline Dyeing (Polyester): A process for high-temperature application of selected disperse dyes from an alkaline bath, normally maintained between pH 8.5 and pH 11.4. The method is said to remove oligimer and soften the fibers.

Batch Dyeing: A process in which separate pieces of fabric are handled sequentially through dyeing and subsequent processes.

Batik: A resist-dyeing process in which portions of a fabric are coated with wax; during the dyeing process, only the uncovered areas take up dye. The process can be repeated so that several colors are used. Batik dyeing is often imitated in machine printing.

Beam Dyeing: Dyeing fabric wound on a perforated stainless-steel cylinder in a process similar to package dyeing of yarn.

Cake Dyeing: Dyeing viscose rayon filament yarn in the cake package that is wound as the yarn is spun. The dyed yarn is then repackaged for further processing.

Chain Dyeing: A method of dyeing yarns and fabrics of low tensile strength by tying them end-to-end and running them through the dyebath in a continuous process.

Cold-Pad-Batch Dyeing: A dyeing process for fabrics of natural cellulosic fibers using fiber-reactive dyes. The fabric is impregnated with unheated dye liquor and batched onto a large roll. The roll containing the wet fabric is slowly rotated until the dyeing is complete.

Continuous Dyeing: A process in which the fabric passes through dyeing and subsequent operations without interruption, as contrasted with batch dyeing. For very long runs of fabric dyed the same color, continuous dyeing offers savings in labor costs and time.

Cross Dyeing: A method of dyeing blend or combination fabrics to two or more shades by the use of dyes with different affinities for the different fibers.

Differential Dyeing: 1. A term used to describe the differences in coloration that occur when modified fibers take up more dye than normal fibers. (Also see DEEP-DYEING VARIANTS.) **2.** The results of variable uptake of dyes in cotton fibers of different maturities.

Dip Dyeing: A process for dyeing hosiery and other knit items.

Garment Dyeing: Any dyeing process for whole garments such as socks. Today, garment dyeing is widely used in the production of stone-washed denim garments.

Gel Dyeing: Passing a wet-spun fiber that is in the gel state (not yet at full crystallinity or orientation) through a dyebath containing dye with affinity for the fiber. This process provides good accessibility of the dye sites.

High-Temperature Dyeing: A dyeing operation in which the aqueous dyebaths are maintained at temperatures greater than 100°C by use of pressurized equipment. Used for many manufactured fibers.

Ingrain Dyeing: A process for dyeing yarn or stock in two or more shades prior to knitting or weaving to create blended color effects in fabrics.

Jet Dyeing: High temperature piece dyeing in which the dye liquor is circulated via a venturi jet that provides the force to move the loop of fabric.

Melt Dyeing: Coloration of melt-spun fiber (yarn, staple, or tow) during the spinning process by introducing pigments or insoluble dyes into the polymer melt prior to extrusion. Usually the colors are fast to most destructive agents.

Muff Dyeing: A form of yarn dyeing in which the cone has been removed.

Package Dyeing: See DYEING, YARN DYEING.

Pad Dyeing: A form of dyeing whereby a dye solution is applied by means of a padder or mangle.

Pad-Steam Dyeing: A continuous open-width dyeing method for fabric containing natural cellulosic fibers. The goods are padded with a bath containing vat pigments, followed by a bath containing the chemicals, usually sodium hydroxide and sodium dithionite, which are required to convert the dyes to a soluble form. The fabric next passes through a steam chamber where the reduction reaction and dyeing occur, then it is treated in an oxidizing bath to return the dyes to their insoluble form.

Piece Dyeing: The dyeing of fabrics "in the piece," i.e., in fabric form after weaving or knitting as opposed to dyeing in the form of yarn or stock.

Pressure Dyeing: Dyeing by means of forced circulation of dye through packages of fiber, yarn, or fabric under superatmospheric pressure.

Reserve Dyeing: 1. A method of dyeing in which one component of a blend or combination fabric is left undyed. The objective is accomplished by the use of dyes that have affinity for the fiber to be colored but not for the fiber to be reserved. **2.** A method of treating yarn or fabric so that in the subsequent dyeing operation the treated portion will not be dyed.

Short-Liquor Dyeing: A term used to describe any yarn or piece dyeing in which the liquor ratio has been significantly reduced. The technique was designed to save water and energy.

Skein Dyeing: The dyeing of yarn in the form of skeins or hanks.

Solution Dyeing: Coloration of solution-spun fiber (yarn, staple, or tow) during the spinning process by introducing pigments or insoluble dyes into the polymer solution prior to extrusion. Usually the colors are fast to most destructive agents.

Solvent Dyeing: A dyeing method based on solubility of a dye in some liquid other than water, although water may be present in the dyebath. The solvent dyeing process using liquid hydrocarbons has become obsolete due to environmental concerns.

Space Dyeing: A yarn-dyeing process in which each strand is dyed with more than one color at irregular intervals. Space dyeing produces an effect of unorganized design in subsequent fabric form. The two primary methods are knit-deknit and warp printing.

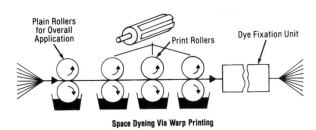

Space Dyeing Via Warp Printing

Spun-Dyed: See DYEING, MELT DYEING and DYEING, SOLUTION DYEING.

Stock Dyeing: The dyeing of fibers in staple form.

Supercritical Dyeing: A dyeing technology using special disperse dyes in a supercritical fluid, supercritical carbon dioxide, which is considered to be environmentally friendly and toxicologically harmless. Above its supercritical point (34°C at a pressure of 74 bar), CO_2 has solvent properties similar to those of liquid hydrocarbons. Fabrics or yarns are wound on a perforated cylinder and dyed in an autoclave under high pressure.

Thermal Fixation: A process for dyeing polyester whereby the color is diffused into the fiber by means of dry heat.

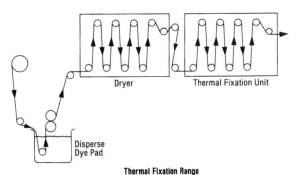

Thermal Fixation Range

Tie Dyeing: A hand dyeing method in which bunched sections of the fabric are tightly tied before dyeing. The method produces a pattern by variable dyeing because the dye liquor does not fully penetrate the tied areas.

Union Dyeing: A method of dyeing a fabric containing two or more types of fibers or yarns to the same shade so as to achieve the appearance of a solid colored fabric.

Vapor-Phase Dyeing: A dyeing method for textiles that is used to apply dyes in their gas phase. (Also see SUBLIMATION.)

Warp Dyeing: Dyeing of warp yarns prior to weaving. The warp is usually wound on a beam and dyed in a pressure vessel.

Yarn Dyeing: The dyeing of yarn before the fabric is woven or knit. Yarn can be dyed in the form of skeins, muffs, packages, cheeses, cakes, chain-warps, and beams.

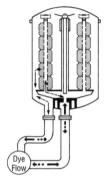

Package Dyeing, a Form of Yarn Dyeing

DYEING AUXILIARIES: Various substances that can be added to the dyebath to aid dyeing. They may be necessary to transfer the dye from the bath to the fiber or they may provide improvements in leveling, penetration, etc. Also called dyeing assistants.

DYE MIGRATION: See MIGRATION, 1.

DYE RANGE: A broad term referring to the collection of dye and chemical baths, drying equipment, etc., in a continuous-dyeing line.

DYE RATE: The rate at which a fiber accepts dye.

DYES: Substances that add color to textiles. They are incorporated into the fiber by chemical reaction, absorption, or dispersion. Dyes differ in their resistance to sunlight, perspiration, washing, gas, alkalies, and other agents; their affinity for different fibers; their reaction to cleaning agents and methods; and their solubility and method of application. Various classes and types are listed below. (Also see COLOUR INDEX [CI].)

Acid Dyes: A class of dyes used on wool, other animal fibers, and some manufactured fibers. Acid dyes are seldom used on cotton or linen since this process requires a mordant. Acid dyes are widely used on nylon when high washfastness is required. In some cases, even higher washfastness can be obtained by aftertreatment with fixatives.

Aniline Dyes: Dyes derived chemically from aniline or other coal tar derivatives.

Anthraquinone Dyes: Dyes that have anthraquinone as their base and the carbonyl group ($>C=O$) as the chromophore. Anthraquinone-based dyes are found in most of the synthetic dye classes.

Azo Dyes: Dyes characterized by the presence of an azo group ($-N=N-$) as the chromophore. Azo dyes are found in many of the synthetic dye classes.

Azoic Dyes: See DYES, NAPHTHOL DYES.

Basic Dyes: A class of positive-ion-carrying dyes known for their brilliant hues. Basic dyes are composed of large-molecule, water-soluble salts that have a direct affinity for wool and silk and can be applied to cotton with a mordant. The fastness of basic dyes on these fibers is very poor. Basic dyes are also used on basic-dyeable acrylics, modacrylics, nylons, and polyesters, on which they exhibit reasonably good fastness.

Cationic Dyes: See DYES, BASIC DYES.

Chrome Dyes: Mordant dyes capable of forming a chelate with chromium ions.

Developed Dyes: Dyes that are formed by the use of a developer. The substrate is first dyed in a neutral solution with a dye base, usually colorless. The dye is then diazotized with sodium nitrite and an acid and afterwards treated with a solution of ß-naphthol, or a similar substance, which is the developer. Direct dyes are developed to produce a different shade or to improve washfastness and lightfastness.

Direct Dyes: A class of dyestuffs that is applied directly to the substrate in a neutral or alkaline bath. Direct dyes produce full shades on cotton and linen without mordanting and can also be applied to rayon, silk, and wool. Direct dyes give bright shades but exhibit poor washfastness. Various aftertreatments are used to improve the washfastness of direct dyes, and such dyes are referred to as "aftertreated direct colors."

Disperse Dyes: A class of slightly water-soluble dyes originally introduced for dyeing acetate and usually applied from fine aqueous suspensions. Disperse dyes are widely used for dyeing most of the manufactured fibers.

Fiber-Reactive Dyes: A type of water-soluble anionic dye having affinity for cellulose fibers. In the presence of alkali, they react with hydroxyl groups in the cellulose and thus are linked with the fiber. Fiber-reactive dyes are used extensively on cellulosics when bright shades are desired.

Macromolecular Dyes: A group of inherently colored polymers. They are useful both as polymers and as dyes with high color yield. The chromophores fit the recognized CI classes, i.e., azo, anthraquinone, etc., although not all CI classes are represented.

Metal-Free Reactive Dyes: Special environmentally friendly reactive dyes for wool and silk.

Metalized Dyes: A class of dyes that have metals in their molecular structure. They are applied from an acid bath.

Naphthol Dyes: A type of azo compound formed on the fiber by first treating the fiber with a phenolic compound. The fiber is then immersed in a second solution containing a diazonium salt that reacts with the phenolic compound to produce a colored azo compound. Since the phenolic compound is dissolved in caustic solution, these dyes are mainly used for cellulose fibers, although other fibers can be dyed by modifying the process. (Also see DYES, DEVELOPED DYES.)

Neutral Dyeing Acid Dyes: Acid dyes that can be applied to wool, silk, and nylon from a neutral dyebath. They generally have poor leveling properties but yield dyeings with good wet fastness.

Nonionic Dyes: Dyes that do not dissociate into anions and cations in aqueous solution.

Premetalized Dyes: Acid dyes that are treated with coordinating metals such as chromium. This type of dye has much better wetfastness than regular acid dye. Premetalized dyes are used on nylon, silk, and wool.

Sulfur Dyes: A class of water-insoluble dyes that are applied in a soluble, reduced form from a sodium sulfide solution and are then reoxidized to the insoluble form on the fiber. Sulfur dyes are mainly used on cotton for economical dark shades of moderate to good fastness to washing and light. They generally give very poor fastness to chlorine.

Vat Dyes: A class of water-insoluble dyes which are applied to the fiber in a reduced, soluble form (leuco compound) and then reoxidized to the original insoluble form. Vat dyes are among the most resistant dyes to both washing and sunlight. They are widely used on cotton, linen, rayon, and other cellulosic fibers.

DYE SITES: Functional groups within a fiber that provide sites for chemical bonding with the dye molecule. Dye sites may be either in the polymer chain or in chemical additives included in the fiber.

DYE STREAK: A dyeing defect consisting of a darker or lighter line or bar through the fabric caused by nonuniform dye uptake.

DYESTUFF: See DYES.

DYNAMIC ADHESION: The ability of a cord-to-rubber bond to resist degradation resulting from flexure.

DYNAMIC LOADING TEST: 1. A test for fabric that measures the effect of repeated application of a load less than the breaking load. **2.** A test for carpet that measures thickness loss when a specimen is repeatedly impacted with a standard weight.

DYNAPOINT PROCESS: A continuous computer-controlled process for manufacturing tufted carpets with intricate patterns from undyed yarn. The carpet is dyed as it is tufted and the colors and pattern are clearly visible through the primary backing of the carpet.

E

EASY-CARE: A term used to characterize fabrics that, after laundering, can be restored to their original appearance with a minimum of ironing or other treatment. An easy-care fabric generally wrinkles only slightly upon laundering. (Also see DURABLE PRESS.)

EDGE ABRASION: Wear on the folded edge of a fabric that has rubbed against another surface. It occurs in items such as cuffs, collars, and furniture upholstery.

EDGE ABRASION TESTER: See STOLL-QUARTERMASTER UNIVERSAL WEAR TESTER.

EDGE CRIMPING: See TEXTURING, 2.

EDGE ROLL: The curl that develops at the edge of a single-knit fabric preventing it from lying flat.

EDGE WIRE: A wire or monofilament drawn through one or both heddles at the edges of the warp on a loom. It is held in place and the fabric slides off as weaving proceeds. Its purpose is to improve the softness and appearance of the selvage.

EDI: Acronym for ELECTRONIC DATA INTERCHANGE.

EFFECTIVE FIBER LENGTH: In testing of fiber fineness, the length of the fiber specimen in the clamps of the VIBROSCOPE.

EFFECT YARN: A special yarn of any type inserted in a fabric construction to produce a novelty effect or pattern.

ELASTIC FABRIC: A fabric that contains elastic threads. Such fabrics are used for girdles, garters, and similar items.

ELASTICITY: The ability of a strained material to recover its original size and shape immediately after removal of the stress that causes deformation.

ELASTIC LIMIT: In strength and stretch testing, the load below which the specimen shows elasticity and above which it shows permanent deformation. (Also see YIELD POINT.)

ELASTIC RECOVERY: The degree to which a fiber, yarn, or cord returns to its original size and shape after deformation from stress.

ELASTOMERIC YARN: Yarn formed from or containing filaments of an elastomer. It must have the ability to return to its original length rapidly after repeated stretching to at least twice its original length. (Also see STRETCH YARN.)

ELASTOMERS: Synthetic polymers having properties of natural rubber such as high stretchability and recovery.

ELECTRICAL CONDUCTIVITY: 1. A measure of the ease of transporting electric charge from one point to another in an electric field. **2.** The reciprocal of resistivity.

ELECTRICAL FINISH: A finish designed to increase or maintain electrical resistivity of a textile material.

ELECTRICAL RESISTIVITY: The resistance to longitudinal electrical flow through a uniform rod of unit length and unit cross-sectional area.

ELECTRONIC DATA INTERCHANGE: An automated system for transferring computerized data or information between locations such as supplier to customer, e.g., information about inventories, orders, shipments, forecasts, and production schedules.

ELECTRONIC JACQUARD: See JACQUARD.

ELECTROSTATIC FLOCKING: A process for applying flock fibers to an adhesive-coated textile substrate in a high-voltage electrostatic field that orients the flock perpendicular to the substrate and assists in achieving a good bond with the coating.

ELECTROSTATIC PRINTING: See PRINTING, 1.

ELECTROSTATIC SPINNING: A type of open-end spinning that uses an electrostatic field as a force for orienting and transporting the fibers to the twister.

ELMENDORF TEAR TESTER: A tester designed to determine the tearing strength of paper. It is also used to measure the tearing strength of very lightweight fabrics and resin-finished apparel fabrics. A trapezoidal fabric sample is employed.

ELONGATION: The deformation in the direction of load caused by a tensile force. Elongation is measured in units of length (e.g., millimeters, inches) or calculated as a percentage of the original specimen length. Elongation may be measured at any specified load or at the breaking load.

ELONGATION AT BREAK: The increase in length when the last component of the specimen breaks.

EMBOSSED CARPET: Carpeting with a pattern formed when heavy twisted tufts are used in a ground of straight yarns to create an engraved appearance. Both the straight and twisted yarns are often of the same color.

EMBOSSING: A calendering process for producing raised or projected figures or designs in relief on fabric surfaces. Embossed surfaces are usually produced on fabrics by engraved, heated rollers that give a raised effect. Embossed velvet or plush is made by shearing the pile to different levels or by pressing part of the pile flat.

EMBROIDERY: Ornamental designs worked on a fabric with threads. Embroidery may be done either by hand or by machine.

EMERIZING: A dry finishing process using emery cloth to produce suede fabrics.

EMULSION: A suspension of finely divided liquid droplets in a second liquid, i.e., oil in water or vice versa.

EMULSION POLYMERIZATION: A three-phase reaction system consisting of monomer, an aqueous phase containing the initiator, and colloidal particles of polymer. Polymerization takes place in the colloidal phase. The process enables the production of very high molecular weights at increased polymerization rates. Only applicable to addition polymers.

EMULSION SPINNING: The process of spinning synthetic polymers in dispersion form, then heating to coalesce the dispersed particles. Normally a matrix polymer provides support until coalescence is completed.

END: 1. An individual warp yarn. A warp is composed of a multitude of ends. **2.** An individual sliver, slubbing, roving, yarn, thread, or cord. **3.** A short length or remnant of fabric.

END DOWN: A broken yarn during spinning or weaving. On a loom, the broken end activates a stop motion.

END GROUP: A functional chemical group that forms the end of a polymer chain.

END OUT: A void caused by a missing warp yarn.

ENERGY ABSORPTION: The energy required to break or elongate a fiber to a certain point.

ENERGY-TO-BREAK: The total energy required to rupture a yarn or cord.

ENGLISH SPINNING SYSTEM: See BRADFORD SPINNING SYSTEM.

ENTANGLED YARNS: See TEXTURED YARNS, 5.

ENTANGLING: 1. A method of forming a fabric by wrapping and knotting fibers in a web about each other, by mechanical means, or by the use of jets of pressurized water, so as to bond the fibers. (Also see HYDROENTANGLING and SPUNLACED FABRIC.) **2.** See INTERMINGLING.

ENTERING: The process of threading each warp yarn on a loom beam through a separate drop wire, heddle, and reed space in preparation for weaving. This process may be done by hand or by a semiautomatic machine.

ENVIRONMENTAL CHAMBER: An enclosure that simulates natural conditions of light, temperature, humidity, and atmospheric gases. It is used to test the effect of exposure to specific environmental conditions on textile materials.

ENZYME FINISHING: Wet processes for textiles that employ enzymes that act as biological catalyst to achieve various effects. For example, cellulases are used to modify the aesthetics of cotton, viscose, and linen fabrics; proteases for degumming raw silk; hydrolases in washing, degreasing, bleaching, and antifelting treatment of wool; and alpha amylases for the bio-conversion of starch size. For denims, enzyme finishing has largely replaced STONE WASHING.

EPITROPIC FIBER: A manufactured fiber with a surface modified to alter a specific property such as electrical conductivity or abrasion resistance.

EPOXY RESIN: In textiles, a compound used in durable-press applications for white fabrics. It provides chlorine resistance but causes loss of tensile strength.

EQUIVALENT SINGLE YARN NUMBER: See YARN NUMBER, EQUIVALENT SINGLE.

EROSION CONTROL FABRICS: See GEOTEXTILES.

ESP: Acronym for extra stretch and performance, used as a descriptor for KoSa's polybutylene terephthalate filament yarn.

ESTERIFICATION: The chemical process of combining an acid and an alcohol to form an ester. Cellulose acetate is an ester formed by the reaction of acetic acid and the hydroxyl groups of cellulose. Polyethylene terephthalate, the most common fiber-forming polyester, is a product of esterification of terephthalic acid with ethylene glycol.

ESTER INTERCHANGE: See TRANSESTERIFICATION.

ESTHETICS: See AESTHETICS.

ETCHING: See PRINTING, 1. BURN-OUT PRINTING.

ETHYLENE: A petroleum derivative (C_2H_4) that is the raw material for polyethylene.

ETHYLENE GLYCOL: A viscous, sweet, colorless liquid (CH_2OHCH_2OH). Principal uses are as an intermediate in the manufacture of polyester fibers and as automobile antifreeze.

EVENNESS TESTING: Determination of the variation in weight per unit length and thickness of yarns or fiber aggregates such as roving, sliver, or top.

EXCESSIVE CLEARER WASTE: A higher than normal amount of short and regular fibers that become attached to the drafting rolls and are transferred to the clearer brushes to accumulate in abnormal amounts until they are removed manually.

EXHAUSTION: During wet processing, the ratio at any time between the amount of dye or substance taken up by the substrate and the amount originally available.

EXPANDER: A device on some textile machines that spreads a fabric to its full width as it advances.

EXTENDED LENGTH: The length of a face pile yarn required to produce one inch of tufted carpet.

EXTENSIBILITY: The ability of a material to undergo elongation on the application of force. (Also see ELONGATION.)

EXTRACTABLES: The material that can be removed from textiles by means of a solvent (in many cases, water).

EXTRACTION: 1. Removal of one substance from another, often accomplished by means of a solvent. **2.** The process of removing water, lint, gum, or excess dye from a substrate by means of a vacuum.

EXTRACT PRINTING: See PRINTING, 1. DISCHARGE PRINTING.

EXTRUDER: 1. Generally a machine in which molten or semisoft materials are forced under pressure through a die to form continuous tubes, sheets, or fibers. It may consist of a barrel, heating elements, a screw, ram or plunger, and a die through which the material is pushed to give it shape. **2.** In fiber manufacture, the machine that feeds molten polymer to an extrusion manifold or that first melts the polymer in a uniform manner, then feeds it to a manifold and associated equipment for extrusion. (Also see SCREW MELTER.)

EXTRUSION: See SPINNING, 2.

EYELET: 1. A series of small holes made to receive a string or tape. A buttonhole stitch is worked around the holes. **2.** A type of yarn guide used on a creel. **3.** A fabric style with areas of cut-outs surrounded by stitching.

F

FABRIC: A manufactured planar structure made of fibers and/or yarns assembled by various means such as weaving, knitting, tufting, felting, braiding, or bonding of webs to give the structure sufficient strength and other properties required for its intended use.

FABRIC CONSTRUCTION: The details of structure of fabric. Includes such information as style, width, type of knit or weave, threads per inch in warp and fill, and weight of goods.

FABRIC CRIMP: The angulation induced between a yarn and a woven fabric via the weaving or braiding process.

FABRIC CRIMP ANGLE: The maximum acute angle of a single weaving yarn's direction measured from a plane parallel to the surface of the fabric.

Crimp Angle

Fabric Crimp Angle

FABRIC SETT: The number of warp threads per inch, or other convenient unit.

FABRIC STABILIZER: Resin or latex treatment for scrims used in coated fabric manufacture to stabilize the scrim for further processing.

FACE: The correct or better-looking side of a fabric.

FACE WEIGHT: See PILE WEIGHT.

FACING: A lining or trim that protects the edges of a garment especially at collars, cuffs, and front closings.

FAÇONNÉ: A broad term for fabrics with a fancy-type weave made on a jacquard or dobby loom.

FADE-OMETER®: Laboratory device used to determine the fastness of a colored fabric to exposure to light. The test pieces are rotated around a light source simulating the sun's rays at 45° N latitude in July between the hours of 9 a.m. and 3 p.m. Fabrics are rated by visual comparison with a gray scale according to degree of fading.

FADING: Loss of color caused by exposure to conditions or agents such as sunlight, washing, perspiration, and atmospheric gases that can remove or destroy the color.

FAILLE: A soft, slightly glossy woven fabric made of silk, rayon, cotton, wool, or manufactured fibers or combinations of these fibers and having a light, flat crossgrain rib or cord made by using heavier yarns in the filling than in the warp.

FALSE-TWISTING: See TEXTURING, 3.

FANCY: 1. A roll about 12 inches in diameter that is located next to the cylinder on a carding machine. The fancy lifts the fibers from the cylinder and presents them to the doffer roll. Fancies are used on all wool cards and on some revolving flat cards. **2.** A roll that cleans the lint from the napping cylinder on a NAPPING machine.

FANCY YARN: See NOVELTY YARN.

FASCIATED YARN: Yarns consisting of a core of discontinuous fibers with little or no twist and surface fibers wrapped around the core bundle.

Fasciated Yarn

FASHIONING: The process of shaping a fabric during knitting by increasing or decreasing the number of needles in action. Fashioning is used in manufacturing hosiery, underwear, and sweaters.

FASLINC: Acronym for Fabric Suppliers Linkage Council.

FASTNESS: See COLORFASTNESS.

FATIGUE: Refers to the resistance of a material to weakening or failure during alternate tension-compression cycles, i.e., in stretch yarns, the loss of ability to recover after having been stretched.

FDY: Acronym for fully drawn yarn.

FEED: In circular knitting, the element that guides yarn to the needles.

FEEDER: Any mechanism that feeds fibers or yarns into a textile machine for processing.

FEED YARN: 1. Manufactured filament yarn with PRODUCER TWIST that is supplied to throwsters for texturing. **2.** Yarn fed to the needles in a knitting machine.

FEEL: See HAND.

FELL: 1. The end of a piece of fabric that is woven last. **2.** In weaving, the last filling pick laid in the fabric at any time.

FELT: 1. A nonwoven sheet of matted material of wool, hair, or fur, sometimes in combination with certain manufactured fibers, made by a combination of mechanical and chemical action, pressure, moisture, and heat. **2.** A woven fabric generally made from wool, but occasionally from cotton or certain manufactured fibers, that is heavily shrunk and fulled, making it almost impossible to distinguish the weave.

FELTING: 1. The process of exposing wool fibers alone or in combination with other fibers to mechanical and chemical action, pressure, moisture, and heat so that they tangle, shrink, and mat to form a compact material. Felting is generally carried out in a fulling mill. (Also see FULLING.) **2.** See NEEDLEPUNCHING and NEEDLED FABRICS.

FESTOON DRYER: A dryer in which cloth is suspended in loops over a series of supporting horizontal poles and carried through the heated chamber in this configuration.

FFACT: Acronym for Fiber, Fabric, and Apparel Coalition for Trade.

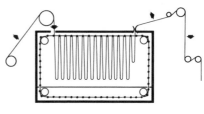

Festoon Dryer

FIBER: A unit of matter, either natural or manufactured, that forms the basic element of fabrics and other textile structures. A fiber is characterized by having a length at least 1000 times its diameter or width. Typically textile fibers are units that can be spun into a yarn or made into a fabric by various methods including weaving, knitting, braiding, felting, and twisting. The essential requirements for fibers to be spun into yarn include a length of at least 5 millimeters, flexibility, cohesiveness, and sufficient strength. Other important properties include elasticity, fineness, uniformity, durability, and luster. While the term *fiber* is often used to refer to staple, it also includes continuous filament and tow. (Also see MANUFACTURED FIBER and NATURAL FIBER.)

FIBER CONTENT LABELING: See TEXTILE FIBER PRODUCTS IDENTIFICATION ACT.

FIBER CROSS SECTION: See CROSS SECTION.

FIBER DISTRIBUTION: In a web, the orientation (random or parallel) of fibers and the uniformity of their arrangement.

FIBER DYEING: See DYEING, STOCK DYEING.

FIBERFILL: Manufactured fibers that have been specially engineered for use as filling material for pillows, mattress pads, comforters, sleeping bags, quilted outerwear, etc. Polyester fibers are widely used.

FIBER FINENESS: See FINENESS.

FIBERGLASS: See GLASS FIBER.

FIBER MIGRATION: See MIGRATION, 2.

FIBER MORPHOLOGY: See MORPHOLOGY.

FIBER NUMBER: The linear density of a fiber expressed in units such as DENIER or TEX. (Also see FINENESS.)

FIBER OPTICS: A term that refers to the ability of some transparent fibers manufactured from glass or polymers to transmit light through their length.

FIBER ORIENTATION: The direction(s) in which fibers are aligned in textile structures, e.g., yarns and webs.

FIBER PLACEMENT: In general, refers to how the plies are laid into their orientation, i.e., by hand, by a textile process, by a tape layer, or by a filament winder. Tolerances and angles are specified. Microprocessor-controlled placement that gives precise control of each axis of motion permits more intricate winding patterns than are possible with conventional winding and is used to make composites that are more complex than usual filament-wound structures.

FIBER-REACTIVE DYES: See DYES.

FIBER-REINFORCED COMPOSITE: Any specialty material composed of textile fibers, yarn, or fabric imbedded in a polymer matrix. The reinforcement adds strength, and depending on its constituents, the composite may have special characteristics such as high chemical, heat, or flame resistance that may be required for advanced technology applications. (Also see COMPOSITE.)

FIBER SHAPE: See CROSS SECTION.

FIBER SIZE: See FIBER NUMBER and FINENESS.

FIBER VARIANT: A manufactured fiber type derived by modification of a generic fiber type. Fiber variants are generally engineered to feature specific properties and are designed for specialized applications. For example, the modification may be achieved by adding end or side functional groups to the fiber-forming polymer, adding materials such as functional dyes or flame retardants to the polymer, changing spinneret geometry, or varying other manufacturing parameters.

FIBRETS: Very short (< 1 mm), fine (diameter < 50 μ) fibrillated fibers that are highly branched and irregular resulting in very high surface area. Fibrets can be produced from a number of substances including acetate, polyester, nylon, and polyolefins. By selection of polymer type and incorporation of additives, they can be engineered to meet a range of specialized requirements.

FIBRIDS: Short, irregular fibrous products, made by mixing a dilute polymer solution with a nonsolvent with agitation. They can also be made by FLASH SPINNING and breaking up the resulting filaments. Used in felts, in papermaking, for filtration products, etc. (Also see FIBRETS.)

FIBRIL: A tiny threadlike element of a synthetic or natural fiber.

FIBRILLATED-FILM YARN: See SLIT-FILM YARN.

FIBRILLATION: 1. The act or process of forming fibrils. The act of breaking up a fiber, plastic sheet, or similar material into the minute fibrous elements from which the main structure is formed. **2.** See COLOR ABRASION.

FIBROIN: A protein compound that is the main constituent of SILK. It is the fiber that remains after degumming.

FIBROUS: A term used to describe a material composed of fibers or having the characteristics of fibers.

FIGURE: See PATTERN, 1.

FILAMENT: A fiber of an indefinite or extreme length such as found naturally in silk. Manufactured fibers are extruded into filaments that are converted into filament yarn, staple, or tow.

FILAMENT COUNT: The number of individual filaments that make up a thread or yarn.

FILAMENT NUMBER: The linear density of a filament expressed in units such as DENIER or TEX. (Also see FINENESS.)

FILAMENT WINDING: In the fabrication of composites, the process of placing reinforcing fibers over a rotating form (mandrel) to make the product shape. Prepreg fibers or dry fibers that are treated in a resin bath immediately prior to winding may be used. The wound form can be cured or consolidated after the fiber winding is complete to product specifications.

FILAMENT YARN: A yarn composed of continuous filaments assembled with or without twist. (Also see YARN.)

FILLER: A nonfibrous material added to a fabric to increase its weight or to modify its appearance or hand. Also referred to as back-sizing. Examples of fillers are insoluble clays or gypsum, starches, and gums.

FILLET: A long, narrow strip of wire card clothing with which the doffer and cylinder of the card are spirally wrapped.

FILLING: In a woven fabric, the yarn running from selvage to selvage at right angles to the warp. Each crosswise length is called a pick. In the weaving process, the filling yarn is carried by the shuttle or other type of yarn carrier.

FILLING BAND: See MIXED END OR FILLING.

FILLING BARRÉ: See BARRÉ.

FILLING BOW: See BOW.

FILLING PILE: Pile that is formed by loops woven into the fabric face using an extra set of filling yarns. The loops are sometimes cut during finishing. (Also see CORDUROY and VELVETEEN.)

FILLING SKEWNESS: See SKEWNESS.

FILLING SNARL: See KINK, 2.

FILM YARN: See SLIT-FILM YARN.

FILTER AID: A powder added to a solution to be filtered that forms a porous bed to improve filtration.

FILTER CLOTH: Any cloth used for filtering purposes. Nylon, polyester, vinyon, PBI, and glass fibers are often used in such fabrics because they are not affected by most chemicals.

FILTER FABRICS: See GEOTEXTILES and FILTER CLOTH.

FINDINGS: 1. Miscellaneous items attached to garments and shoes during manufacture. Included are buttons, hooks, snaps, and ornaments. **2.** Miscellaneous fabrics in garments such as zipper tapes, linings, pockets, waistbands, and facings.

FINE END: 1. A warp yarn of smaller diameter than that normally used in the fabric. **2.** A term for a defect in silk warp yarn consisting of thin places that occur when all the filaments required to make up the full ply are not present. This condition is generally caused by poor reeling.

FINENESS: 1. A relative measure of fiber size expressed in DENIER or TEX for manufactured fibers. For cotton, fineness is expressed as the mean fiber weight in micrograms per inch. For wool, fineness is the mean fiber width or mean fiber diameter expressed in microns (to the nearest 0.001 millimeter). **2.** For yarn fineness, see YARN NUMBER. **3.** For fineness of knit fabrics, see GAUGE, 4.

FINES: Particles or dust of polymer formed during the process of cutting to produce chip.

FINE STRUCTURE: Orientation, crystallinity, and molecular morphology of polymers, including fiber-forming polymers.

FINGER MARK: A defect of woven fabrics that is seen as an irregular spot showing variation in picks per inch for a limited width. Causes are spreading of warp ends while the loom is in motion and pressure on the fabric between the reed and take-up drum.

FINISH: 1. A substance or mixture of substances added to textile materials to impart desired properties. **2.** A process, physical or chemical, performed on textile materials to produce a desired effect. **3.** A property, such as smoothness, drape, luster, water repellency, flame retardancy, or crease resistance that is produced by 1 and/or 2 above. **4.** The state of a textile material as it leaves a process. (Also see FINISHING.)

FINISH COMPOSITION (YARN): Physical and chemical analysis of the lubricant applied to yarns to reduce friction and improve processibility.

FINISHED FABRIC: Fabric that is ready for the market, having passed through the necessary finishing processes.

FINISHING: 1. All the processes through which fabric is passed after bleaching, dyeing, or printing in preparation for the market or use. Finishing includes such operations as heat-setting, napping, embossing, pressing, calendering, and the application of chemicals that change the character of the fabric. The term finishing is also sometimes used to refer collectively to all processing operations above, including bleaching, dyeing, printing, etc. **2.** In carpet manufacture, processes carried out after pile formation and dyeing, including application of the secondary backing, application of attached foam cushion, application of soil retardant, shearing, and brushing.

FINISHING BAR: A noticeable streak across the entire width of a fabric, usually caused by machine stoppage during processing.

FINISHING SPOT: A discolored area on a fabric caused by foreign material such as dirt, grease, or rust.

FINISH TURNS: The actual degree of twist in the final yarn product.

FIRE-BLOCKING LAYER: A fabric layer composed of fibers with flame-retardant properties used in aircraft seat cushions and other upholstery constructions to decrease the overall flammability of the total construction by preventing access of flame to the body of the construction.

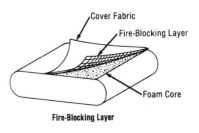

Fire-Blocking Layer

FIREPROOF: A term used to describe a material, treated or untreated, that will not support combustion when subjected to a flame. While few textile materials are truly fireproof, many can be treated with flame-retardants to impart flame resistance. (Also see FLAME RESISTANT.)

FIRST-ORDER TRANSITION TEMPERATURE: The temperature at which a polymer freezes or melts.

FIRST QUALITY: See YARN QUALITY.

FISH EYE: See PINHOLE.

FISSURE: A very minute crack or opening in a material that frequently leads to the breaking or rupture of the material.

FIXATION: The process of setting a dye after dyeing or printing, usually by steaming or other heat treatment or by converting a dye to an insoluble form by chemical treatment.

FIXING AGENT: A chemical used in dyeing or printing to form a complex with a soluble dye in or on the fiber so that it becomes insoluble.

FLAKE: The granular form in which cellulose acetate and triacetate polymers exist prior to dissolving or feeding into the extrusion or molding unit.

FLAKE YARN: Yarn in which roving or short, soft staple fibers are inserted at intervals between long filament binder yarns.

FLAKY WEB: A web at the card that shows thick and thin places, approximately 1–6 square inches in size. This indicates that, instead of a free flow of fibers through the card, either an uneven amount has been fed into the card, or groups of fibers have hesitated in the card and then dropped back into production.

FLAME BONDING: See BONDING, 1.

FLAME RESISTANCE TESTS: See FLAMMABILITY TESTS.

FLAME RESISTANT: A term used to describe a material that burns slowly or is self-extinguishing after removal of an external source of ignition. A fabric or yarn can be flame resistant because of the innate properties of the fiber, the twist level of the yarn, the fabric construction, or the presence of flame retardants, or because of a combination of these factors. (Also see FLAME RETARDANT and INHERENT FLAME RESISTANCE.)

FLAME RETARDANT: A chemical compound that can be incorporated into a textile fiber during manufacture or applied as a topical treatment to a fiber, fabric, or other textile item during processing or use to reduce its flammability. (Also see FLAME RESISTANT.)

FLAMMABILITY TESTS: Many procedures have been developed for assessing the flame resistance of textiles. The most common currently in use are detailed below:

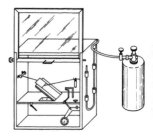

Diagonal (45°) Flame Test: In this test for flame resistance, a specimen is mounted at a 45° angle and exposed to an open flame for a specific time. This test measures the ease of ignition and rate of burning of the samples.

Diagonal Flame Test Apparatus

Horizontal Flame Test: A test for flame resistance in which a specimen is mounted in a horizontal holder and exposed to an open flame for a specific time to measure burning rate and char-hole diameter.

Methenamine Pill Test: A test for the flame resistance of carpets or rugs in which a methenamine tablet is ignited on a test sample under controlled conditions and the size of the burn hole is measured.

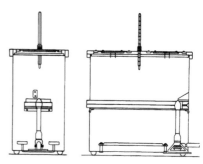

Mushroom Apparel Flammability Test: This test method involves igniting a cylinder of fabric around a core containing heat sensors and measuring the rate of heat transfer from the burning material to the sensors. (See diagram on the next page.)

Horizontal Flame Test Apparatus

Radiant Panel Test: A test for the flammability of carpets or rugs in which the specimen is mounted on the floor of the test chamber and exposed to intense radiant heat from above. The rate of flame spread is assessed.

Smoke Chamber Test: This method assesses the smoke generating characteristics of a sample due to pyrolysis and combustion by measuring the attenuation of a light beam by smoke accumulating in a closed chamber under controlled conditions. Results are expressed in terms of specific optical density.

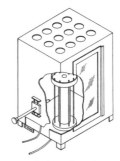

Mushroom Apparel Flammability Tester

Tablet Test: See FLAMMABILITY TESTS, METHENAMINE PILL TEST.

Thermo-Man: This instrumented mannequin system, interfaced with a computer, allows full-scale testing of garments for protection capability or degree of flammability. The system was developed by Accurex Corporation for the U.S. Air Force.

Tunnel Test: Test for the flammability of floor coverings in which a sample is placed on the ceiling of a tunnel of specific dimensions and ignited under controlled conditions to determine the extent to which it will burn. (Also called Steiner Tunnel Test.)

Radiant Panel Test Apparatus

Vertical Flame Test: A test for flame resistance in which a specimen is mounted in a vertical holder and exposed to an open flame for a specific time. The open flame is then extinguished and continued flaming time and char length of the sample are measured.

FLANGE CRIMPING: Simultaneous crimping of two ends of yarn by using heated snubber pins, then combining both ends on a draw roll after they contact a rubber flange on the draw roll.

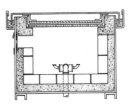

Tunnel Test Apparatus

FLANNEL: Mediumweight plain- or twill-weave, slightly napped fabric, usually of wool or cotton, but may be made of other fibers.

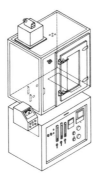

Smoke Chamber Test Apparatus

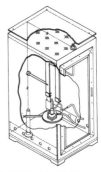

Vertical Flame Test Apparatus

FLAPPER: The movable side of a fiber-crimping chamber that periodically opens or flaps to permit crimped fiber to be expelled from the chamber.

FLASH AGEING: A process for rapid reduction and fixation of vat dyes obtained when the printed fabric is padded with caustic soda and sodium hydrosulfite and immediately steamed in air-free steam.

FLASHOVER: Rapid combustion of all flammable material in a given space.

FLASH SPINNING: See SPINNING, 5.

FLASH-SPUN NONWOVEN: A nonwoven structure produced by extrusion of a dilute solution of polymer resin in a low-boiling solvent that has been heated under pressure in a gaseous environment. Upon extrusion into a high-velocity air stream, the solvent evaporates rapidly leaving a filament web. (Also see SPUNBOND.)

FLASH STEAMING: See FLASH AGEING.

FLAT: 1. In carding, one of the parts forming an endless chain that partially surrounds the upper portion of the cylinder and gives the name to a revolving flat card. Flats are made of cast iron, T-shaped in section, about 1 inch wide, and as long as the width of the cylinder. One side of the flat is nearly covered with fine card clothing, and the flats are set close to the teeth of the cylinder so as to work point against point. A chain of flats contains approximately 110 flats and operates at a surface speed of about 3 inches per minute. **2.** A fabric defect caused by weaving two yarns together. **3.** A term used to describe dullness of color.

FLAT ABRASION: A form of abrasion that occurs as a result of friction that is generated when two flat surfaces rub together.

FLAT ABRASION TESTER: See STOLL-QUARTERMASTER UNIVERSAL WEAR TESTER.

FLAT-BED SCREEN PRINTING: See PRINTING, 1.

FLAT CARD: The type of card used for cotton fibers and for cotton-system processing. It is named for the flat wire brushes called flats that are assembled on an endless chain that partially surrounds the main cylinder. The staple is worked between the flats and cylinder, transferred to a doffer roll, and peeled off as a web that is condensed into a sliver. (Also see FLAT, 1.)

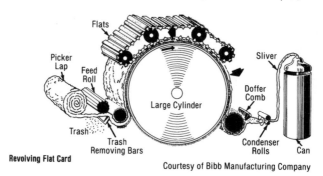

Revolving Flat Card

Courtesy of Bibb Manufacturing Company

FLAT DUCK: See DUCK.

FLAT-KNIT FABRIC: 1. A fabric made on a flat-knitting machine, as distinguished from tubular fabrics made on a circular-knitting machine. While tricot and milanese warp-knit fabrics (non-run) are knit in flat form, the trade uses the term flat-knit fabric to refer to weft-knit fabrics made on a flat machine, rather than warp-knit fabrics. **2.** A term used in the underwear trade for plain-stitch fabrics made on a circular-knitting machine. These fabrics have a flat surface and are often called flat-knit fabrics to differentiate them from ribbed-knit or Swiss rib fabrics. In this case, the term refers to the texture, not the type of machine on which the fabric was knit.

FLAT KNITTING: See KNITTING, 2.

FLAT-KNITTING MACHINE: A weft-knitting machine with needles arranged in a straight line in a flat plate called the bed. The yarn travels alternately back and forth, and the fabric may be shaped or varied in width, as desired, during the knitting process. Lengthwise edges are selvages. Flat-knitting machines may be divided into two types: latch-needle machines for sweaters, scarves, and similar articles and fine spring-needle machines for full-fashioned hosiery.

FLAT SEAM: A plain seam as contrasted with a thicker seam composed of several layers of fabric.

FLATSPOTTING: A characteristic of certain tire cords. It occurs with all materials but is more noticeable with nylon cord and is associated with nylon cord by users. Nylon exerts a shrinkage force as it becomes heated in tire operation. When the tire is stopped under load, the cord in the road-contact portion of the tire is under less tension than that in other portions of the tire, and it shrinks to conform to the flat surface of the road. When cooled in this position, the cord maintains the flat spot until it again reaches its glass transition temperature in use.

FLAT STITCH: A plain knit stitch.

FLAT-TOP CARD: See FLAT CARD.

FLAT YARN: A fully drawn, untextured, manufactured continuous filament yarn with a small amount of twist. (Contrast with TEXTURED YARNS.)

FLAX: The plant *Linum usitatissimum* from which the cellulose fiber LINEN is obtained. The stems of the plant are processed into long, strong fibers by HACKLING, RETTING, and SCUTCHING processes.

FLEECE: 1. Wool from sheep, generally shorn at one time, in one large piece. **2.** A thick but lightweight fabric with a deep nap. It may be a knit fabric or a woven fabric made in a plain weave or twill construction or a variation of either. The term can be correctly applied only to wool, but there are so-called fleeces of other fibers.

FLEECE FABRIC: A fabric with a thick, heavy surface resembling sheep's wool. It may be a pile or napped fabric of either woven or knit construction.

FLEX ABRASION: Wear resulting from repeated bending and straightening of a fabric.

FLEXIBILITY: 1. The ability to be flexed or bowed repeatedly without rupturing. **2.** A term relating to the hand of fabric, referring to ease of bending and ranging from pliable (high) to stiff (low).

FLEXING AND ABRASION TESTER: See STOLL-QUARTERMASTER UNIVERSAL WEAR TESTER.

FLEXURAL FATIGUE: A physical property expressed by the number of times a material can be bent on itself through a prescribed angle before it ruptures or loses its ability to recover.

FLEXURAL RIGIDITY: This measure of a material's resistance to bending is calculated by multiplying the material's weight per unit area by the cube of its bending length.

FLOAT: 1. The portion of a warp or filling yarn that extends over two or more adjacent filling picks or warp ends in weaving for the purpose of forming certain designs. **2.** In a knit fabric, a portion of yarn that extends for some length without being knitted in. **3.** A fabric defect consisting of an end lying or floating on the cloth surface instead of being woven in properly. Floats are usually caused by slubs, knot-tails, knots, or fly waste, or sometimes by ends being drawn in heddle eyes incorrectly or being twisted around heddle wires.

FLOATING ENDS: See FLOAT, 3.

FLOAT STITCH: See MISS-STITCH.

FLOCCULATING: Coagulating or coalescing a material into a small, loosely aggregated mass.

FLOCK: The material obtained by reducing textile fibers to fragments by cutting or grinding. There are two main types: (1) precision cut flock, where all fiber lengths are approximately equal, and (2) random cut flock, where the fibers are ground or chopped to produce a broad range of lengths.

FLOCKED CARPET: Carpet produced by embedding very short fibers (flock) in an adhesive-coated backing fabric.

FLOCKING: A method of cloth ornamentation in which adhesive is printed or coated on a fabric, and finely chopped fibers are applied all over by means of dusting, air-blasting, or electrostatic attraction. In flock printing, the fibers

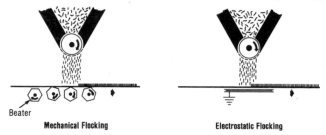

Beater

Mechanical Flocking　　　　　　**Electrostatic Flocking**

adhere only to the printed areas and are removed from the unprinted areas by mechanical action.

FLOCK PRINTING: See PRINTING, 1.

FLOOR COVERING (TEXTILE): A broad term for carpets or rugs made by a variety of methods such as weaving, tufting, braiding, hooking, and knitting.

FLUFFING: A term describing the appearance of a carpet after loose fiber fragments left during manufacture have worked their way to the surface. Fluffing is not a defect; it is simply a characteristic of new carpets that disappears with vacuuming.

FLUORESCENCE: Emission of electromagnetic radiation, usually as visible light, that is caused by the flow of energy into the emitting body. The emission ceases abruptly when the excitation ceases.

FLUORESCENT BRIGHTENER: See OPTICAL BRIGHTENER.

FLUOROCARBON FIBER: A manufactured fiber in which the fiber forming substance is a long-chain synthetic polymer of fluorocarbon aliphatic monomer, e.g., tetrafluoroethylene polymer. This strong, highly chemically resistant fiber is used primarily for industrial applications such as packings for machinery.

FLUOROCARBON FINISH: A polymeric finish applied to the surface of textile materials to impart soil/stain resistance and oil/water repellency.

FLY: The short, waste fibers that are released into the air in textile processing operations such as picking, carding, spinning, and weaving.

FLYER: 1. A device used to insert twist into slubbing, roving, or yarn, and to serve as a guide for winding it onto a bobbin. The flyer is shaped like an inverted U that fits on the top of the spindle and revolves with it. One arm of the U is solid and the other is hollow. The yarn enters through the top of the hollow arm, travels downward, and emerges at the bottom where it is wound around a presser finger onto the take-up package. **2.** See LOOM FLY.

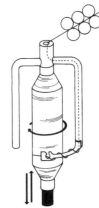

FLYER SPINNING: A method of spinning by means of a driven flyer. It is used primarily for spinning worsted and coarser yarns. (Also see FLYER, 1.)

FLYER SPINNING FRAME: See SPINNING FRAME.

FLYER WASTE: During the roving operation, flyer waste refers to fibers that free themselves by centrifugal force from the regular bulk of roving and accumulate on the flyers and adjacent machinery.

FLY FRAME: See ROVING FRAME.

Flyer Spinning

FOAM: Dispersion of gas in a liquid or solid. The gas bubbles may be any size. The term covers a wide range of useful products such as insulating foam and cushions. It also describes the undesirable froth in polymer melts, dyebaths, etc.

FOAM BONDING: See BONDING, 1.

FOAM FINISHING: A finishing method for fabric in which air is incorporated into the finishing liquid to produce a foam. The foam can be applied evenly to fabric at low wet pickup, greatly reducing drying time and thus energy cost.

FOLDED SELVAGE: A curled SELVAGE.

FOLDED YARN: See PLIED YARN.

FOLDING: 1. See PLYING. **2.** The process of laying finished fabric in layers in preparation for garment cutting.

FOREIGN WASTE: Thread waste or lint that is twisted in the yarn or woven in the fabric. If such foreign matter is of a different fiber, it may dye differently and thus show plainly.

FORMALDEHYDE: A one-carbon aldehyde (CH_2O). It is a colorless, pungent gas at room temperature. This compound is used primarily as a disinfectant and preservative and in synthesizing other compounds and resins.

FORMED FABRIC: See NONWOVEN FABRIC.

FOULARD: A lightweight, lustrous 2 x 2 twill that is usually printed with small figures on a solid background, foulard is frequently used in men's ties. Foulards are made of silk, filament polyester, acetate, etc.

FOY: 1. Acronym for fully oriented yarn. **2.** Acronym for the amount of finish on yarn, usually expressed as a percentage.

FR: Acronym for FLAME RESISTANT.

FRAME: 1. A general term for many machines used in yarn manufacturing such as the drawing frame, roving frame, and spinning frame. **2.** See TENTER FRAME. **3.** In carpet production, a rack at the back of a Wilton loom to hold the spools that feed yarns to the loom. Each frame holds yarns of separate color.

FRAMEWORK KNITTING: See KNITTING, WEFT KNITTING.

FRAMING: The process of drying fabric to a specific width on a TENTER FRAME.

FRAYING: The slipping or raveling of yarns from unfinished edges of cloth.

FRC: Acronym for fiber-reinforced composite.

FREE-WHEELING: In reference to rolls, spinning without the application of either driving or braking force.

FRENCHBACK: A fabric with a corded twill backing of different weave than the face. The backing, which is frequently of inferior yarn, gives added weight, warmth, and stability to the cloth.

FRENCH COMB: A machine employed in the FRENCH SPINNING SYSTEM for combing wool fibers in worsted yarn manufacture.

FRENCH PIQUÉ: A type of DOUBLE PIQUÉ knit fabric.

FRENCH SPINNING SYSTEM: A type of worsted spinning system that generally utilizes shorter fibers than those processed in the BRADFORD SPINNING SYSTEM.

FREQUENCY: In uniform circular motion or in any periodic motion, the number of revolutions or cycles completed in unit time.

FRICTION CALENDERING: A type of calendering that produces a highly polished finish on fabrics. The fabric passes between heated calender rolls that rotate at slightly different speeds, creating a friction effect that imparts a lustrous surface to the fabric.

FRICTION FALSE-TWIST TEXTURING: See TEXTURING, FALSE-TWIST METHOD.

FRICTION SPINNING: A type of OPEN-END SPINNING in which the yarn receives its twist by being rolled along the longitudinal axis in the nip between two revolving surfaces. The surfaces may rotate at the same or different speeds in the same or opposite directions depending on the particular machine design. Potential advantages include high production capacity, low stress on the fiber in processing, and the capacity to produce very fine counts.

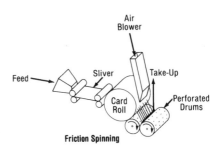

Friction Spinning

FRICTION TEST: A method for measuring frictional forces that occur when textile materials are rubbed against each other or another surface. (Also see FLAT ABRASION.)

FRIEZÉ: 1. A term applied when the pile of a velvet, plush, velour, or other pile fabric is uncut. A friezé fabric is sometimes patterned by shearing the loops at different lengths. Friezé fabrics are widely used for upholstery. **2.** A cut-pile carpet made of highly twisted yarns normally plied and heat-set. A kinked or curled yarn effect is achieved. Excellent durability results from the hard-twist pile yarns.

FROSTING: 1. See COLOR ABRASION. **2.** See STONE WASHING.

FROST MARKS: A defect of woven fabric consisting of surface highlights that give a frosted appearance. Frost marks are caused by improper sizing or insufficient warp tension as a result of uneven bending of some warp ends over the picks.

FTC: Acronym for U.S. Federal Trade Commission.

FUGITIVE TINT: Very light, nonpermanent color added to textiles for identification purposes. It is removed during normal wet processing operations. (Also see TINT.)

FULL-FASHIONED: A term applied to fabrics produced on a flat-knitting machine, such as hosiery, sweaters, and underwear, that have been shaped by adding or reducing stitches.

FULLING: A finishing process used in the manufacture of woolen and worsted fabrics. The cloth is subjected to moisture, heat friction, chemicals, and pressure which cause it to mat and shrink appreciably in both the warp and filling directions, resulting in a denser, more compact fabric.

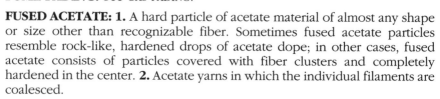

Sectional View of a
Rotary Fulling Mill

FULLY DRAWN YARN: See HIGHLY ORIENTED YARN.

FULLY ORIENTED YARN: See HIGHLY ORIENTED YARN.

FUME FADING: See GAS FADING.

FUSED ACETATE: 1. A hard particle of acetate material of almost any shape or size other than recognizable fiber. Sometimes fused acetate particles resemble rock-like, hardened drops of acetate dope; in other cases, fused acetate consists of particles covered with fiber clusters and completely hardened in the center. **2.** Acetate yarns in which the individual filaments are coalesced.

FUSED FILAMENTS: A group of filaments bonded together in a tow by drips or frictional effects and thereby resistant to filament separation and crimp deregistering.

FUSED RIBBON: Acetate fabrics in wide widths may be cut into narrow ones by the application of heat. A hot knife·blade causes the edges to sear and bead, thereby doing away with selvages on the edges of the goods.

FUSING: 1. Melting. **2.** Uniting, as by melting together, then resolidifying.

FUSION BONDING: See BONDING, 2.

FUZZ BALL: See BALLING UP.

FUZZINESS: 1. A term describing a woven fabric defect characterized by a hairy appearance due to broken fibers or filaments. Principal causes are underslashed warp; rough drop wires, heddles, or reed; fabric slippage on take-up drum; rough shuttles; cut glass, dents, or reeds in warper; and damage in slashing. **2.** A term describing a fabric intentionally made with a hairy surface; such fabrics are usually produced from spun yarns.

G

GABARDINE: A firm, durable, warp-faced cloth, showing a decided twill line, usually a 45° or 63° right-hand twill. (See diagram on the next page.)

GAGE: See GAUGE.

GAITING: See GATING.

GALATEA: A sturdy, serviceable, warp-effect, five-shaft, left-hand twill-weave fabric, frequently cotton or a cotton blend, used for children's play clothes.

GAMMA CELLULOSE: One of the three forms of cellulose. With beta cellulose it is called hemicellulose. (Also see ALPHA CELLULOSE and BETA CELLULOSE.)

GARMENT DYEING: See DYEING.

Gabardine

GARNETTING: A process for reducing various textile waste materials to fiber by passing them through a machine called a garnett, that is similar to a card.

GAS FADING: A change of shade of dyed fabric caused by chemical reaction between certain disperse dyes and acid gases from fuel combustion, particularly oxides of nitrogen.

GASSING: See SINGEING.

GATING: The relative positioning of knitting elements on dial-and-cylinder and flat-knitting machines: (1) In interlock gating, two sets of needles are in direct alignment and only one set of the opposed needles operates at a time. (Also see INTERLOCK KNIT.) (2) In purl gating on flat or circular links-links machines, the needle guides of two beds are lined up on the same plane, and a double headed needle passes from one bed to the other. (Also see PURL.) (3) In rib gating, two sets of needles are alternately aligned and both sets operate concurrently. (Also see RIB KNIT.)

GAUGE: 1. A generic term for various measurement instruments such as pressure or thickness gauges. **2.** The number of needles per given distance in a knitting machine. **3.** The thickness of the knitting needle in the shank and the hook. **4.** The number of wales per inch in a knit fabric. **5.** On spinning or twisting frames, the distance from the center of one spindle to the center of the next spindle in the same row. **6.** In tufted carpeting, the number of surface yarn ends per unit width, expressed as a fraction; e.g., carpet made on a 1/8-gauge tufting machine has 8 ends per inch. (Also see PITCH.)

GAUGE WIRE: Used with an extra filling yarn during weaving, this type of standing wire controls the height of fabric pile.

GAUZE: A thin, sheer-woven fabric in which each filling yarn is encircled by two warp yarns twisted around each other, gauze is similar to cheesecloth. It may be made of silk, cotton, wool, or manufactured fibers. Cotton gauze is used primarily for surgical dressings.

Gauze

GEAR CRIMPING: See TEXTURING, 4.

GEL: 1. A colloid in which the dispersed particles have combined with the continuous phase to produce a viscous, jelly-like product. **2.** Degraded polymer occurring in process lines. Usually seen as specks in polymer or yarn.

GEL DYEING: See DYEING.

GEL SPINNING: See SPINNING, 2.

GEOGRID: Manufactured polymer constructions characterized by large openings made by one of the following methods: (1) coating woven or knit products to form a grid; (2) welding oriented strands to form a grid; (3) punching holes in flat sheets then drawing them to align the polymer molecules. Used for soil stabilization, drainage, and erosion control applications. (Also see GEOTEXTILES.)

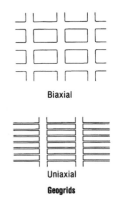

Biaxial

GEOMEMBRANE PROTECTION FABRIC: See GEOTEXTILES.

GEOTEXTILES: Manufactured fiber products made into fabrics of various constructions for use in a wide variety of civil engineering applications including several described below.

Uniaxial

Geogrids

Asphalt Overlay Fabrics: Fabric systems installed between the old and new asphalt layers during pavement resurfacing. The fabric absorbs the tack coat sprayed on the old surface thus forming a permanent moisture barrier to protect the subgrade from strength loss due to water intrusion. The fabric system also helps retard reflective cracking by serving as a flexible layer to diffuse stress.

Drainage Fabrics: Fabrics used as filter media or separators in subsurface drainage systems. The fabric is installed around the drainage pipe, or coarse stone in the drain; it allows water to pass freely from the soil to the drain, but prevents soil particles from migrating into the drain system. These fabrics are also used as outer coverings in prefabricated drainage composites and serve the same function as a filtering medium.

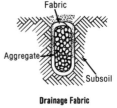

Fabric

Aggregate

Subsoil

Drainage Fabric

Erosion Control Fabrics: Fabrics used in the stabilization of embankments and the containment of silt run-off from erodible slopes. In embankment stabilization, the fabric functions as a filter medium behind stabilizing rip-rap revetments. In siltation control, the fabric acts as a filter to contain silt while allowing excess water to drain freely. In turf reinforcement, the mat is used to retain soil while allowing roots and stems to grow through. In fabric-forming systems for the construction of revetments, a double-layer, water-permeable fabric is positioned, then pumped full of structural grout. These systems are alternatives to rip-rap.

Geomembrane Protection Fabrics: Fabric systems used in the construction of landfills to protect the membrane liner from puncture and installation damage. The fabric may be installed on one or both sides of the liner. It can also be used in the leachate collection system since it is permeable to fluids and gases.

Horticultural and Agricultural Textiles: Geotextiles are used in several applications to assist plant growers, both commercial and domestic: (1) fabric that is laid over the soil to provide weed control, (2) bulky capillary mats that assist in watering, (3) lightweight fabrics that protect plants from pests and weather damage, and (4) grain storage covers that protect against pests.

Reinforcement Fabrics: Fabric systems used in the construction of steep slopes and retaining walls. By stabilizing the soil mass, they reduce the stress on the retaining wall with corresponding decrease in load-bearing requirements for the wall design. In slope reinforcement, the stabilization permits steeper slope construction than would be possible based on soil properties.

Subsurface Stabilization Fabrics: Fabrics used in the construction of access roads, railroads, parking and storage areas over soft, unstable soils. The fabric is placed between the subgrade and the stabilizing fill material where it provides separation of subsoil and fill, filtration of moisture at the subsoil/fill interface, and added tensile reinforcement of the compacted fill.

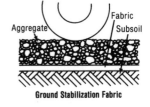

Ground Stabilization Fabric

GIGGING: See NAPPING.

GILLING: See PIN DRAFTING.

GIN: A machine used to separate cotton fiber from the seed.

GINGHAM: A woven fabric characterized by a block or check effect produced by weaving in dyed yarns at fixed intervals in both the warp and the filling.

GLACÉ: A lustrous, glossy effect imparted to fabrics by finishing.

GLASS FIBER: A manufactured fiber in which the fiber-forming substance is glass (FTC definition). In the continuous filament process, glass marbles are melted in an electric furnace and the liquid flows in fine streams through small orifices at the bottom of the melting chamber. The resultant filaments are caught and drawn by a high-speed draw-winding mechanism. In the staple fiber process, the streams of molten glass are attenuated into fibers by jets of high-pressure steam or air. These fibers are gathered on a revolving drum and then wound on tubes to form staple fiber sliver or bands that can be drafted, twisted, and plied.

CHARACTERISTICS: Glass fiber is incombustible and will tolerate heat up to 1000°F without material damage. Potential strength is not realized in woven fabrics or even in yarns, because the fiber is brittle and fracture points may develop, but nevertheless, very high tensile strength is obtained in woven fabrics, and is retained at elevated

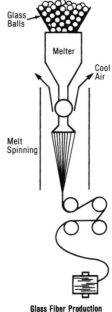

Glass Fiber Production

temperatures. The fiber originally was difficult to color but methods have been developed to accomplish this. Moisture absorption is low. Electrical and insulation resistance is high.

END USES: Glass fiber is used for heat and electrical insulation, filter cloth in the chemical and dye industries, reinforcing belts in tires, novelty fabrics, tablecloths, and fireproof draperies. Because of its brittleness, it is not used in wearing apparel or in household fabrics that have to withstand frequent flexing.

GLASS TRANSITION TEMPERATURE: See SECOND-ORDER TRANSISTION TEMPERATURE.

GLAZED THREAD: Thread to which a sizing compound has been applied to impart a smooth, lustrous surface.

GLAZING: 1. A finishing process that produces a smooth, highly polished, or lustrous surface on a fabric such as chintz. The fabric is treated with starch, glue, paraffin, or shellac, then friction calendered. Synthetic resins are used for a more permanent finish. **2.** A shiny fabric appearance produced unintentionally, e.g., by pressing at excessive temperature.

GLOBAL RADIATION: The wavelength distribution of sunlight under a given environment (e.g., under windowpane glass).

GLYOXAL RESINS: Low-formaldehyde finishing for crosslinking cotton and other cellulosic fibers. Glyoxal resins were developed to reduce the usage of formaldehyde compounds as finishing agents because of environmental concerns.

GODET: Roll used for transporting and controlling the movement of bundles of fibers and yarns in the processing of these materials.

GOUT: Foreign matter that is accidentally woven into a fabric. It is usually fly or waste that drops into the loom during weaving or that catches in yarns during spinning.

GRAB STRENGTH TEST: A method for measuring the breaking strength of a fabric sample by mounting the sample in the tensile tester so that only a part of the width of the specimen is gripped in the clamps.

GRAFT COPOLYMER: A copolymer formed when side chains of one polymer are built along a main chain composed of another polymer.

```
                        C — C — C — C
                                |
A — A — A — A — A — A — A — A — A — A
        |
    C — C — C
```

Graft Copolymer

GRAM BREAK FACTOR: See BREAK FACTOR.

GRAPHICS TUFTING MACHINE: Machine for making patterned tufted carpeting, usually by the use of shifting needle bars that may be individually controlled or by individually controlled needles or a combination of the two. Through the use of computer technology, graphics machines are able to produce tufting patterns closer to those possible in woven carpets.

GRAPHITE FIBER: Although the terms carbon and graphite are used interchangeably to describe these fibers, graphite fibers are more accurately defined as fibers that are 99+% carbonized while the term carbon is used for any fiber carbonized to 93–95% or more. (Also see CARBON FIBER.)

GRAY FABRIC: See GREIGE FABRIC.

GRAY SCALE FOR COLOR CHANGE: A nine-step scale of gray chips distributed by AATCC and used as comparison standards for rating degrees of color change resulting from colorfastness tests.

GRAY SCALE FOR STAINING: A nine-step scale of gray chips distributed by AATCC and used as comparison standards for rating degrees of color transfer from other materials onto undyed textiles in colorfastness tests.

GREASE WOOL: Wool shorn from sheep in its natural state before scouring.

GREEN TACK: A term used in fabric bonding for the preliminary bond created in the first stage of curing by the wet adhesive process. At this point, the bond is not fully cured and hence is "green."

GREIGE FABRIC: An unfinished fabric just off the loom or knitting machine.

GRENADINE: 1. A fine, loosely woven fabric in leno weave made with dyed filling yarns and having a clipped dobby design. **2.** A silk cord constructed by twisting together several twisted strands.

GREX: An obsolete direct yarn numbering system. A grex unit is equal to the weight in grams of 10 kilometers of a textile strand.

GREY FABRIC: See GREIGE FABRIC.

GRINNING: 1. A flaw in fabric, especially a ribbed fabric, that occurs when warp threads show through the covering filling threads or when the threads have slipped leaving open spaces on either side. **2.** A condition that occurs when the carpet backing shows through the pile. **3.** A printing term referring to either poor cover where the background shade shows through the print, or to the "two-tone" appearance of a shade printed with incompatible dyes.

GRIPPER LOOMS: Shuttleless looms. These looms employ a projectile with a jaw that grips the end of the filling yarn during the insertion of the pick.

GROSGRAIN: A heavy fabric with prominent ribs, grosgrain has a dressy appearance and is used in ribbons, vestments, and ceremonial cloths.

GROUND COLOR: A term describing the plain background color against which a design is created.

GROWTH: See SECONDARY CREEP.

GUIDE BAR: A mechanism on a warp-knitting machine that directs warp threads to the latch needles.

GUIDES: Fittings of various shapes for controlling the path of a threadline. (See diagram on the next page.)

GUILLOTINE: Cutting device that consists of a single blade that descends between guides for chopping fibers, plastic strands, etc.

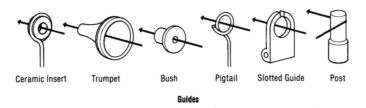

Ceramic Insert　　Trumpet　　Bush　　Pigtail　　Slotted Guide　　Post

Guides

GUM: A term covering a wide range of substances. Strictly, gums are carbohydrate high polymers, either soluble or dispersible in water, that are derived from vegetable origins. Loosely, the term gum is used to mean resins, saps, natural rubber, chicle, starch, cellulose derivatives, and many other products. In textile printing, the term refers to print-paste thickeners.

H

HACKLING: In the production of linen fiber from FLAX, a combing and straightening process for scutched flax, which leaves the fibers in condition for further processing.

HAIRY: See FUZZINESS.

HAND: The tactile qualities of a fabric, e.g., softness, firmness, elasticity, fineness, resilience, and other qualities perceived by touch.

HAND-BLOCKED PRINT: A fabric that has been printed by hand with wooden or linoleum blocks. (Also see PRINTING, 1.)

HANDLE: See HAND.

HANG PICK: A pick that is caught on a warp yarn knot for a short distance which produces a triangular hole in the fabric. Hang picks usually result from knots that are tied incorrectly, shuttle tension that is too loose, or harness that is timed too early.

HANG SHOT: See HANG PICK.

HANK: 1. A skein of yarn. **2.** A standard length of slubbing, roving, or yarn. The length is specified by the yarn numbering system in use; e.g., cotton hanks have a length of 840 yards. **3.** A term applied to slubbing or roving that indicates the yarn number (count); e.g., a 1.5 hank roving.

HANK DYEING: See DYEING, SKEIN DYEING.

HANK ROVING: See HANK.

HARD FIBER: Stiff, elongated fibers obtained from leaves or stems of plants. Coarse and stiff, they are used in matting and industrial products.

HARDNESS: 1. When used in reference to water, hardness is the total parts per million (ppm) of calcium as $CaCO_3$ plus the magnesium expressed as equivalent CaCO$_3$ [ppm hardness (as CaCO$_3$) = (ppm Ca x 2.497 + ppm Mg x 4.116)]. **2.** Used in reference to pulp to denote the degree of delignification.

HARD SIZE: A condition found in areas of a fabric where the warp contains an excessive quantity of sizing.

HARD TWIST: A term, usually applied to spun yarn, to describe a yarn with a high number of turns of twist per unit length.

HARNESS: A frame holding the heddles in position in the loom during weaving.

HARNESS CHAIN: A mechanism used to control the vertical movements of the harness, or shaft, on a loom.

HARSH FIBER: Fiber that is rough or coarse to the touch, but not fused or bonded filaments.

HAWSER: A very large-diameter marine rope for mooring and towing ships. It is formed by three twisted strands wound around the same central axis with Z twist.

HAZARD COMMUNICATION: A program administered by the U.S. Occupational Safety and Health Administration to ensure that manufacturers, suppliers, and importers of chemicals supply product labeling and information to customers about any hazards associated with these products, and to inform their own employees about any risks they may encounter in handling such chemical substances.

HDPE: Acronym for high-density polyethylene. (Also see HIGH-DENSITY POLYETHYLENE FIBER.)

HEAD END: 1. The beginning of a new piece of fabric in the loom that bears appropriate identification. **2.** A short sample of fabric dyed for quality evaluation. **3.** A small sample of fabric that may be submitted to a customer for approval.

HEATHER YARN: A term describing mottled or melange-type yarns.

HEAT RESISTANCE: A property of certain fibers or yarns whereby they resist degradation at high temperature. Heat resistance may be an inherent property of the fiber-forming polymer or it may be imparted by additives or treatment during manufacture. (Also see HEAT STABILIZED.)

HEAT-SETTING: The process of conferring dimensional stability and often other desirable properties such as wrinkle resistance and improved heat resistance to manufactured fibers, yarns, and fabrics by means of either moist or dry heat.

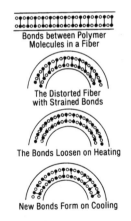

Bonds between Polymer
Molecules in a Fiber

The Distorted Fiber
with Strained Bonds

The Bonds Loosen on Heating

New Bonds Form on Cooling

**Representation of the
Heat-Setting Process
for Thermoplastic Polymers**

HEAT STABILIZED: A term to describe fiber or yarn heat-treated to reduce the tendency of the fiber to shrink or elongate under load at elevated temperature. (Also see HEAT RESISTANCE.)

HEAT-TRANSFER PRINTING: See PRINTING, 1.

HEAVY END: 1. The higher boiling fraction in distillation. **2.** See COARSE THREAD.

HEAVY FILLING: See COARSE THREAD.

HEAVY PICK: See COARSE THREAD.

HEDDLE: A cord, round steel wire, or thin flat steel strip with a loop or eye near the center through which one or more warp threads pass on the loom so that the thread movement may be controlled in weaving. The heddles are held at both ends by the harness frame. They control the weave pattern and shed as the harnesses are raised and lowered during weaving.

HELIX ANGLE: 1. The angle formed by the path of a ply and the major axis in a yarn or tire cord. **2.** The angle between the tangent to a yarn and the minor axis of the package on which it is wound. Also called wind angle.

HEMICELLULOSES: The principal noncellulosic polysaccharides in wood. Wood contains 28–35% hemicelluloses, the balance being cellulose and lignin.

HEMP: A coarse, durable bast fiber of *Cannabis sativa* found all over the world. Used primarily for twines, cordage, halyards, and tarred riggings.

HENEQUEN: A bast fiber from one type of agave plant and used in twine and ropes. Henequen is less resistant to water damage than sisal, for example.

HEPTALOBAL CROSS SECTION: Fiber cross-sectional shape having seven lobes.

HERRINGBONE: A broken twill weave characterized by a balanced zigzag effect produced by having the rib run first to the right and then to the left for an equal number of threads.

HESSIAN: A name for burlap used in the United Kingdom, India, and parts of Europe. (Also see BURLAP.)

HETEROFILAMENT: Also called Heterofil. See BICOMPONENT FIBER.

HEXALOBAL CROSS SECTION: Fiber cross-sectional shape having six lobes.

HEXAMETHYLENEDIAMINE: 1,6-diaminohexane, $[H_2N(CH_2)_6NH_2]$. It is used in the polymerization reaction to form nylon 66.

HIGH-BULK YARN: See TEXTURED YARNS.

HIGH DENSITY: A term to describe a material with heavier than normal weight per unit volume. (Also see DENSITY.)

HIGH-DENSITY POLYETHYLENE FIBER: A high-performance manufactured fiber with excellent chemical and electrical resistance, very high strength and good abrasion resistance. The fiber has a specific gravity of only 0.97. This combination of properties makes it suited for end uses that require toughness and light weight such as marine ropes and cables that float, body armor, and cut-resistant gloves. HDPE fiber has a relatively low melting point of 250°F, which restricts its use in heat-resistant applications. The fiber is not dyeable but can be bleached and sterilized.

HIGHLOFT: A low-density fiber structure having a high ratio of thickness to weight per unit area. Specifically, highloft battings contain at least 90% air by volume and are at least 3 millimeters thick. They are used for applications such as fiberfill, insulation, healthcare, and personal protection.

HIGH-LOW PILE: A pile construction characterized by the presence of two or more pile heights. High-low pile carpets sometimes combine looped and cut surface yarns.

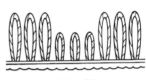

High-Low Pile

HIGHLY ORIENTED YARN: Melt-spun yarn that has been stretched in a drawing process to achieve a high degree of alignment of its polymer molecules in the axial direction.

HIGH MODULUS: A term that refers to a material with a higher than normal resistance to deformation. (Also see MODULUS.)

HIGH-PERFORMANCE FIBER: Any fiber with very high strength and/or resistance to heat, flame, or chemical exposure. Such fibers are in demand for industry, aerospace, and the military, for example.

HIGH pH FINISH: A finish, basic in nature rather than acidic or neutral, that is applied to yarn or fiber.

HIGH-SHRINKAGE FIBER: Staple fiber with a greater-than-normal propensity to shrink. When blended with the same generic fiber of normal shrinkage and treated under conditions to promote shrinkage, it produces a bulky product.

HIGH-SPEED SPINNING: A melt-spinning process in which the filaments are extruded and drawn at high speeds, currently over 6000 meters per minute.

HIGH-TEMPERATURE DYEING: See DYEING.

HIGH TENACITY: A term to describe a material with a higher than normal tensile strength. (Also see TENACITY.)

HIGH-WET-MODULUS RAYON FIBER: See POLYNOSIC FIBER and RAYON FIBER.

HITCH-BACK: See STICKER, 1.

HMLS: Acronym for high modulus, low shrinkage.

HOLES (TOW): In tow opening processes, partial or complete filament breakage within a confined spread of tow, usually circular or oval in shape. Not to be confused with splitting or partial crimp deregistration, which are linear.

HOLLAND: See SHADECLOTH.

HOLLAND FINISH: A glazed or unglazed finish containing oil and a filling material. The finish is applied to cotton fabrics to make them opaque or semiopaque. The resultant fabric resembles a beetled linen fabric called Holland fabric.

HOLLOW FIBERS: Manufactured, continuous filament fibers, having voids created by introduction of air or other gas in the polymer solution or by melt spinning through specially designed spinnerets. The fibers are used in fiberfill applications such as quilted outerwear and sleeping bags.

HOLLOW SPINDLE SPINNING: A spinning method for producing wrapped or core-spun yarns. The core yarn passes through a rotating hollow spindle. A bobbin containing the wrapping yarn is mounted over the hollow spindle, and both yarns are passed through the hollow tube. The rotation of the spindle winds the wrapping yarn around the core yarn.

HOMESPUN: Coarse plain-weave fabric of uneven yarns that have a hand-spun appearance.

HOMOPOLYMER: A polymer consisting of repeating units of only one monomer.

HONAN: A pongee-type fabric of the very best Chinese wild silk. Honan is sometimes woven with blue edges.

HOOK REED: See REED.

HOPSACKING: A coarse, open, basket-weave fabric that gets its name from the plain-weave fabric of jute or hemp used for sacking in which hops are gathered.

Roving
Drafting Zone
Hollow Spindle with Yarn Package
Belt
Take-Off Rolls

Hollow-Spindle Spinning

HORIZONTAL FLAME TEST: See FLAMMABILITY TESTS.

HORIZONTAL LINE: See RING.

HOT-AIR SHRINKAGE: Generally, the reduction in the dimensions of a fabric, yarn, or fiber induced by exposure to dry heat. Specifically, a fundamental property of fibers.

HOT DRAWING: The process of stretching manufactured filaments under heated conditions to improve their properties. It is used for processing filaments that cannot be drawn at ambient conditions. (Also see DRAWING, 2, and COLD DRAWING.)

HOT-HEAD PRESS: A pressing machine capable of generating high temperatures and pressures. Used for pressing and processing permanent-press fabrics.

HOT-MELT ADHESIVE: A solid material that melts quickly upon heating, then sets to a firm bond upon cooling. Use of this type adhesive provides almost instantaneous bonding.

HOUNDSTOOTH: A term describing a medium-sized broken-check effect; the check is actually a four-pointed star. (See diagram on the next page.)

HOY: Acronym for highly oriented yarn.

HUCKABACK: A heavy, serviceable toweling made with slackly twisted filling yarns to aid absorption. The cloth has a honeycomb effect.

HUMIDITY: See ABSOLUTE HUMIDITY, RELATIVE HUMIDITY, and SPECIFIC HUMIDITY.

Houndstooth

HYBRID COMPOSITE: Advanced composite with a combination of different high-strength continuous fila- ments in the matrix. Also, composite in which continuous and staple fibers are used in the same matrix.

HYBRID FABRIC: Fabric for composite manufacture in which two or more different yarns are used in the fabric construction. This provides design flexibility to meet performance requirements and controls cost by permitting some lower priced fibers to be used.

HYBRID NONWOVEN: A nonwoven made by two or more manufacturing methods to produce a structure with properties that are unattainable with a single process; e.g., a composite nonwoven.

HYBRID YARN: In aerospace textiles, a yarn having more than one com- ponent. (Also see COMMINGLED YARN.)

HYDRAULIC ENTANGLEMENT: See HYDROENTANGLING.

HYDROENTANGLING: Process for forming a fabric by mechanically wrap- ping and knotting fibers in a web through the use of high-velocity jets or curtains of water. (Also see SPUNLACED FABRIC.)

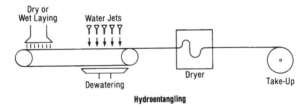

Hydroentangling

HYDROEXTRACTOR: See CENTRIFUGE.

HYDROGENATION: The process of passing hydrogen into an unsaturated chemical in the presence of a catalyst to convert the material to a more saturated state (i.e., containing more combined hydrogen).

HYDROLYSIS: A double decomposition reaction involving the addition of the elements of water and the formation of an acid and a base, an acid and an alcohol, or an acid and phenol.

HYDROLYTIC STABILITY: The resistance of any material to hydrolysis on exposure to wet conditions.

HYDROPHILIC: Having strong affinity for or the ability to absorb water.

HYDROPHOBIC: Lacking affinity for or the ability to absorb water.

HYDROSCOPIC: Having the ability to absorb moisture from the atmosphere. All fibers have this property in varying degrees.

HYDROXYL END GROUP: A polymer chain-terminating (–OH) group.

HYGROSCOPIC: See HYDROSCOPIC.

HYPOCHLORITE BLEACHING: Whitening of textile materials using a sodium hypochlorite solution as the bleaching agent.

HYPOCRITICAL DYEING: See DYEING, SUPERCRITICAL DYEING.

HYSTERESIS: 1. In general, a lag in the effect that occurs when the forces acting on a material are changed. **2.** In tire cord, a measurement of work lost through heat during dynamic operation. **3.** In tensile testing, loss of linear recovery following repeated loading and relaxation.

I

ICE WASHING: A wet process to produce a frosted appearance on garments (such as denim jeans) by stone washing with pebbles that have been soaked in potassium permanganate to bleach the surface fibers. (Also see STONE WASHING.)

IFAI: Acronym for the Industrial Fabrics Association International.

IMBIBITION: A measure of the liquid or water-holding capacity of a textile material.

IMMEDIATE ELASTIC DEFORMATION: Recoverable deformation that is essentially independent of time, i.e., occurring in (a time approaching) zero time and recoverable in (a time approaching) zero time after removal of the applied load.

IMPACT RESISTANCE: 1. The resistance of a material to fracture by a blow, expressed in terms of the amount of energy absorbed before fracture. **2.** In yarn or cord, the ability to withstand instantaneous or rapid rate of loading.

IMPACT STRENGTH: See IMPACT RESISTANCE.

IMPREGNATED FABRIC: A fabric in which the interstices between the yarns are completely filled, as compared to sized or coated materials where the interstices are not completely filled. Not included in the definition is a woven fabric constructed from impregnated yarns, rather than one impregnated after weaving.

INDA: Association of the Nonwoven Fabrics Industry.

INDEX OF REFRACTION: Ratio of the velocity of light in one medium to its velocity in a second medium as the light passes from medium to medium. If a medium is crystalline, the velocity may depend on the direction of the light with respect to the crystalline axes and the substance may have several indexes of refraction, i.e., it may be birefringent. (Also see BIREFRINGENCE.)

INDIGO: Originally, a natural blue vat dye extracted from plants, especially the *Indigofera tinctoria* plant. Most indigo dyes today are synthetic. They are frequently used on dungarees and denims.

INDIRECT WARPING: See SECTION WARPING.

INDIRECT YARN NUMBER: See DIRECT YARN NUMBER.

INDOOR/OUTDOOR CARPET: A carpet with indoor appearance features designed for outdoor use. Components are designed to withstand exposure to outdoor conditions such as moisture, temperature extremes, and UV radiation.

INDUSTRIAL FABRIC: A broad term for fabrics used for nonapparel and nondecorative uses. They fall into several classes: (1) a broad group including fabrics employed in industrial processes (e.g., filtering, polishing, and absorption), (2) fabrics combined with other materials to produce a different type of product (e.g., rubberized fabric for hose, belting, and tires; fabric combined with synthetic resins to be used for timing gears and electrical machinery parts; coated or enameled fabrics for automobile tops and book bindings; and fabrics impregnated with adhesive and dielectric compounds for applications in the electrical industry), and (3) fabrics incorporated directly in a finished product (e.g., sails, tarpaulins, tents, awnings, and specialty belts for agricultural machinery, airplanes, and conveyors). Fabrics developed for industrial uses cover a wide variety of widths, weights, and constructions and are attained, in many cases, only after painstaking research and experiment. Cotton and manufactured fibers are important fibers in this group, but virtually all textile fibers have industrial uses. The names mechanical fabrics or technical fabrics sometimes have been applied to certain industrial fabrics.

INFLATED DIAPHRAGM ABRASION TESTER: An apparatus for determining the abrasion resistance of woven and knit fabrics. The specimen is abraded in one or multiple directions while held in position on a rubber diaphragm that is inflated at constant pressure.

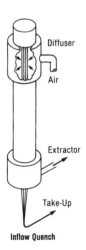

Diffuser

Air

Extractor

Take-Up

Inflow Quench

INFLATABLE STRUCTURES: Structures opened or enlarged by input of air and, once enlarged, able to retain the air to maintain the distended position.

INFLOW QUENCH: Cooling air for extruded polymer filaments that is directed radially inward across the path of the filaments. The threadline is completely enclosed in a quench cabinet in inflow quenching.

INGRAIN: See DYEING.

INHERENT FLAME RESISTANCE: As applied to textiles, flame resistance that is derived from an essential characteristic of the fiber from which the textile is made.

INHERENT VISCOSITY: See INTRINSIC VISCOSITY.

INHIBITOR: A substance that retards or prevents a chemical or physical change. In textiles, a chemical agent that is added to prevent fading, degradation, or other undesirable effects.

INITIAL MODULUS: A measure of a material's resistance to small deformations. It is the slope of the initial straight portion of a stress-strain curve. The modulus is the ratio of the change in stress, expressed in newtons per tex, grams-force per tex, or grams-force per denier, to the change in strain expressed as a fraction of the original length.

INITIATOR: A chemical added to start a reaction such as polymerization. Unlike catalysts, initiators may be consumed during the reaction.

INK-JET PRINTING: See BUBBLE-JET PRINTING and PRINTING, 1.

INSPECTION: The process of examining textiles for defects at any stage of manufacturing and finishing.

INSTRON TENSILE TESTER: A high precision electronic test instrument designed for testing a variety of materials under a broad range of test conditions. It is used to measure and chart the load-elongation properties of fibers, yarns, fabrics, webbings, plastics, films, rubber, leather, paper, etc. May also be used to measure such properties as tear resistance and resistance to compression.

INTAGLIO: 1. Printing style in which the design is cut into the surface of the cylinder and is thus below the surface. **2.** A lustrous, brocade pattern knitted in a tricot fabric.

INTEGRATED COMPOSITE SPINNING: See BOBTEX ICS YARN SYSTEM.

INTENSITY: 1. The amount of energy per unit (space, charge, time). **2.** The brilliance of a color. **3.** The brightness of light.

INTERFACIAL POLYMERIZATION: Polymerization in which two reactive monomers, each dissolved in different solvents that are mutually immiscible, react at the interface between the two solutions.

INTERFACING: See INTERLINING.

INTERLINING: A padding or stiffening fabric used in garment manufacture to provide shape retention. Interlining is sandwiched between layers of fabric.

INTERLOCK GATING: See GATING.

INTERLOCK KNIT: To produce an interlock knit, long and short needles are arranged alternately in both the dial and cylinder; the needles in the dial and cylinder are also positioned in direct alignment. When the long and short needles knit in alternate feeds in both needle housings, a fabric with a type of cross 1 x 1 rib effect is produced.

Interlock Knit
Construction

INTERMINGLING: 1. Use of air jets to create turbulence to entangle the filaments of continuous filament yarns, without forming loops, after extrusion. Provides dimensional stability and cohesion for further processing but is not of itself a texturing

Air Jet   Intermingling   Take-Up

process. It is compatible with high-speed spin-drawing and high-speed take-up. When compared with twisting processes, it also permits increased take-up package size. **2.** Combining two or more yarns via an intermingling jet. Can be used to get special effect yarns, i.e., mixing dye variants to get heather effects upon subsequent dyeing.

INTERMITTENT PATTERN: A pattern occurring in interrupted sequence.

INTERNAL DYE VARIABILITY: The change from point to point in dye uniformity across the diameter and along the length of the individual filaments. Affects appearance of the dyed product and is a function of fiber, dye, dyeing process, and dyebath characteristics.

INTERNATIONAL SYSTEM OF MEASUREMENT: See SI METRIC SYSTEM.

INTIMATE BLEND: A technique of mixing two or more dissimilar fibers in a very uniform mixture. Usually the stock is mixed before or at the picker.

INTRINSIC VISCOSITY: Ratio of the specific viscosity (R.V. − 1) of a solution of known concentration to the concentration of solute extrapolated to zero concentration. Also called the limiting viscosity number. It is directly proportional to the polymer-average molecular weight.

$$I.V. = \lim_{c \to 0} (\ln R.V. \div concentration).$$

IONOMER: A polymer having covalent bonds between the constituents of the long-chain molecules and ionic bonds between the chains.

ISLANDS-IN-THE-SEA: A type of component fiber described as multiple-interface or filament-in-matrix. The "islands" are fibrils of one or more polymers embedded in the "sea" (or matrix) consisting of another polymer. The matrix is often dissolved away to leave filaments of very low denier per filament. These fibers have been used in ion-exchange products and in imitation fur products as well as to produce textile products with a different hand.

Islands-in-the-Sea

ISO: Acronym for International Organization for Standardization.

ISO 9000: Product quality assurance and quality management systems developed by ISO. Companies must meet a set of minimum requirements to qualify for ISO 9000 status. The purposes of the systems are to help companies to produce goods and services that meet customer expectations and to minimize the cost of waste, rework, etc.

…IC POLYMER: A polymer struc-
…in which there is a regular spatial or
…reo relationship from one repeat unit to
the next. (Contrast with ATACTIC POLYMER,
SYNDIOTACTIC POLYMER and TACTIC POLYMER.)

$$-\overset{\displaystyle H}{\underset{\displaystyle H}{C}}-\overset{\displaystyle H}{\underset{\displaystyle CH_3}{C}}-\overset{\displaystyle H}{\underset{\displaystyle H}{C}}-\overset{\displaystyle H}{\underset{\displaystyle CH_3}{C}}-\overset{\displaystyle H}{\underset{\displaystyle H}{C}}-\overset{\displaystyle H}{\underset{\displaystyle CH_3}{C}}-\overset{\displaystyle H}{\underset{\displaystyle H}{C}}-\overset{\displaystyle H}{\underset{\displaystyle CH_3}{C}}-$$

Isotactic Structure

ISOTHERM: Constant temperature line used
on graphs of climatic conditions or thermodynamic relations, such as
pressure-volume relations at constant temperature.

ISOTROPIC: Having the same physical properties in every direction in the
plane of a fabric. It is related to the random distribution of fibers in nonwoven
manufacture.

ITCB: Acronym for the International Textiles and Clothing Bureau.

ITMA: Acronym for the International Textile Machinery Association.

IWS: Acronym for the International Wool Secretariat.

J

JACK: 1. A blade having high and/or low butts used to actuate the movement
of latch knitting needles. **2.** Part of a dobby head designed to serve as a lever
in the operation of the harness of a loom.

JACKET: 1. A woven or felted tubular sleeve for covering and shrinking on
a machine roll. **2.** A short coat. **3.** In polymer manufacture, an external shell
around a reaction vessel. For example, jacketed vessels are used when heat-
transfer medium is circulated around the vessel.

JACQUARD: A system of weaving that utilizes a highly versatile pattern
mechanism to permit the production of large, intricate designs. The weave
pattern is achieved by a series of punched cards. Each card perforation
controls the action of one warp thread for the passage of one pick. The
machine may carry a large number of cards, depending on the design, because
there is a separate card for each pick in the pattern. Today, much jacquard
weaving is done with an electronic pattern mechanism, which is quieter and
much smaller than the conventional jacquard apparatus. Jacquard weaving is
used for tapestry, brocade, damask, brocatelle, figured necktie and dress
fabrics, and some floor coverings. A similar device is used for the production
of figured patterns on some knit goods. (Also see JACQUARD KNIT FABRIC.)

JACQUARD KNIT FABRIC: A patterned fabric made on a knitting machine.
The design may be multicolored or formed by different types of knit stitches.
Jacquard double-knits can be produced by joining the two layers of loops in
some areas and leaving the layers separate in others to form a raised design.
(Also see DOUBLE-KNIT FABRIC.)

JACQUARD LOOM: See JACQUARD.

JASPÉ: 1. A fabric used for suiting, draperies, or upholstery characterized by a series of faint stripes formed by dark, medium, and light yarns of the same color. **2.** A term describing carpets having a faint striped effect.

JAWS: The devices on a tensile tester that grip the specimen at both ends so that strain can be applied.

J-BOX: A J-shaped holding device used in continuous operations to provide varying amounts of intermediate material storage such as in wet processing of fabrics and in tow production. The material is fed to the top and pleated to fill the long arm before being withdrawn from the short arm.

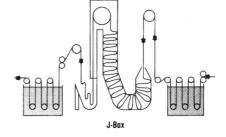

J-Box

J-CUT: In tufting cut-pile carpet constructions, uneven cutting of the loops caused by poor adjustment of knives and hooks or excessive tension.

JEAN: 1. A cotton twill fabric, similar to denim, but lighter and finer, in a 2 x 1 weave. It is used for sportswear, work clothing, and some industrial applications. **2.** A term sometimes used for denim.

JERK-BACK: See PULLED-IN FILLING.

JERKED-IN FILLING: See PULLED-IN FILLING.

JERSEY: 1. A circular-knit or flat-knit fabric made with a plain stitch in which the loops intermesh in only one direction. As a result, the appearance of the face and the back of a jersey fabric is wholly different. **2.** A tricot fabric made with a simple stitch, characterized by excellent drape and wrinkle recovery properties.

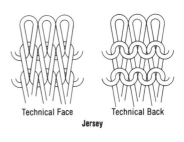

Technical Face   Technical Back

Jersey

JET: 1. A device used to bulk yarns by introducing curls, coils, and loops that are formed by the action of a high velocity stream, usually of air or steam. (Also see TEXTURING, 1.) **2.** A spray nozzle that applies dye to the face of fabric in a continuous dyeing machine. **3.** See SPINNERET.

JET CRATER: In spinning viscose rayon, a deposit that forms around the spinneret hole.

JET DYEING MACHINE: A high-temperature piece-dyeing machine that circulates the dye liquor through a venturi jet, thus imparting a driving force to move the fabric. The fabric, in rope form, is sewn together to form a loop.

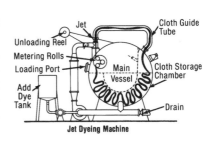

Jet Dyeing Machine

JET LOOM: A shuttleless loom that employs a jet of water or air to carry the filling yarn through the shed.

JET PRINTING: See BUBBLE-JET PRINTING.

JET SPINNING: See AIR JET SPINNING.

JIG: A machine in which fabric in open-width form is transferred repeatedly from one roller to another, passing each time through a bath of relatively small volume. Jigs are used for scouring, dyeing, bleaching, and finishing.

Jig

JIT: Acronym for JUST-IN-TIME.

JUST-IN-TIME: A streamlined inventory control method designed to improve cash flow and customer satisfaction through quick response to orders for production goods. Materials are timed to arrive shortly before they are required for production. An element of the QUICK RESPONSE program.

JUTE: A bast fiber used for sacking, burlap, and twine as a backing material for tufted carpets.

JUTE BUTT: The flaggy lower end of jute fiber that is cut off in preparing jute for market. The fibers are 0.4 to 1 inch in length. Jute butts are used in twines and coarse bagging.

JUTE COUNT: The weight in pounds of a spindle of 14,400 yards of yarn.

K

KAPOK: Short, lightweight cotton-like fibers from the seed pod of trees of the family *Bombacaceae*. A very brittle fiber, it is generally not spun. It is used for stuffing cushions, mattresses, etc., and for life jackets because of its buoyancy and moisture resistance.

KARAKUL: 1. A type of African sheep that produces a coarse wool sometimes used in carpets. **2.** A type of lamb pelts with glossy black fur in a wavy pattern that is less curly than Astrakhan.

KARAKUL FABRIC: A heavy pile fabric, knit or woven, simulating karakul fur. It is used for trimming coats and jackets.

KDK: Acronym for KNIT-DEKNIT.

KERATIN: The basic protein constituent of wool and other hair fibers.

KERSEY: A heavily fulled or milled woolen fabric having a high lustrous nap and a "grainy" face, kersey is frequently used in overcoats.

KETTLE: See BECK.

K-FACTOR: A numerical expression of the heat conduction rate of a material.

KHAKI: 1. A light yellowish brown. **2.** A khaki-colored cloth of cotton, wool, or combinations of these fibers with manufactured fibers used primarily in military uniforms and workclothes.

KIER: A large metal tank, capable of being heated uniformly, used for wet processing.

KIER BOILING: Process of boiling cellulosic materials in alkaline liquors in a kier at or above atmospheric pressure.

KINK: 1. In fabrics, a place where a short length of yarn has spontaneously doubled back on itself. **2.** In yarn, see SNARL.

KINKING: The doubling back of a yarn on itself to relieve torque imparted by twisting or texturing.

KINKY THREAD: See KINK.

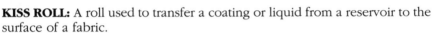

Kier

KISS ROLL: A roll used to transfer a coating or liquid from a reservoir to the surface of a fabric.

KNEE BREAK-OUT TEST: A method to evaluate the performance of fabrics, especially boys' wear, when subjected to abrasion, stretch, and impact forces under conditions which simulate ordinary wear at the knee.

KNEEING: Abnormal behavior of a spinning threadline (especially in melt spinning) in which one or more filaments form an angle (knee).

KNIT-DEKNIT: See TEXTURING, 5.

KNIT FABRIC: A structure produced by interlooping one or more ends of yarn or comparable material. (Also see KNITTING.)

KNIT-MISS: A form of tricot knitting in which yarns on each bar of a two-bar machine are knit at alternate courses only. This type of knitting permits the use of heavy-denier yarns without creating undesirable bulkiness in the fabric.

KNITTING: A method of constructing fabric by interlocking series of loops of one or more yarns. The two major classes of knitting are warp knitting and weft knitting, as follows:

1. Warp Knitting: A type of knitting in which the yarns generally run lengthwise in the fabric. The yarns are prepared as warps on beams with one or more yarns for each needle. Examples of this type of knitting are tricot, milanese, and raschel knitting.

　Milanese Knitting: A type of run-resistant warp knitting with a diagonal rib effect using several sets of yarns.

　Raschel Knitting: A versatile type of warp knitting made in plain and jacquard patterns; the latter can be made with intricate eyelet and lacy patterns and is often used for underwear fabrics. Raschel fabrics are coarser than other warp-knit fabrics, but a wide range of fabrics can be made. Raschel knitting machines have one or two sets of latch needles and up to thirty sets of guides.

Tricot Knitting: A run-resistant type of warp knitting in which either single or double sets of yarn are used. (Also see TRICOT.)

2. Weft Knitting: A common type of knitting, in which one continuous thread runs crosswise in the fabric making all of the loops in one course. Weft knitting types are circular and flat knitting.

Circular Knitting: The fabric is produced on the knitting machine in the form of a tube, the threads running continuously around the fabric.

Flat Knitting: The fabric is produced on the knitting machine in flat form, the threads alternating back and forth across the fabric. The fabric can be given shape in the knitting process by increasing or decreasing loops. Full-fashioned garments are made on a flat-knitting machine. (Also see FLAT-KNIT FABRIC.)

KNITTING MACHINE: A machine for constructing fabric by the formation of interconnected loops. The two main types of machines are weft knitting and warp knitting. (Also see KNITTING.)

KNOT STRENGTH: The tensile strength of a textile strand that has a knot tied in the specimen between the clamps of the tensile tester.

KNOTTING: 1. The process of tying two yarn ends together. **2.** Tying the yarn ends from a replacement beam to the ends of the depleted beam on the loom for continuation of weaving.

KRAFTCORD: Yarn produced by tightly twisting plant fiber is sometimes used in carpet backings.

KRAFT PULP: Wood pulp prepared in an alkaline liquor consisting of sodium hydroxide, sodium carbonate, and sodium sulfide. Also called sulfate pulp.

KRAFT YARN: A yarn made by twisting a strip of paper manufactured from kraft pulp.

KROY® SHRINKPROOFING PROCESS: Continuous process for shrinkproofing wool tops in which there is a direct chlorination step with no intervening chemical reaction followed by anti-chlorination and neutralization. Provides better hand and strength than does conventional shrinkproofing.

KÜSTERS DYEING RANGE: Continuous dye range for carpets. The unit wets the carpet, applies dyes and auxiliary chemicals by means of a doctor blade, fixes the dyes in a festoon steamer, and washes and dries the carpet in one pass through the range. An optional auxiliary unit may be installed to randomly drip selected dyes onto the background shade for special styling effects. This process is called TAK® dyeing.

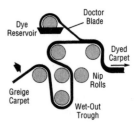

Küsters Carpet Dyeing Range

L

LACE: Ornamental openwork fabric, made in a variety of designs by intricate manipulation of the fiber by machine or by hand.

LACE STITCH: In this knitting stitch structure, loops are transferred from the needles on which they are made to adjacent needles to create a fabric with an open or a raised effect.

LA COSTA STITCH: A cross-tuck knit fabric with alternating courses of plain jersey stitch. Made on a spring needle machine, it is widely used in sportswear.

LADDER: See RUNNER.

LAID-IN FABRIC: A knit fabric in which an effect yarn is tucked in, not knitted into, the fabric structure. The laid-in yarns are held in position by the knitted yarns.

LAID-IN YARN: See AXIAL YARN.

LAMB'S WOOL: Very soft wool from lambs under seven months old. The fibers have a natural tapered tip that is lost after the first clipping. It has superior spinning characteristics. (Also see FLEECE, 1.)

LAMÉ: A fabric woven with flat metal threads, usually silver or gold, that form either the background or the pattern.

LAMINAR FLOW: Streamline flow in a viscous fluid, such as molten polymer, near a solid boundary.

LAMINATED FABRIC: 1. Fabric composed of a high-strength reinforcing scrim or base fabric between two plies of flexible thermoplastic film. Usually open scrims are used to permit the polymer to flow through the interstices and bond during calendering. **2.** See BONDED FABRIC, 1.

LAP: A continuous, considerably compressed sheet of fibers that is rolled under pressure into a cylindrical package, usually weighing between 40 and 50 pounds. The lap is used to supply the card.

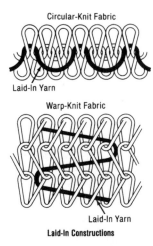

Circular-Knit Fabric

Laid-In Yarn

Warp-Knit Fabric

Laid-In Yarn

Laid-In Constructions

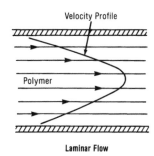

Velocity Profile

Polymer

Laminar Flow

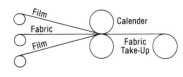

Film

Fabric

Film

Calender

Fabric Take-Up

Laminated Fabric Formation

LAPPING: A term describing the movement of yarn guides between needles, at right angles to the needle bar, or laterally in relation to the needle bar during warp knitting.

LAP SPLITTING: A condition caused by a lap that will not unwind in carding in the same thickness as it was wound in picking. This splitting of the sheet of fiber can result in either a thicker or thinner sheet being fed into the card.

LASE: An acronym for load at specified elongation: the load required to produce a given elongation of a yarn or cord.

LASER: A device for producing an intense beam of coherent light. It is used for cutting, spectroscopy, photography, biomedical investigations, etc.

LASER CUTTING: A cutting process using a special narrow-beam laser to vaporize the fabric on contact.

LASER ENGRAVING: A process for engraving rotary printing screens using a laser.

LASER FABRIC INSPECTION: Electronic inspection of fabric with a laser device that greatly increases the efficiency of the cloth inspection process. A human inspector is also required to evaluate identified defects and make any possible repairs.

LASHED-IN FILLING: See PULLED-IN FILLING.

LASTRILE FIBER: A manufactured fiber in which the fiber-forming substance is a copolymer of acrylonitrile and a diene composed of at least 10% by weight, but not more than 50% by weight, of acrylonitrile [$-CH_2-CH(CN)-$] units (FTC definition).

LATCH NEEDLE: One of the two types of knitting machine needles. The latch needle has a small terminal hook with a latch that pivots automatically in knitting to close the hook. The fabric loop is cast off. The latch then opens, allowing a new loop to be formed by the hook, and loop-forming and casting-off proceed simultaneously. (Also see SPRING NEEDLE.)

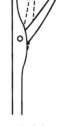

Head of
Latch Needle

LATENT CRIMP: Crimp in fibers that can be developed by a specific treatment. Fibers are prepared specially to crimp when subjected to specific conditions, e.g., tumbling in a heated chamber or wet processing.

LATEX: A milky fluid found in certain cells of some families of seed plants. Latex is the raw material from which rubber is made.

LAUNDER-OMETER®: The trademark for a laboratory machine for testing the fastness of fabrics to washing and dry cleaning (Manufactured by Atlas Electric Devices.)

LAWN: A light, thin cloth made of carded or combed yarn, this fabric is given a crease-resistant, crisp finish. Lawn is crisper than voile but not as crisp as organdy.

LAYING: A doubling process for ropes and cordage.

LCL: Acronym for LOWER CONTROL LIMIT.

LCP: See LIQUID CRYSTAL POLYMER.

LEA: 1. One-seventh of an 840-yard cotton hank, i.e., 120 yards. **2.** A standard skein with 80 revolutions of 1.5 yards each (total length of 120 yards). It is used for strength tests. **3.** A unit of measure, 300 yards, used to determine the yarn number of linen yarn. The number of leas in one pound is the yarn number.

LEACHING: The removal of any substance or dye from textiles by the percolating action of a suitable liquid.

LEA COUNT CONSTANT: See BREAK FACTOR.

LEADER CLOTH: A length of fabric left threaded through a printing or finishing machine to which a new piece is attached to thread it through the machine.

LEADER MARK: See DECATING MARK.

LEA PRODUCT: See BREAK FACTOR.

LEASE: The orderly arrangement of yarns in a warp sheet to facilitate handling during preparation and weaving. The most common method is passing two sets of yarns alternately over and under two rods, called lease rods, to keep them in position.

LEFT-HAND TWILL: A twill construction in which the diagonal runs from the lower right to the upper left on the fabric face when viewed in the warp direction.

LEFT-HAND TWIST: S twist. See DIRECTION OF TWIST.

LENGTH DISTRIBUTION: Analysis of a fiber sample for the proportion of different fiber lengths it contains.

LENO WEAVE: A weave in which the warp yarns are arranged in pairs with one twisted around the other between picks of filling yarn as in marquisette. This type of weave gives firmness and strength to an open-weave fabric and prevents slippage and displacement of warp and filling yarns.

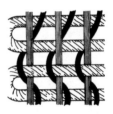

Full Leno Weave

LET-OFF MOTION: A device for controlling the delivery and tension of the warp during weaving.

LEVELING: Migration leading to uniform distribution of dye in a dyed material. Leveling may be a property of the dye or it may require chemical assistance.

LEVEL LOOP: A term describing a tufted or woven carpet with uncut, equal-length loops composing the pile surface.

LICKERIN: A part of the feed mechanism of the card. It consists of a hollow, metal roll with a spirally grooved surface containing a special saw-toothed wire. The lickerin opens up the tufts of the picker lap as it is fed to the card and transfers the fibers to the main cylinder.

LICKERIN LOADING: A condition in which fibers are imbedded in the lickerin wire clothing so as to resist transfer to the cylinder clothing.

LIGHT END: 1. The low boiling fraction in distillation. **2.** See FINE END, 1.

LIGHTFASTNESS: The degree of resistance of dyed textile materials to the color-destroying influence of sunlight. Two methods of testing are in use: (1) exposure to sunlight, either directly or under glass, and (2) accelerated testing in a laboratory apparatus equipped with any of several types of artificial light sources.

LIGNIN: The major noncarbohydrate portion of wood. It is an amorphous polymeric substance that cements the fibrous portions together.

LIMITING OXYGEN INDEX: A relative measure of flammability that is determined as follows: A sample is ignited in an oxygen/nitrogen atmosphere. The oxygen content is adjusted to the minimum amount required to sustain steady burning. The higher the value, the lower the flammability.

LINEAR DENSITY: Mass per unit length expressed as grams per centimeter, pounds per foot, or equivalent units. It is the quotient obtained by dividing the mass of a fiber or yarn by its length.

LINEN: Cellulose fibers derived from the stem of the FLAX plant or a fabric made from these fibers. Linen is the oldest fabric known to man, dating to at least 4000 B.C., when it was produced in Egypt. Flax plants are pulled from the ground to preserve the stems, which then undergo a process called RETTING to decompose the woody components. In the next processing stage, SCUTCHING, the stems are crushed to separate the decomposed materials from the fibers, followed by HACKLING, a combing process. Then the linen fibers are lightly twisted and spun into yarns.

CHARACTERISTICS: Linen fibers are stronger and more lustrous than cotton; they yield cool, absorbent fabrics that wrinkle easily. Fabrics with linen-like texture and coolness but with good wrinkle resistance can be produced from blends with other fibers.

END USES: Linen fabrics are used in dresses, blouses, and suitings, home furnishing fabrics, wall coverings, towels, and canvas. Household linens such as tablecloths are prized for their beauty and durability, often becoming family heirlooms. Linen fiber is blended with silk for apparel and with spandex for comfort stretch.

LINEN LEA: See LEA, 3.

LINEN WEAVE: See PLAIN WEAVE.

LINEN YARN COUNT: See LEA, 3.

LINET: A French-made lining fabric of unbleached linen.

LINING FABRIC: Fabric that is used to cover inner surfaces, especially when the inner surface is of a different material than the outer. May refer to garment lining, lining for boxes, coffins, etc. Generally of smooth, lustrous appearing fabrics, but also of felt and velvet. Both manufactured fibers and natural fibers are used.

LINKED PROCESSES: Refers to the connection of the various steps of fiber-to-yarn processing via pneumatic fiber-transport systems, on-line monitoring, and process control. Process linking results in less labor-intensive processing. A typical linked system might include all stages from bale opening through carding.

LINKS-LINKS KNITTING MACHINE: A type of flat or circular knitting machine for producing PURL stitches. The needles can be transferred from one needle bed to the opposite one to produce novelty fabric effects.

LINON A JOUR: A gauze-like linen fabric used as dress goods.

LINT: Particles and short fibers that fall from a textile product during the stresses of use. Also called FLY.

LINT BALL: See BALLING UP.

LINTERS: The short cotton fibers that are not removed from the seed during the first ginning. The linters are cut from the seed and used as a source for cellulose derivatives such as nitrocellulose or viscose rayon.

LIQUID AMMONIA TREATMENT: Process for treating cotton fabric with anhydrous liquid ammonia to impart a softer handle and improve smoothness after drying.

LIQUID CRYSTAL: A liquid in which the molecules are oriented parallel to each other resulting in birefringence and interference patterns visible in polarizing light.

LIQUID CRYSTAL POLYMER: Polymers such as aramids or the thermotropic polyesters that form liquid crystals when in the appropriate state, (concentrated solution or melt). Most liquid crystal polymers have in their structure a succession of para-ring structures. The liquid crystal formation is thought to relate to the fact that there is a limiting concentration of rod-like chains that can exist in a random arrangement in a solution or melt. Once this concentration is reached, ordering or alignment of the chains is necessary to accommodate them. Fibers from liquid crystal polymers generally have high modulus and tenacity, good chemical resistance, and high-temperature resistance. They are used in a wide range of applications including protective apparel, tire cord, composites, ropes and cables, etc.

Random Orientation

Parallel Orientation

Liquid Crystal

LIQUOR RATIO: In wet processing, the ratio of the weight of liquid used to the weight of goods treated.

LISLE YARN: A high-quality cotton yarn made by plying yarns spun from long combed staple. Lisle is singed to give it a smooth finish.

LISTING: 1. A fabric dyeing defect consisting of variable colorant across the width. **2.** A damaged selvage.

LIVELY: A term used to describe yarn that tends to twist on itself when not under tension. (Also see KINKING and SNARL.)

LIVING RING: See REVOLVING SPINNING RING.

LOAD-DEFORMATION CURVE: A graphical representation of the relationship between the change in dimension (in the direction of the applied force) of the specimen resulting from the application of an external load, and the magnitude of that load. The load may be expressed in units of weight (such as pounds or kilograms) and the deformation in either units of length (such as inches or millimeters) in tension or compression tests, or degrees in shear tests. In a tension test, a load-deformation curve becomes a load-elongation curve.

LOAD-ELONGATION CURVE: See STRESS-STRAIN CURVE.

LOADING: Increasing the weight or body of a fabric by applying materials such as starch, gum, or clay. (Also see FILLER.)

LOCKING COURSE: The final course on a garment or garment component knit on a rib or purl machine. It is designed to prevent unraveling of cast off stitches.

LOFT: The properties of firmness, resilience, and bulk of a fiber batting, yarn, fabric, or other textile material.

LOI: Acronym for LIMITING OXYGEN INDEX.

LONG STAPLE: A long fiber. In reference to cotton, long staple indicates a fiber length of not less than 1$\frac{1}{8}$-inches. In reference to wool, the term indicates fiber 3 to 4 inches long suitable for combing.

LOOM: A machine for weaving fabric by interlacing a series of vertical, parallel threads (the warp) with a series of horizontal, parallel threads (the filling). The warp yarns from a beam pass through the heddles and reed, and the filling is shot through the "shed" of warp threads by means of a shuttle or other device and is settled in place by the reed and lay. The woven fabric is then wound on a cloth beam. The primary distinction between different types of looms is the manner of filling insertion (see WEFT INSERTION, 1). The principal elements of any type of loom are the shedding, picking, and beating-up devices. In shedding, a path is formed for the filling by raising some warp threads while others are left down. Picking consists essentially of projecting the filling yarn from one side of the loom to the other. Beating-up forces the pick, that has just been left in the shed, up to the fell of the fabric. This is accomplished by the reed, which is brought forward with some force by the lay. (Also see JACQUARD.)

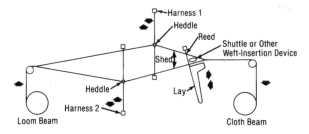

Elements of the Loom

LOOM BARRÉ: A repeated unevenness in the fabric, usually running from selvage to selvage, and caused by uneven let-off or take-up or by a loose crank arm.

LOOM EFFICIENCY: See WEAVING EFFICIENCY.

LOOM FINISHED: A term describing fabric sold as it comes from the loom, without further finishing.

LOOM FLY: Waste fibers that are inadvertently woven into a fabric.

LOOM STATE: See GREIGE FABRIC.

LOOM WINDER: In weaving on a shuttle loom, a device that automatically refills quills during weaving by winding yarn from cones.

LOOP: The basic stitch in all knit constructions.

LOOP BREAKING STRENGTH: See LOOP TENACITY.

LOOPED FILLING: A woven-in loop caused by the filling sloughing off the quill or by the shuttle rebounding in the box.

LOOPED PILE: A pile surface made of uncut looped yarns.

LOOPED YARN: See KINK, 1.

LOOP ELONGATION: The maximum extension of a looped yarn at maximum load, expressed as a percentage of the original gauge length.

LOOPER: Component of a tufting machine that picks up the yarn from the tufting needle at the bottom of the downstroke and holds it while the needle retracts from the backing.

LOOPING: Generally, a method of uniting knit fabrics by joining two courses of loops on a machine called a looper.

LOOPING BAR: A bar inserted in the bottom of an extrusion metier around which the dried filaments pass as they leave the spinning cabinet.

LOOP-KNOT: See KINK.

LOOP PILE: Carpet construction in which the tufts are formed into loops from the supply yarn.

LOOP SELVAGE: See PICOT.

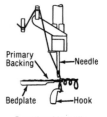

Primary Backing — Needle

Bedplate — Hook

Formation of Loop Pile

LOOP TENACITY: The strength of a compound strand formed when one strand of yarn is looped through another strand, then broken. It is the breaking load in grams divided by twice the measured yarn denier or decitex. Loop tenacity, when compared with standard tenacity measurements, is an indication of the brittleness of a fiber.

LOOPY SELVAGE: A weaving defect at the selvage of excessive thickness or irregular filling loops that extend beyond the outside selvages.

LOOSE EDGE: See SLACK SELVAGE.

LOOSE END: See TIGHT OR LOOSE END.

LOOSE FILLING: A fabric defect that is usually seen as short, loose places in the filling caused by too little tension on the yarn in the shuttle or by the shuttle rebounding in the box. Loose filling can often be felt by an examiner when passing a hand over the surface of the fabric.

LOOSE PICK: See SLACK PICK.

LOST END: An end on a section or tricot beam that has been broken at some stage in warping and has not been repaired by a knot.

LOT: A unit of production or a group of other units or packages that is taken for sampling or statistical examination, having one or more common properties and being readily separable from other similar units.

LOWER CONTROL LIMIT: In statistical quality control, the lowest value of a specific parameter that is acceptable for a process. On a control chart, it is represented by a straight line drawn parallel to the time axis 3 standard deviations below the expected mean value. (Also see STATISTICAL PROCESS CONTROL.)

LOW-ORIENTATION YARN: A manufactured filament yarn with a low level of alignment of its polymer molecules. It can be drawn down at a high draw ratio. (Also see PARTIALLY ORIENTED YARN and HIGHLY ORIENTED YARN.)

LOW POWER STRETCH: A term used to describe fabric that will stretch easily when a low load is applied and recover readily when the load is removed. (Also see COMFORT STRETCH and POWER STRETCH.)

LOW ROWS: A carpet defect characterized by rows of unusually low pile height across the width of the goods.

LOW WET PICKUP: A method of applying a minimal amount of a dyeing or finishing bath to reduce material waste and energy required for drying.

LOY: Acronym for low-orientation yarn.

LUANA: A fabric characterized by a crosswise rib effect, usually made with a filament yarn warp and a spun yarn filling.

LUBRICANT: An oil or emulsion finish applied to fibers to prevent damage during textile processing or to knitting yarns to make them more pliable.

LUMEN: A hollow channel of varying lengths that runs longitudinally in each cell of an animal or vegetable fiber.

LUMINESCENCE: Emission of light not caused by incandescence but rather by physiological processes, chemical action, friction or electrical action. (Also see FLUORESCENCE and PHOSPHORESCENCE.)

LUSTER: The quality of shining with reflected light. With reference to textile materials, the term is frequently associated with the adjectives bright or dull to distinguish between varieties of manufactured fibers.

LUSTERING: The finishing of yarn or fabric by means of heat, pressure, steam, friction calendering, etc., to produce luster.

LUSTER WOOL: See BRAID, 3.

LYOCELL FIBER: A manufactured cellulose fiber made by direct dissolution of wood pulp in an amine oxide solvent, N-methylmorpholine-N-oxide. The clear solution is extruded into a dilute aqueous solution of amine oxide, which precipitates the cellulose in the form of filaments. The fiber is then washed before it is dried and finished.

The solvent spinning process for making lyocell fiber is considered to be environmentally friendly because the non-toxic spinning solvent is recovered, purified, and recycled as an integral part of the manufacturing process. No chemical intermediates are formed, the minimal waste is not hazardous, and energy consumption is low. Wood pulp is a renewable resource, and the fiber is biodegradable.

CHARACTERISTICS: Lyocell fiber is stronger than other cellulosic fibers. It is inherently absorbent, having a water imbibition of 65%–75%. Lyocell retains 85% of its dry tenacity when wet, making it stronger when wet than cotton. The fiber has a density of 1.51 g/cm^3.

END USES: Lyocell fiber is suitable for blending with cotton or other manufactured fibers. Because of its molecular structure, lyocell has the tendency to develop surface fibrils that can be beneficial in the manufacture of hydroentangled and other nonwovens, and in specialty papers. For apparel uses, the fiber's unique fibrillation characteristic has enabled the development of fabrics with a soft luxurious hand. The degree of fibrillation is controlled by cellulase enzyme treatment.

LYOTROPIC POLYMER: Polymers that decompose before melting but that form liquid crystals in solution under appropriate conditions. They can be extruded from high concentration dopes to give fibers of high modulus and orientation for use in advanced composites, tire cord, ballistic protective devices, etc.

M

MACE SNAG TEST: A test for evaluation of snagging performance. A fabric sample is mounted on a revolving drum in contact with a miniature mace that tracks randomly across the sample. The spikes of the mace effect the snagging. The test predicts results in actual wear.

MACHINE DIRECTION: The long direction within the plane of the fabric, i.e., the direction in which the fabric is being produced by the machine.

MACHINE TWIST: A hard-twist sewing thread, usually of 3-ply construction spun with S twist and plied with Z twist, especially made for use in sewing machines.

MACHINE WASHABLE: A term used to describe a textile item that is suitable for laundering in a domestic washing machine.

MACROLATTICE: A repeating structure in very small microfibrils of alternating crystalline and amorphous regions. Yarn properties are thought to be governed by morphology at the macrolattice scale.

MADRAS: A lightweight, plain-weave fabric with a striped, checked, or plaid pattern. True madras is "guaranteed to bleed."

MAGAZINE BAR: In full fashioned knitting, a transfer bar that holds a supply of garment components prior to looping.

Mace Snag Tester

Macrolattice

MALLORY FATIGUE TEST: A test to measure the endurance properties of tire cord.

MANDREL: The core around which the impregnated filaments are placed to form a specified shape in composite manufacture.

MANILA: Fiber obtained from the leaf stalks of the abaca plant. It is generally used for cordage.

MAN-MADE FIBER: See MANUFACTURED FIBER.

MANUFACTURED FIBER: A class name for various genera of fibers (including filaments) produced from fiber-forming substances which may be: (1) polymers synthesized from chemical compounds, e.g., acrylic, nylon, polyester, polyethylene, polyurethane, and polyvinyl fibers; (2) modified or transformed natural polymers, e.g., alginic and cellulose-based fibers such as acetates and rayons; and (3) minerals, e.g., glasses. The term manufactured usually refers to all chemically produced fibers to distinguish them from the truly natural fibers such as cotton, wool, silk, flax, etc.

MARKER: In the floor coverings industry, a distinctive threadline in the back of a carpet that enables the installer to assemble breadths of carpet so that the pile lays in one direction or so that patterns match.

MARK-OFF: See CROCKING.

MARL YARN: A yarn made from two rovings of contrasting colors drafted together, then spun. Provides a mottled effect.

MARQUISETTE: A lightweight, open-mesh fabric made of cotton, silk, or manufactured fibers in a leno, doup, or gauze weave. Marquisettes are used for curtains, dresses, mosquito nets, and similar end uses.

MARRIED FIBER CLUMP: A defect that occurs in converter top. It consists of a group of unopened, almost coterminous fibers with the crimp in register.

MATELASSÉ: A soft, double or compound fancy-woven fabric with a quilted appearance. Heavier types are used as draperies and upholsteries. Crepe matelassé is used for dresses, wraps, and other apparel. Matelassé is usually woven on a jacquard loom.

MATERIAL BALANCE: A mathematical representation of material flow through a reaction system. The input material is accounted for throughout its various transformations.

MATRIX BICOMPONENT FIBER: See BICOMPONENT FIBER.

MATRIX FIBER: 1. A manufactured fiber that is essentially a physical combination or mixture of two or more chemically distinct constituents or components combined at or prior to the time of extrusion (i.e., produced in fiber form), which components, if separately extruded, would each fall within different definitions of textile fibers (FTC definition). Matrix-fibril fibers have the fibril constituent randomly arranged across the cross section of the matrix. When the fibril component is in high concentration, it may actually form a fibrillar network in the matrix. **2.** In aerospace textiles, a thermoplastic fiber used with reinforcing fiber to form a composite after consolidation with heat and pressure. **3.** In nonwovens manufacture, fibers that are blended with low-melt fibers to form a thermally bonded fabric.

MATRIX-FIBRIL BICOMPONENT FIBER: See BICOMPONENT FIBER.

MATTED STAPLE: Fiber in the bale that is compressed and entangled in a manner indicating that the fiber was either too wet at the baling operation or that excessive baling pressure was used.

MATT EFFECT: See BASKET WEAVE.

MECHANICAL FINISHING: Changing the appearance or physical properties of a fabric by a mechanical process such as calendering, embossing, bulking, compacting, or creping.

MELAMINE FIBER: One of the newest high-performance manufactured fibers, produced by dry spinning of melamine formaldehyde polymer. It has high chemical and temperature resistance and a high LOI, making it of interest for technical applications such as protective apparel and hot-gas filtration. Because of its low tenacity and variability in denier and staple lengths, melamine fiber has experienced processing difficulties, but developments in spinning technology are allowing blends of melamine fiber to be spun satisfactorily for some end uses.

MELDED FABRIC: A nonwoven fabric of a base fiber and a thermoplastic fiber. The web is hot-calendered or embossed at the softening point of the thermoplastic fiber to form the bond.

MELT: A material in the molten state.

MELT BLEND: See BICONSTITUENT FIBER, 1.

MELT BLOWING: The formation of a nonwoven by extruding molten polymer through a die then attenuating and breaking the resulting filaments with hot, high-velocity air or steam. This results in short fiber lengths. The short fibers are then collected on a moving screen where they bond during cooling.

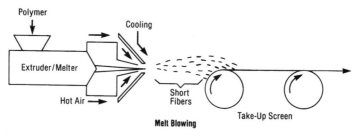

MELT-DYEING: See DYEING.

MELT INDEX: The weight in grams of a thermoplastic material that can be forced through a standard orifice within a specified time.

MELTING POINT: The temperature at which the solid and liquid states of a substance are in equilibrium; generally, the temperature at which a substance changes from a solid to a liquid.

MELTON: A heavily fulled, hard, plain coating fabric that was originally all-wool but is now also seen in wool blends.

MELT SPINNING: See SPINNING, 2.

MELT VISCOSITY: The resistance of molten polymer to shear deformation. It is primarily a factor of intrinsic viscosity and temperature. It is an apparent polymer viscosity measurement in that it is only true at a specific shear stress and shear rate combination.

MENDING: 1. A process in woven fabric manufacture in which weaving imperfections, tears, broken yarns, and similar defects are repaired after weaving; especially on woolen and worsted fabrics to prepare them for dyeing, finishing, or other processing. **2.** Hand repair of carpet at the tufting machine to replace missing tufts.

MERCERIZATION: A treatment of cotton yarn or fabric to increase its luster and affinity for dyes. The material is immersed under tension in a cold sodium hydroxide (caustic soda) solution in warp or skein form or in the piece, and is later neutralized in acid. The process causes a permanent swelling of the fiber and thus increases its luster.

MERGE: A group to which fiber production is assigned based on properties and dyeability. All fibers within a merge can be expected to behave uniformly, and for this reason, can be mixed or used interchangeably.

MERINO: 1. Wool from pure-bred Merino sheep. Merino wool usually has a mean fiber diameter of 24 microns or less. **2.** A yarn of blended wool and cotton fibers.

MESH FABRICS: A broad term for fabric characterized by open spaces between the yarns. Mesh fabrics may be woven, knit, lace, net, crochet, etc.

META: A chemical prefix, usually abbreviated *m*, that denotes that two substituents on a benzene ring are separated by one carbon atom.

META-ARAMID FIBER: A high-performance manufactured fiber with high strength and heat resistance. The fibers do not ignite, melt or drip making them suitable for flame-resistant applications. They retain their integrity and mechanical properties during long-term exposure to elevated temperatures. Meta-aramid fibers have a soft hand and good processing characteristics. Major uses are flame-resistant apparel and filtration. (Also see ARAMID FIBER and PARA-ARAMID FIBER.)

METAL-COMPLEX DYES: See DYEING, PREMETALIZED DYES.

METAL-FREE REACTIVE DYES: See DYES.

METALLIC CLOTHING: A serrated metal strip used to wrap card cylinders and doffers. The teeth face out and form the working surface for web formation and transfer.

METALLIC FIBER: A manufactured fiber composed of metal, plastic-coated metal, metal-coated plastic, or a core completely covered by metal (FTC definition). They are available in "yarn" form as well as in staple form for spinning with other fibers. A core yarn with a metal surface is produced by twisting a strip of metal around yarn of natural or manufactured fibers. The most important characteristic of metallic fiber and the chief reason for its use in textiles is glitter. Metallic fibers are used as a decorative accent in fabrics for apparel, bedspreads, towels, draperies, and upholstery. A relatively new application for metallic fibers is in carpet pile, where they are being used in small percentages for control of static electricity.

METALIZED DYES: See DYES

METALIZED FABRIC: 1. A fabric containing metalized yarns. **2.** A fabric with a metalized surface. The metalized layer can be applied chemically, electrically, or by lamination to the fabric substrate.

METAMERIC COLOR MATCH: A color match between two materials in which the colors are identical under some lighting conditions but not under others. Metameric color matches are common when different pigments or dyestuffs are used to color the two materials.

METAP WEAVE-KNIT PROCESS: A technique combining weaving and knitting in one operation with two independent yarn systems wound on warp beams. In the fabrics produced, woven strips are linked together with wales of stitches. Generally, the fabrics have 75%–85% woven and 25%–15% knitted structure.

METERING PUMP: A positive displacement device that pumps a measured amount of polymer solution to the spinnerets.

METHENAMINE PILL TEST: See FLAMMABILITY TESTS.

METIER: A spinning machine for producing manufactured fibers. The bank of cells or compartments and associated equipment used in the dry spinning of fibers, such as cellulose acetate and cellulose triacetate.

METIER TWIST: The amount of twist present in yarn wound at the metier.

METRIC COUNT: The number of kilometers per kilogram of yarn.

METRIC SYSTEM: See SI METRIC SYSTEM.

MICROBIAL DEGRADATION: Deterioration of natural fibers caused by bacteria or fungi. (Also see ANTIBACTERIAL FINISH.)

MICRODENIER: See MICROFIBER.

MICROENCAPSULATION: Enclosing materials in capsules of less than one micron to over 2000 microns in diameter. These can contain polymer additives that can then be released under certain conditions of use or processing.

MICROFIBER: An ultrafine fiber of less than 1.0 denier per filament or 0.1 tex per filament, or having a diameter less than 10 microns. Microfiber is used to produce ultrasoft, lightweight fabrics.

MICRONAIRE METHOD: A means of measuring fiber fineness by determining the resistance of a sample to a flow of air forced through it.

MICROSAFE®: Registered trademark of Celanese Acetate for manufactured acetate fibers made from polymer to which an antimicrobial agent has been added prior to extrusion. The agent provides built-in protection against a broad range of bacteria and fungi such as mold, mildew, and yeasts. Microsafe fibers find wide use in products used in medical, food service, and many other applications.

MICROSTRUCTURE: A term referring to the internal structure of a fiber. (Also see MORPHOLOGY.)

MIGRATION: 1. Movement of dye from one area of dyed fabric to another. Includes movement of color from the dyed area to the undyed area of cloth. **2.** Movement of fibers which go from the center to the outside surface of yarn and back again periodically.

MIL: A unit of length, 0.001 inch, commonly used for measuring the diameter of wires and textile monofilaments.

MILANESE KNITTING: See KNITTING, 1.

MILDEW: A whitish growth caused by spore-forming fungi that grow in a warm, moist, confined atmosphere. The formation of mildew may cause discoloration, tendering, or variation in dyeing properties in cellulosic fibers.

MILDEW RESISTANCE: The degree to which fabrics are unaffected by certain fungi that cause odor and discoloration.

MILL END: A remnant or short length of finished fabric.

MILLING: 1. The process of treating fabric in a fulling mill, i.e., fulling. **2.** In silk manufacturing, the twisting of the filaments into yarn. **3.** A grinding process, i.e., ball-milling of dyes and pigments.

MILLITRON® PROCESS: See PRINTING, 2.

MILL RUN: A yarn, fabric, or other textile product that has not been inspected or that does not come up to the standard quality.

MINERAL FIBERS: A generic term for all non-metallic, inorganic fibers, which may be natural, such as asbestos, or manufactured from such sources as rock, ore, alloys, slag, or glass.

MINIMUM CARE: A term describing home laundering methods. Minimum care fabrics, garments, and household textile articles can be washed satisfactorily by normal home laundering methods and can be used or worn after light ironing. Light ironing denotes ironing without starching or dampening and with a relatively small expenditure of physical effort. (Also see DURABLE PRESS and EASY-CARE.)

MISCLIP: See SCALLOPED SELVAGE.

MISPICK: A weaving defect in which a pick is improperly interlaced, resulting in a break in the weave pattern. Mispicks can result from starting the loom on the incorrect pick after a pick-out.

MISSING END: See END OUT.

MISS-STITCH: A knitting construction formed when the needle holds the old loop and does not receive new yarn. It connects two loops of the same course that are not in adjacent wales. Also known as float-stitch.

MITTER PRINTING MACHINE: See PRINTING, 2.

MIXED END OR FILLING: Warp or filling yarn differing from that normally used in the fabric, e.g., yarn with the incorrect twist or number of plies, yarn of the wrong color, or yarn from the wrong lot.

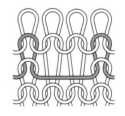

Miss-Stitch

MIXING: Blending fibers from different lots of the same fiber to improve product uniformity. (Also see BLENDING.)

MOCK DYEING: A heat stabilization process for yarns. The yarns are wound onto packages and subjected to package dyeing conditions (water, pressure, temperature) but without dye and chemicals in the bath.

MOCK LENO: A combination of weaves having interlacings that tend to form the warp ends into groups (with empty spaces intervening) in the cloth, thereby giving an imitation of the open structure that is characteristic of leno fabrics. Mock leno fabrics are used for summer shirts, dresses, and other apparel, and as a shading medium in Jacquard designs.

MODACRYLIC FIBER: A manufactured fiber in which the fiber-forming substance is any long chain synthetic polymer composed of less than 85% but at least 35% by weight of acrylonitrile units (FTC definition). Both wet and dry spinning are used.

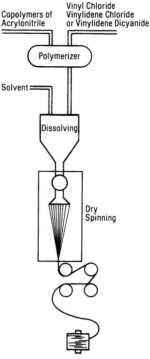

Modacrylic Fiber Production

CHARACTERISTICS: Although modacrylics are similar to acrylics in properties and applications, certain important differences exist. Modacrylics have superior resistance to chemicals and combustion, but they are more heat sensitive (lower safe ironing temperature) and have a higher specific gravity (less cover).

END USES: The principal applications of modacrylic fibers are in pile fabrics, flame-retardant garments, draperies, and carpets.

MODIFIED STRETCH YARN: See TEXTURED YARNS, 6.

MODIFIED WORSTED SPINNING SYSTEM: A system for spinning manufactured fibers that is based on the WORSTED SPINNING SYSTEM for long-staple wool fibers. The combing operation is omitted and parallelization of the sliver is accomplished during pin drafting.

MODULUS: The ratio of change in stress to change in strain following the removal of crimp from the material being tested; i.e., the ratio of the stress expressed in either force per unit linear density or force per unit area of the original specimen, and the strain expressed as either a fraction of the original length or percentage elongation. (Also see YOUNG'S MODULUS.)

MOHAIR: See ANGORA, 1.

MOIRÉ: 1. A wavy or watered effect on a textile fabric, especially a corded fabric of silk, rayon, or one of the manufactured fibers. Moiré is produced by passing the fabric between engraved cylinders which press the design into the material, causing the crushed and uncrushed parts to reflect light differently.

124

2. An unintentional moiré effect produced on fabric when an impression of the weave of one layer is left on the face of another layer during wet processing of rolled goods under heat and pressure.

MOISTURE-FREE WEIGHT: 1. The constant weight of a specimen obtained by drying at a temperature of 105°C in a current of desiccated air. **2.** The weight of a dry substance calculated from an independent determination of moisture content (e.g., by distillation with an immiscible solvent or by titration with Fischer reagent).

MOISTURE PROPERTIES: All fibers when exposed to the atmosphere pick up some moisture; the quantity varies with the fiber type, temperature, and relative humidity. Measurements are generally made at standard conditions, which are fixed at 65% RH and 70°F. Moisture content of a fiber or yarn is usually expressed in terms of percentage regain after partial drying.

MOISTURE REGAIN: The percentage of moisture in a textile material brought into equilibrium with a standard atmosphere after partial drying, calculated as a percentage of the moisture-free weight. (Also see STANDARD MOISTURE REAGAIN.)

MOLESKIN: A heavy sateen-weave fabric made with heavy, soft-spun filling yarns. The fabric is sheared and napped to produce a suede effect.

MONK'S CLOTH: A rough, substantial, rather bulky fabric made of very coarse yarn in a 4 x 4 or similar basket-weave construction.

MONOFIL: See MONOFILAMENT.

MONOFILAMENT: Any single filament of a manufactured fiber, usually of a denier higher than 14. Instead of a group of filaments being extruded through a spinneret to form a yarn, monofilaments generally are spun individually. Monofilaments can be used for textiles such as hosiery or sewing thread or for nontextile uses such as bristles, papermaker's felts, fishing lines, etc.

MONOMER: The simple, unpolymerized form of a compound from which a polymer can be made.

MORDANT: A chemical used in some textile fibers to provide affinity for dyes.

MORESQUE: A multicolored yarn formed by twisting or plying single strands of different colors.

MORPHOLOGY: The study of the fine structure of a fiber or other material.

MOTE: A small piece of seed or vegetable matter in cotton. Motes are removed by boiling the fiber or fabric in sodium hydroxide, then bleaching. When not removed, they can leave a dark spot in the fabric.

MOY: Acronym for medium-orientation yarn.

MUFF: A loose skein of textured yarn prepared for dyeing or bulking. In the bulking operation, the yarn contracts and the resulting skein resembles a muff.

MUFF DYEING: See DYEING.

MULE SPINNING FRAME: A spinning machine invented by Samuel Crompton in 1782 and termed "mule" because it was a combination of the machines invented by Arkwright and Hargreaves. It was once widely used for spinning wool and to a lesser extent for very fine counts of cotton yarn. Its action was intermittent and slower than that of the more current ring spinning frame. It drew out and twisted a length of yarn and then wound it in the form of a cop, or bobbin, then repeated the cycle. (Also see SPINNING FRAME.)

MULLEN BURSTING STRENGTH: An instrumental test method that measures the ability of a fabric to resist rupture by pressure exerted by an inflated diaphragm.

MULTIFILAMENT: A yarn consisting of many continuous filaments or strands, as opposed to monofilament, which is one strand. Most textile filament yarns are multifilament.

MULTILOBAL CROSS SECTION: See CROSS SECTION.

MURATA® SPINNING: See AIR JET SPINNING.

MUSHROOM TEST: See FLAMMABILITY TESTS.

MUSLIN: A broad term describing a wide variety of plain-weave cotton or polyester/cotton fabrics ranging from lightweight sheers to heavier shirting and sheeting.

MUSSINESS: A fabric defect on the surface that is characterized by undesirable unevenness caused by many minor deformations. Mussiness is independent of the presence of soil.

N

NAINSOOK: A fine, lightweight, plain-weave fabric, usually of combed cotton. The fabric is often mercerized to produce luster and is finished soft. Nainsook is chiefly used for infants' wear, lingerie, and blouses.

NAP: 1. A downy surface given to a cloth when part of the fiber is raised from the basic structure. **2.** The surface of a pile carpet.

NAPHTHALENE: A solid aromatic hydrocarbon ($C_{10}H_8$) derived from coal tar. Naphthalene is used as moth flakes and as the basis of certain dye components.

NAPHTHOL DYES: See DYES.

NAPPING: A finishing process that raises the surface fibers of a fabric by means of passage over rapidly revolving cylinders covered with metal points or teasel burrs. Outing, flannel, and wool broadcloth derive their downy appearance from this finishing process. Napping is also used for certain knit goods, blankets, and other fabrics with a raised surface.

NARROW CARPET: Carpet woven in widths of 27 or 36 inches.

NARROW FABRIC: Any nonelastic woven fabric, 12 inches or less in width, having a selvage on either side, except ribbon and seam binding.

NARROWING: Reducing the width of a knit fabric by knitting two wale loops as one, thereby reducing the number of wales in a course.

NATURAL FIBER: A class name for various genera of fibers (including filaments) of: (1) animal (i.e., silk and wool); (2) mineral (i.e., asbestos); or (3) vegetable origin (i.e., cotton, flax, jute, and ramie).

NAVEL: A device in rotor spinning through which the yarn is withdrawn. It is aligned on the axis of the rotor.

NCC: Acronym for National Cotton Council of America.

NECKING: 1. The sudden reduction in the diameter of an undrawn manufactured filament when it is stretched. **2.** Narrowing in width of a fabric or film when it is stretched.

NEEDLE: 1. A thin, metal device, usually with an eye at one end for inserting the thread, used in sewing to transport the thread. **2.** The portion of a knitting machine used for intermeshing the loops. Several types of knitting needles are available. (Also see SPRING NEEDLE and LATCH NEEDLE.) **3.** In nonwovens manufacture, a barbed metal device used for punching the web's own fibers vertically through the web. **4.** In a tufting machine, a needle with an eye that holds the tufting yarn and punches it through the backing fabric.

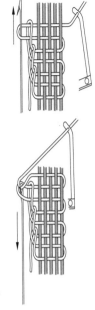

Narrow Fabric Weaving

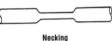

Necking

NEEDLE BAR: The component of a tufting machine that holds the needles and moves them up and down through the backing fabric.

NEEDLE BED: Flat metal plate with slots at regular intervals in which the knitting needles slide on the knitting machine.

NEEDLE DAMAGE: Fabric damage in sewing caused by cutting of yarns by the needle or fusion of yarns due to heat generated by friction as the needle passes through the fabric at high speed.

NEEDLED FABRICS: The product of the NEEDLE LOOM. Needled fabrics are used for rug pads, papermaker's felts, paddings, linings, etc.

NEEDLE LOOM: A machine for bonding a nonwoven web by mechanically orienting fibers through the web. The

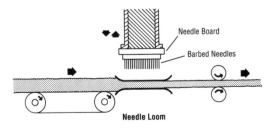

Needle Loom

127

process is called needling, or needlepunching. Barbed needles set into a board punch fiber into the batt and withdraw, leaving the fibers entangled. The needles are spaced in a nonaligned arrangement. By varying the strokes per minute, the advance rate of the batt, the degree of penetration of the needles, and the weight of the batt, a wide range of fabric densities can be made. For additional strength, the fiber web can be needled to a woven, knit, or bonded fabric. Bonding agents may also be used.

NEEDLE LOOP: A loop of yarn drawn through a loop made previously.

NEEDLEPUNCHING: The process of converting batts or webs of loose fibers into a coherent nonwoven fabric on a NEEDLE LOOM.

NEEDLE SET-OUT: A term that refers to long periods of time when certain needles are removed from the knitting cycle. The process is used to make sweater cuffs.

NEEDLE SLOT: A groove that houses a needle in the cylinder or dial of a circular-knitting machine or the needle bed of a flat-bed machine.

NEEDLING: See NEEDLEPUNCHING.

NEP: A small knot of entangled fibers that usually will not straighten to a parallel position during carding or drafting.

NET: An open fabric made by knotting the intersections of thread, cord, or wires to form meshes. Net can be made by hand or machine in a variety of mesh sizes and weights matched to varying end uses, i.e., veils, curtains, fish nets, and heavy cargo nets.

NET RATE: In a fiber production process, the total throughput less waste and inferior or off-grade material.

NETTING: The process of knotting threads into meshes that will not ravel.

NEUTRAL DYEING ACID DYES: See DYES.

NEUTRON-ABSORBING FIBER: Polyethylene fiber modified with boron used in the nuclear industry for reducing neutron transmission.

NINON: A lightweight fabric of silk or manufactured fibers made in a plain weave with an open mesh. Used for curtains and evening wear.

Net

NIP: 1. The line or area of contact between two contiguous rollers. **2.** A defect in yarn consisting of a thin place.

NIP CREASES: Creases occurring at regular intervals along a fabric selvage subsequent to a nipping operation such as calendering or padding. Such creases are caused by a loosely wound selvage or improper let-off tension which allows the fabric to fold over or gather at the selvage prior to entering the nip of the rolls.

NIST: Acronym for National Institute of Standards and Technology.

NOBLE COMB: A machine for combing wool, particularly in the bradford system of worsted spinning. It separates the short fibers (noils) from the longer fibers to produce top. (Also see TOP, 1.)

NOIL: A short fiber that is rejected in the combing process of yarn manufacture.

NOMINAL GAUGE LENGTH: In tensile testing, the length of the specimen under a specified pre-tension between the nips of the jaws before strain is applied.

NONELASTIC WOVEN TAPE: A woven narrow fabric, weighing less than 15 ounces per square yard, made principally of natural and/or manufactured fibers, including monofilaments, but not containing rubber or other similar elastic strands.

NONFIBROUS MATTER: Soluble materials present in fibers, such as oils, fats, waxes, finishes, and salts, that must be removed before qualitative analysis of the fibers.

NONFLAMMABLE: See FIREPROOF and FLAME RESISTANT.

NONIONIC DYES: See DYES.

NONRECOVERABLE: See PERMANENT DEFORMATION.

NONTORQUE YARN: See TEXTURED YARNS, 7.

NONWOVEN FABRIC: A manufactured sheet, batting, webbing, or fabric that is held together by various methods, e.g., thermal fusion, resin and solvent bonding, or mechanical interlocking of fibers, sometimes concurrently with their extrusion. The term is sometimes used broadly to cover other structures such as those held together by interlacing of yarns (stitch bonding) or those made from perforated or porous films. The term excludes woven, knitted, and tufted structures, paper, and felts made by wet milling processes. In its most common usage, the term includes fibrous structures made by such processes as dry, wet, or air laying, needlepunching, spunbond processes, and hydro-entanglement. The fibers in these structures may be directionally or randomly oriented, depending on the nature of their production process. The wet-laying process is similar to papermaking but uses fibers of greater length—300:1 length-to-diameter ratio.

Nonwoven fabrics are used in a wide variety of applications such as disposable diapers, sanitary items, hospital gowns, and wiping cloths; computer diskette linings; base materials for coated fabrics; interlinings; and engineering fabrics, to name a few.

NOTATION: A representation on graph paper of the stitch construction of a knit fabric.

NOVELTY WEAVE: A woven construction that is a variation or combination of the basic weaves—plain, satin, and twill.

NOVELTY YARN: A yarn produced for a special effect. Novelty yarns are usually uneven in size, varied in color, or modified in appearance by the presence of irregularities deliberately produced during their formation. In singles yarns, the irregularities may be caused by inclusion of knots, loops, curls, slubs, and the like. In plied yarns, the irregularities may be effected by variable delivery of one or more yarn components or by twisting together dissimilar singles yarns. Nub and slub yarns are examples of novelty yarns.

NOVOLOID FIBER: A manufactured fiber containing at least 85% by weight of a cross-linked novolac (FTC definition). Novoloid is flame resistant and nonmelting. Novoloid fiber is no longer produced in the U.S.

NOZZLE: 1. The spout through which something is discharged, i.e., oil in finish application or fibers in web laying. **2.** A term sometimes used to refer to spinnerets.

NTI: Acronym for the Northern Textile Association.

NUB YARN: A novelty yarn containing slubs, beads, or lumps introduced intentionally.

NUCLEATION: A process by which crystals are formed. Crystals form initially on minute traces of foreign substances that act as the nucleus, then grow by external addition.

NUN'S VEILING: A soft, lightweight, plain-weave fabric that usually comes in black and white, nun's veiling is a rather flimsy, open fabric but always of high quality. It may be made from fine woolen yarn or yarns spun from manufactured fibers such as nylon, acrylic, or polyester.

NYLON FIBER: A manufactured fiber in which the fiber-forming substance is any long chain synthetic polyamide having recurring amide groups (–NH–CO–) as an integral part of the polymer chain (FTC definition). The two principal nylons are nylon 66, which is polyhexamethylenediamine adipamide, and nylon 6, which is polycaprolactam. Nylon 66 is so designated because each of the raw materials, hexamethylenediamine and adipic acid, contains six carbon atoms. In the manufacture of nylon 66 fiber, these materials are combined, and the resultant monomer is then polymerized. After polymerization, the material is hardened into a translucent ivory-white solid that is cut or broken into fine chips, flakes, or pellets. This material is melted and extruded through a spinneret while in the molten state to form filaments that solidify quickly as they reach the cooler air. The filaments are then drawn, or stretched, to orient the

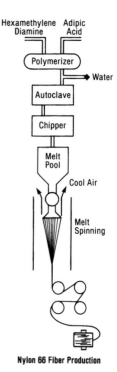

Nylon 66 Fiber Production

130

long molecules from a random arrangement to an orderly one in the direction of the fiber axis. This drawing process gives elasticity and strength to the filaments.

Nylon 6 was developed in Germany where the raw material, caprolactam, had been known for some time. It was not until nylon 66 was developed in the U.S. that work was initiated to convert caprolactam into a fiber. The process for nylon 6 is simpler in some respects than that for nylon 66. Although nylon 6 has a much lower melting point than nylon 66 (a disadvantage for a few applications), it has superior resistance to light degradation and better dyeability, elastic recovery, fatigue resistance, and thermal stability.

There are several other nylons of varying commercial importance. Nylon 11 is a polyamide made from 11-amino-undecanoic acid. Nylon 610 is made from the condensate product of hexamethylenediamine and sebacic acid. It has a lower melting point than nylon 66. Nylon 4 has a greater moisture regain and nylon 612 a lower moisture regain than other nylons.

CHARACTERISTICS: Although the properties of the nylons described above vary in some respects, they all exhibit excellent strength, flexibility, toughness, elasticity, abrasion resistance, washability, ease of drying, and resistance to attack by insects and microorganisms.

END USES: Nylon is used for apparel such as hosiery, lingerie, dresses, bathing suits, foundation garments, and easy-care linings; for floor coverings; for tire cord and industrial fabrics; and in-home furnishings such as upholstery fabrics.

NYTRIL FIBER: A manufactured fiber containing at least 85% by weight of a long chain polymer of vinylidene dinitrile $[-CH_2-C(CN)_2-]$ and having the vinylidene dinitrile group in no less than every other unit in the polymer chain (FTC definition). Nytril fiber is no longer manufactured in the U.S.

O

OATMEAL CLOTH: A heavy, soft linen fabric with a pebbled or crepe effect.

OCTALOBAL CROSS SECTION: Fiber cross-sectional shape having eight lobes.

OE: Acronym for open-end. See OPEN-END SPINNING.

O-FADING: See OZONE FADING.

OFF-CLIP: See SCALLOPED SELVAGE.

OFF-GRAIN: See SKEWNESS.

OFF-SQUARE: 1. A term to describe the difference between the percentage of warp crimp and the percentage of filling crimp. **2.** A term referring to a fabric in which the number of ends and the number of picks per inch are not equal.

OILCLOTH: Any fabric treated with linseed-oil varnish to make it waterproof. It comes in plain colors and printed designs and is most commonly used for table covers or shelf covering. It has now been widely replaced by plastic-coated fabrics.

OILPROOF: A term describing fabrics that are impervious to oil.

OIL-REPELLENT: A term applied to fabrics that have been treated with finishes to make them resistant to oil stains.

OLEFIN FIBER: A manufactured fiber in which the fiber-forming substance is any long-chain synthetic polymer composed of at least 85% ethylene, propylene or other olefin units by weight, except amorphous (noncrystalline) polyolefins qualifying as rubber (FTC definition). Polyolefin fibers combine light weight with high strength and abrasion resistance. They are used in rope, indoor-outdoor carpeting, lawn furniture upholstery and many other uses. (Also see POLYETHYLENE FIBER, HIGH-DENSITY POLYETHYLENE FIBER, and POLYPROPYLENE FIBER.)

OLEOPHILIC: A term describing a substance that has a strong affinity for oils.

OLEOPHOBIC: A term describing a substance that does not have a strong affinity for oils.

OLIGOMER: A polymer molecule consisting of only a few monomer units.

OLT: Acronym for ON-LINE TESTING.

OMBRÉ: A color effect in which the shade is changeable from light to dark, generally produced by using warp yarns of different tones. Ombré effects may also be produced by printing.

ONDULE: A general term for plain-weave fabrics of silk, cotton, or manufactured fiber having a wavy effect produced by weaving the warp or filling, but usually the filling, in a wavy line. An ondule reed is generally used to produce this effect, often in a leno weave to emphasize the wave. Ondule is used for dress fabrics.

ON-LINE TESTING: Automated quality control measurements on textile materials as they move through production processes. Known in texturing as OLT, Unitens or Qualitens.

ON-STREAM: The state of having been brought into production. The term is usually used for chemical and metallurgical plants or processes.

ON WEIGHT OF FIBER: A term to define the amount of dyes or chemicals applied to textile materials in a wet process. The amount is a percentage of the fiber weight, independent of the bath liquor.

OPEN-END SPINNING: A system of spinning spun yarns from sliver by introducing twist into the yarn without package rotation by simply rotating the yarn end at a gap or break in the flow of the fibers between the delivery system and the yarn package. The element that inserts the twist can be a rotor or other mechanical device, a friction device, or an air jet. Because the twisting element can be compact and the mass of material to be rotated is small, very high twisting speeds can be attained. The process, in a sense, combines the traditional processes of roving and spinning in one operation.

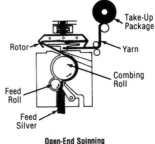

Open-End Spinning

OPEN FACE: A fabric defect consisting of an open appearance of the fabric which permits the filling to "grin" through the warp ends in the center portion of the fabric.

OPENING: 1. A preliminary operation in the processing of staple fiber. Opening separates the compressed masses of staple into loose tufts and removes the heavier impurities. **2.** An operation in the processing of tow that substantially increases the bulk of the tow by separating the filaments and deregistering the crimp. **3.** A stage in open-end spinning in which staple fibers are separated from the sliver and fed to the spinning element.

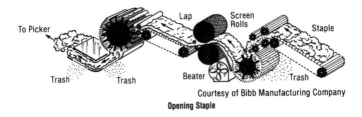

Courtesy of Bibb Manufacturing Company

Opening Staple

OPEN-WIDTH PROCESSING: Treating of fabric spread to its fullest width, as contrasted with fabric treatment in rope form.

OPTICAL BRIGHTENER: 1. A colorless compound that, when applied to fabric, absorbs the ultraviolet radiation in light but emits radiation in the visible spectrum. **2.** Fluorescent materials added to polymer in manufactured fiber production that emit light in the visible spectrum, usually with a blue cast.

OPTICAL FIBER: Fine glass filaments used in telecommunications to transmit messages via modulated light beams.

OPTICAL PROPERTIES: A general term used to refer to the relations of yarn or fibers with light. It includes such parameters as birefringence, refractive index, reflectance, optical density, etc.

OPTIMUM TWIST: In spun yarns, a term to describe the amount of twist that gives the maximum breaking strength or the maximum bulk at strength levels acceptable for weaving or knitting.

ORGANDY: A very thin, transparent, stiff, wiry, muslin fabric used for dresses, neckwear, trimmings, and curtains. Swiss organdy is chemically treated and keeps its crisp, transparent finish through many launderings. Organdy without chemical treatment loses its crispness in laundering and has to be restarched.

Organdy crushes or musses but is easily pressed. Shadow organdy has a faint printed design in self-color.

ORGANZA: A stiff, thin, plain-weave fabric made of silk, nylon, acrylic, or polyester, organza is used primarily in evening and wedding attire for women.

ORGANZINE YARN: Two or more threads twisted in the singles and then plied in the reverse direction. The number of turns per inch in the singles and in the ply is usually in the range of 10–20 turns. Organzine yarn is generally used in the warp.

ORIENTATION: In linear polymeric structures, the degree of parallelism of the chain molecules. (Also see FIBER ORIENTATION.)

ORIFICE: Generally, an opening. Used specifically to refer to the small holes in spinnerets through which the polymer flows in the manufacture of fibers.

ORIGINAL TWIST: The twist that was in a plied yarn or cable component before it was plied.

ORTHO: A chemical prefix, usually abbreviated *o*, signifying that two substituents appear in adjacent positions on a benzene ring.

OSCILLATORY CYLINDER ABRASION MACHINE: An abrasion tester for woven fabrics that subjects the specimen to unidirectional rubbing action.

OSHA: Acronym for (U.S.) Occupational Safety and Health Administration.

OSNABURG: A coarse cotton or polyester/cotton fabric, often partly of waste fiber, in a plain weave, medium to heavy in weight, that looks like crash. Unbleached osnaburg is used for grain and cement sacks, and higher grades are used as apparel and household fabrics.

OTEXA: Acronym for the Office of Textiles and Apparel (U.S. Department of Commerce).

OTTOMAN: Heavy, large, filling rib yarns, often of cotton, wool, or waste yarn, covered in their entirety by silk or manufactured fiber warp yarns, characterize this fabric used for womenswear and coats.

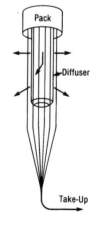

OUTFLOW QUENCH: Air for cooling extruded polymer that is directed radially outward from a central dispersion device around which the filaments descend.

OUT-OF-CONTROL PROCESS: A term used in STATISTICAL PROCESS CONTROL for a process that varies to the degree that product conformance to specifications is unpredictable.

OVEN-DRY WEIGHT: The constant weight of a specimen obtained by drying in an oven under prescribed conditions of temperature and humidity.

OVERCUT: A staple fiber that is longer than nominal length. Usually, the length is a multiple of 2, 3, or more times the

Outflow Quench

134

nominal length. An overcut is caused by the failure of filaments to be cut to the desired length during staple manufacture.

OVERDYEING: See TOP DYEING.

OVERLENGTH: See OVERCUT.

OVERPRINTING: See PRINTING, 1.

OVERSHOT: A term used to describe a woven fabric with a design formed by extra filling yarns that float over a plain-weave ground.

OVERSPRAYING: A term sometimes used to describe the application, by spraying, of a fiber lubricant to staple fibers during opening and blending.

OVER-THE-COUNTER: A term that usually refers to direct sales to a retail customer in a store, as opposed to wholesale marketing.

OWF: Acronym for ON WEIGHT OF FIBER.

OWG: Acronym for on weight of goods. See ON WEIGHT OF FIBER.

OXFORD CLOTH: 1. A soft but stout shirting fabric in a modified basket weave with a large filling yarn having no twist woven under and over two single, twisted warp yarns. The fabric is usually made from cotton or polyester/cotton blends and is frequently given a silk-like luster finish. **2.** A knit fabric constructed of gray heather yarns.

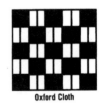

Oxford Cloth

OXYGEN BLEACH: A stain removal and whitening process for textiles using a nonchlorine bleach such as sodium perborate or hydrogen peroxide. Compared to chlorine bleaches, oxygen bleaches have inferior whitening power but are generally less destructive to textiles.

OXYGEN INDEX: See LIMITING OXYGEN INDEX.

OZONE FADING: The fading of a dyed textile material, especially those in blue shades, caused by atmospheric ozone (O_3).

P

PACK: 1. The complete assembly of filters and spinneret through which polymer flows during extrusion. **2.** A unit of weight for wool, 240 pounds.

PACKAGE BUILD: A general term that applies to the shape, angles, tension, etc., of a yarn package during winding. Package build affects performance during subsequent processing.

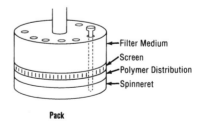

Pack

PACKAGE DYEING: See DYEING, YARN DYEING.

PACKAGE OVERFEED: In yarn processing, the ratio of the surface speed of a yarn input roll to the package take-up roll.

PACKAGES: A large selection of forms for winding yarn is available to meet the requirements of existing machinery, and a variety of package builds is used to ensure suitable unwinding in later stages of manufacturing. Since a package with flanges cannot be unwound easily and quickly by pulling the yarn off overend, most packages are flangeless with self-supporting edges. Some can be unwound at speeds up to 1500 yd/min. The accompanying diagram shows six common types of yarn packages.

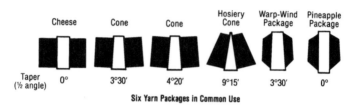

Six Yarn Packages in Common Use

PACK LIFE: The time during which a pack assembly can remain in use and produce good-quality yarn.

PADDING: The application of a liquor or paste to textiles either by passing the material through a bath and subsequently through squeeze rollers, or by passing it between squeeze rollers, the bottom one of which carries the liquor or paste.

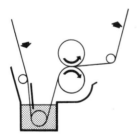

Single-Dip, Single-Nip Padding

Double-Dip, Double Nip Padding

PADDLE DYEING MACHINE: A machine used for dyeing garments, hosiery, and other small pieces that are packaged loosely in mesh bags. The unit consists of an open tank and revolving paddles that circulate the bags in the dyebath.

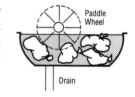

Paddle Dyeing Machine

PAD DYEING: See DYEING.

PAD-STEAM DYEING: See DYEING.

PAF: Acronym for producer-applied fluorocarbon. (Also see FLUOROCARBON FINISH.)

PAISLEY: A drop-shaped pattern that is extremely popular for men's ties and womenswear.

PALMER FINISHING: A combined drying and surface finishing operation to impart a smooth, flat finish to fabrics such as satin and taffeta. The fabric is pressed between a large-diameter heated cylinder and an endless belt that partially wraps the cylinder.

PAN: Acronym for POLYACRYLONITRILE.

PANELS (HOSIERY): Knitted panels used for testing purposes.

PANNÉ SATIN: A satin fabric with an unusually high luster because of the application of very heavy roll pressure in finishing. Panné satin is made of silk or one of the manufactured fibers.

PANNÉ VELVET: Velvet of silk or a manufactured fiber, with a finish in which the pile is flattened and laid in one direction. Panné velvet is a lustrous, lightweight fabric.

PAPERMAKER'S FELT: Formerly, a heavy, wide, coarse, worsted or woolen fabric that was threaded between the rolls of the papermaking machine to form an endless conveyer belt for pulp or wet paper in its passage through the machine. These products are now also made of various constructions, woven and nonwoven, of manufactured fibers and monofilaments.

PARA: A chemical prefix, usually abbreviated *p*, indicating that two substituents on a benzene ring are separated by two carbon atoms.

PARA-ARAMID FIBER: A manufactured fiber with very high tenacity, high modulus, and high heat resistance. While para-aramid fibers have an operating temperature range comparable to that of meta-aramid fibers, they have much higher strength and modulus due to their highly oriented molecular structure. These properties make them suitable for reinforcement and protective uses such as cut-resistant gloves and ballistic applications. Para-aramid fibers tend to have relatively poor resistance to strong acids, alkalies, and chlorine bleaches, but some types have been developed with better chemical resistance. (Also see ARAMID FIBER and META-ARAMID FIBER.)

PARALLELING: The process of aligning fibers to produce a more uniform, smoother, stronger yarn.

PARALLEL SPINNING: The spinning method most commonly used to convert staple fiber into carpet yarn, usually involving modified worsted fiber preparation and sliver-to-yarn spinning.

PARTIALLY ORIENTED STAPLE: Staple fibers cut from tow that has been drawn less than normal so that only partial longitudinal orientation of the polymer molecules exists.

PARTIALLY ORIENTED YARN (POY): Filament yarn in which the draw ratio is less than normal, resulting in only partial longitudinal orientation of the polymer molecules.

PART RUN: A partially filled bobbin that occurs when an end breaks before the completion of a doff cycle. The total weight of yarn normally wound during a cycle is not obtained on the bobbin at the break position. The number of part runs is used as a measure of spinning performance.

PATTERN: 1. An arrangement of form; a design or decoration such as the design of woven or printed fabrics. **2.** A model, guide, or plan used in making things, such as a garment pattern.

PATTERN WHEEL: In a circular-knitting machine, a slotted device for controlling individual needles so that patterns can be knit in the fabric.

PBI: See POLYBENZIMIDAZOLE FIBER.

PBO: Acronym for polyphenylenebenzobisoxazole. See POLYPHENYLENEBENZO-BISOXAZOLE FIBER.

PBT: Acronym for polybutylene terephthalate. See POLYBUTYLENE TEREPHTHA-LATE FIBER.

PEARL: See PURL, 2.

PEAU DE SOIE: A heavyweight, soft satin of silk or manufactured fiber with a fine cross rib and a dull luster. The term is French for "skin of silk."

PEBBLE-WEAVE FABRIC: A fabric with an irregular or rough surface texture formed by either a special weave or by the use of highly twisted yarns that shrink when they are wet.

PECE: Post-chlorinated vinyl chloride polymer. The post-chlorination process increases chlorine content from 57%–64%. The resulting polymer is soluble in acetone and can be wet spun.

PEEK: Acronym for polyetheretherketone. See POLYETHERETHERKETONE FIBER.

PEEL ADHESION: The force required to delaminate a structure or to separate the surface layer from a substrate. Peel adhesion is the usual measure of the strength of the bond between fiber reinforcements and rubber in tires and other mechanical rubber goods.

PEELER: In beaming, a defect caused by a portion of an end sticking or remaining on the beam, causing the filament to strip back or peel until it is broken. Although they are often associated with ringers, peelers are not necessarily defects that will circle the beams.

PEGGING: A finishing process for velveteen consisting of applying friction with blocks of wood or soapstone to impart a gloss or sheen to the fabric.

PEGGING JETS: A technique for freeing a plugged hole in a spinneret by rubbing the face with a piece of wood. Use of the technique has been discouraged because of damage to the spinneret.

PEI: Acronym for polyetherimide. See POLYETHERIMIDE FIBER.

PELERINE: A device for transferring stitches from the cylinder to the dial or vice versa on a circular-knitting machine.

PEN: Acronym for polyethylene naphthalate. See POLYETHYLENE NAPHTHALATE FIBER.

PENTALOBAL CROSS SECTION: Fiber cross-sectional shape having five lobes.

PERCALE: A closely woven, plain-weave, spun fabric used for dress goods and sheeting, generally 80 x 80 threads per inch or better.

PERCHING: Inspection of cloth for defects while it is run over a roller.

PERMANENT DEFORMATION: The change in length of a sample after removal of an applied tensile stress and after the removal of any internal strain (e.g., by boiling off the sample and allowing it to dry without tension). The permanent deformation is expressed as a percentage of the original sample length.

PERMANENT FINISH: A term for various finishing treatments, chemical and/or mechanical, applied to fabric so that it will retain certain properties, such as glaze of chintz, crispness of organdy, smoothness of cotton table damask, and crease, crush, and shrinkage resistance of many apparel fabrics during the normal period of wear and laundering.

PERMANENT GROWTH: See SECONDARY CREEP.

PERMANENT PRESS: See DURABLE PRESS.

PERMANENT SET: See SECONDARY CREEP.

PERMEABILITY: The state or quality of being penetrable by fluids or gases.

PERMITTIVITY: See DIELECTRIC CONSTANT.

PES: Acronym for polyethersulfone. See POLYETHERSULFONE FIBER.

PET: Acronym for POLYETHYLENE TEREPHTHALATE.

pH: Value indicating the acidity or alkalinity of a material. It is the negative logarithm of the effective hydrogen ion concentration. A pH of 7.0 is neutral; less than 7.0 is acidic; and more than 7.0 is basic.

PHASED BEAM: A beam on which each of the ends is wound from the same depth of each of the bobbins on the creel. Phased beams are prepared when yarn properties vary from the inside to the outside of the bobbins in order to prevent warp streakiness in the finished fabric.

PHASE-SEPARATION SPINNING: See SPINNING, 2.

PHENOLIC: 1. A resin or plastic made by the condensation of a phenol with an aldehyde and used particularly in coatings and adhesives. **2.** Containing or pertaining to phenol.

PHENYL: A chemical radical (C_6H_5-) derived from benzene. It is the basis of many aromatic derivatives.

PHOSPHORESCENCE: Emission of light that persists for a noticeable time after the removal of the excitation source.

PHOSPHORIC ACID: An inorganic acid having the formula (H_3PO_4).

PHOTOGRAPHIC PRINTING: See PRINTING, 1.

PHTHALIC ACID: An organic acid obtained by oxidation of various benzene derivatives and having two adjacent (ortho) acid (COOH) groups on the benzene ring.

PI: Acronym for polyimide. See POLYIMIDE FIBER.

PICK: A single filling thread carried by one trip of the weft-insertion device across the loom. The picks interlace with the warp ends to form a woven fabric. (Also see FILLING.)

PICK COUNT: The number of filling yarns per inch or per centimeter of fabric.

PICK COUNTER: 1. A mechanical device that counts the picks as they are inserted during weaving. **2.** A mechanical device equipped with a magnifying glass used for counting picks (and/or ends) in finished fabrics.

PICKER: 1. A machine that opens staple fiber and forms a lap for the carding process used in the production of spun yarns. **2.** That part of the picking mechanism of the loom that actually strikes the shuttle.

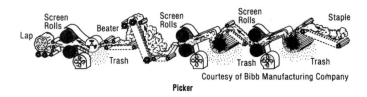

Courtesy of Bibb Manufacturing Company

Picker

PICKER LAP: A continuous, considerably compressed sheet of staple that is delivered by the picker and wound into a cylindrical package. It is used to feed the card.

PICKER STICKS: The two sticks that throw the shuttles from box to box at each end of the raceplate of the loom.

PICKING: 1. A process that continues the opening and cleaning of staple and forms a continuous fiber sheet (or lap), which is delivered to the card. **2.** The operation of passing the filling through the warp shed during weaving.

PICK-OUT MARK: A fillingwise band or bar characterized by a chafed or fuzzy appearance due to pulled-out picks.

PICOT: 1. A small loop woven on the edge of ribbon, or a purl on lace. A picot edge may also be produced by a hemstitching machine. **2.** A run-resistant loop usually found at the top of hosiery.

PIECE: A standard length of a fabric, such as 40, 60, 80, or 100 yards.

PIECE DYEING: See DYEING.

PIECING: The joining of two or more ends of sliver, roving, yarn, etc.

PIGMENT: An insoluble, finely divided substance, such as titanium dioxide, used to deluster or color fibers, yarns, or fabrics.

PIGMENTED YARN: A dull or colored yarn spun from a solution or melt containing a pigment.

PIGMENT PRINTING: See PRINTING, 1.

PILE: 1. A fabric effect formed by introducing tufts, loops, or other erect yarns on all or part of the fabric surface. Types are warp, filling, and knotted pile, or loops produced by weaving an extra set of yarns over wires that are then drawn out of the fabric. Plain wires leave uncut loops; wires with a razor-like blade produce a cut-pile surface. Pile fabric can also be made by producing a double-cloth structure woven face to face, with an extra set of yarn interlacing with each cloth alternately. The two fabrics are cut apart by a traversing knife, producing two fabrics with a cut-pile face. Pile should not be confused with nap. Corduroys are another type of pile fabric, where long filling floats on the surface are slit, causing the pile to stand erect. **2.** In carpets, pile refers to the face yarn, as opposed to backing or support yarn. Pile carpets are produced by either tufting or weaving. (Also see CUT PILE and LOOP PILE.)

PILE CRUSH: The bending of upholstery or carpet pile that results from heavy use or the pressure of furniture.

PILE DENSITY: Pile weight per unit area divided by pile height.

PILE HEIGHT: The height of pile measured from the surface of the backing to the top of the pile, not including the thickness of the backing.

PILE WEAVE: A weave in which an additional set of yarns, either warp or filling, floats on the surface and is cut to form the pile. Turkish toweling is a pile-weave fabric with uncut loops on one or both sides.

PILE WEIGHT: The total weight of the face yarn in a unit area of a carpet or pile fabric.

PILE WIRE: A metal rod over which yarn is woven to generate a pile fabric.

PILL: A small accumulation of fibers on the surface of a fabric. Pills, which can develop during wear, are held to the fabric by an entanglement with the surface fibers of the material, and are usually composed of the same fibers from which the fabric is made.

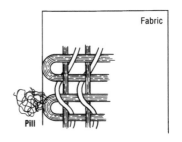

PILLING: The tendency of fibers to work loose from a fabric surface and form balled or matted particles of fiber that remain attached to the surface of the fabric.

PILLING TEST: See RANDOM TUMBLE PILLING TESTER.

PILL TEST: See FLAMMABILITY TESTS, METHENAMINE PILL TEST.

PILOT: A woolen cloth generally made in navy blue and used for seamen's coats. It is usually a heavily milled 2 x 2 twill with a raised, brushed finish.

PIN DRAFTING: Any system of drafting in which the orientation of the fibers relative to one another in the sliver is controlled by pins.

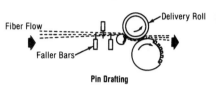

Pin Drafting

PINHEAD: A small pinhead-sized opening usually found about 10–12 inches from a selvage. Pinheads usually run in a fairly straight line along the warp and are formed by the shuttle pinching the filling, causing small kinks that show up as small holes in transmitted light.

PINHOLE: A very small hole in hosiery or fabric.

PINION BARRÉ: A fine, fillingwise fabric defect appearing as one or two pick bars in an even repeat. It is caused by a faulty loom pinion.

PIN MARK: See CLIP MARK.

PINNING: See PIN DRAFTING.

PINSONIC® THERMAL JOINING MACHINE: A rapid, efficient quilting machine that uses ultrasonic energy rather than conventional stitching techniques to join layers of thermoplastic materials. The ultrasonic vibrations generate localized heat by causing one piece of material to vibrate against the other at extremely high speed, resulting in a series of welds that fuse the materials together.

PIN TENTER: See TENTER FRAME.

PIQUÉ: 1. A mediumweight to heavyweight fabric with raised cords in the warp direction. **2.** A double-knit fabric construction knit on multifeed circular machines.

PIRN: 1. A wood, paper, or plastic support, cylindrical or slightly tapered, with or without a conical base, on which yarn is wound. **2.** The double-tapered take-up yarn package from drawtwisting of nylon, polyester, and other melt-spun yarns.

PIRN BARRÉ: A fabric defect consisting of crosswise bars caused by unequal shrinkage of the filling yarn from different points on the original yarn package.

PITCH:1. In woven carpeting, the number of warp ends per unit width, usually 27 inches. **2.** In tufted pile carpeting, the number of surface yarn ends per inch in the width direction. Also called GAUGE. **3.** In handmade carpets, the number of knots per square inch in the pile.

PLAIN-KNIT FABRIC: See FLAT-KNIT FABRIC.

142

PLAIN WEAVE: One of the three fundamental weaves: plain, satin, and twill. Each filling yarn passes successively over and under each warp yarn, alternating each row.

PLAITING: See BRAIDING.

PLASMA FINISHING: A treatment employing ionized gases to modify the surface morphology of a textile substrate.

Plain Weave

PLASTIC: A high polymer, usually combined with other ingredients such as curatives, plasticizers, and fillers. It can be molded under heat and pressure and then machined accurately in its hardened state. General term for a wide range of substances.

PLASTICIZER: 1. A chemical added to polymers and resins to impart flexibility, workability, or stretchability. **2.** A bonding agent that acts by solvent action on fibers.

PLATED: 1. A term to describe a fabric that is produced from two yarns of different colors, characters, or qualities, one of which appears on the face and the other on the back. **2.** A term to describe a yarn covered by another yarn.

PLEAT: Three layers of fabric involving two folds or reversals of direction; the back fold may be replaced by a seam.

PLIED YARN: A yarn formed by twisting together two or more singles yarns in one operation.

PLIED YARN DUCK: See DUCK.

PLISSÉ: A cotton, rayon, or acetate fabric with a crinkled or pleated effect. The effect is produced by treating the fabric, in a striped or spotted motif, with a caustic-soda solution which shrinks parts of the goods.

PLUCKING: A condition found at the feed roll and lickerin section of the card when larger-than-normal clusters of fiber are pulled from the lap by the lickerin. This situation is normally caused by uneven laps or the inability of the feed rolls to hold the lap sheet while small clusters of fibers are being pulled from the lap by the lickerin. Plucking inevitably produces flaky webs.

PLUGGING VALUE: In the manufacture of acetate fibers, a measure of filterability. It is the weight of solids in an acetate dope that can be passed through a fixed area of filter before the filter becomes plugged. It is expressed as weight of solids per square unit of filter area, e.g., g/cm^2.

PLUSH: A term describing a cut-pile carpet in which the pile yarns are only slightly twisted, dense, and very evenly sheared. A plush carpet has the look of a solid, flat velvet surface. Similar pile constructions are also used in upholstery fabric.

PLY: 1. The number of singles yarns twisted together to form a plied yarn, or the number of plied yarns twisted together to form cord. **2.** An individual yarn in a plied yarn or cord. **3.** One of a number of layers of fabric (ASTM). **4.** The number of layers of fabric, as in a shirt collar, or of cord in a tire.

PLYFIL®: A proprietary system of making two-fold long-and-short staple yarns by using ultrahigh drafting. The slightly twisted ends produced are not useable yarns but are well-suited for subsequent processing, i.e., twisting.

PLYING: Twisting together two or more singles yarns to form plied yarns or plied yarn to form cord.

PLY TWISTING: See PLYING.

POINT BONDING: See BONDING, 2.

POLYACETAL FIBER: A very strong manufactured fiber spun from polyoxymethylene and super-drawn under high pressure.

POLYACRYLONITRILE: Homopolymer of acryonitrile (CH_2=CH–COOH) used in the production of ACRYLIC FIBER and ACRYLIC RESIN.

POLYAMIDE: A synthetic polymer and the fibers made from it in which the simple chemical compounds used for its production are linked together by amide linkages (–NH–CO–). (Also see NYLON FIBER.)

POLYARYLATE: High-temperature-resistant aromatic polyesters from bisphenols.

POLYBENZIMIDAZOLE FIBER (PBI): A manufactured fiber in which the fiber-forming substance is a long chain aromatic polymer having recurrent imidazole groups as an integral part of the polymer chain. (FTC definition). The polymer is made from tetraaminobiphenyl and diphenyl isophthalate and is dry spun from a dope with dimethylacetamide as the solvent.

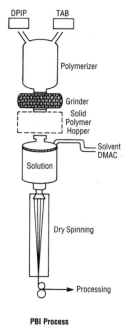

PBI Process

CHARACTERISTICS: A high-performance fiber with high chemical resistance that does not burn in air. It has no melting point and does not drip when exposed to flame. The fiber and fabrics from PBI retain their flexibility, dimensional stability, and significant strength without embrittlement even when exposed to flame or extreme heat. The fiber emits little smoke in extreme conditions. It processes well on conventional textile equipment, having processing characteristics similar to polyester. It can be used in 100% form or blended with other fibers. It has a high moisture regain and low modulus with comfort properties similar to cotton. The natural color of PBI is a gold-khaki shade, but it can be dyed to almost any medium to dark shade with conventional basic dyes.

END USES: With excellent thermal, flame, and chemical resistance, combined with good comfort properties, PBI is a good fiber for many critical uses including: firefighter's protective apparel, aluminized proximity gear, industrial apparel such as pants, shirts and underwear, protective gloves, welder's apparel, aircraft fire-blocking layers, aircraft wall fabrics, rocket motor insulation, race car driver's apparel, and braided packings, among others.

POLYBLENDS: See BICONSTITUENT FIBER.

POLYBUTYLENE TEREPHTHALATE FIBER (PBT): A polyester fiber with inherent comfort stretch properties. It is used in garments such as jeans where a small amount of stretch is desirable. The polymer is produced by the reaction of 1,4-butanediol and terephthalic acid and the fiber is melt-spun.

POLYCHLAL FIBER: A manufactured, bicomponent fiber of polyvinyl alcohol and polyvinyl chloride. Some vinyl chloride is grafted to the polyvinyl alcohol (Japanese Chemical Fibers Association definition). The fiber is emulsion spun into tow and staple.

CHARACTERISTICS: Polychlal fibers have a soft, lamb's wool-like hand and moderate moisture regain. The fibers are also characterized by high flame resistance and high abrasion resistance.

END USES: Polychlal fibers are suitable for end uses such as children's sleepwear, blankets, carpets, curtains, bedding, upholstery, nonwovens, and paper-making.

POLYESTER FIBER: A manufactured fiber in which the fiber-forming substance is any long-chain synthetic polymer composed of at least 85% by weight of an ester of a substituted aromatic carboxylic acid, including but not restricted to substituted terephthalate units:

$$p(-R-O-\underset{\underset{O}{\|}}{C}-C_6H_4-\underset{\underset{O}{\|}}{C}-O-)$$

and parasubstituted hydroxybenzoate units:

$$p(-R-O-C_6H_4-\underset{\underset{O}{\|}}{C}-O-)$$

(FTC definition).

The most widely used polyester polymer in the production of fiber is polyethylene terephthalate, which is produced by the reaction of ethylene glycol and terephthalic acid or its derivatives. Polymerization is accomplished at high temperature, using a vacuum, by one of two methods: (1) the glycol and a terephthalate ester react to form a polyester chain, releasing methanol; or (2) the glycol and terephthalate acid

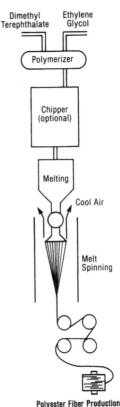

Dimethyl Terephthalate | Ethylene Glycol

Polymerizer

Chipper (optional)

Melting

Cool Air

Melt Spinning

Polyester Fiber Production

145

react directly to form the polymer, with water as the by-product. The filaments are spun in a melt-spinning process, then stretched several times their original length to orient the long-chain molecules and give the fiber strength. Fiber forms produced are staple, filament yarn, and tow. The polymer is also used as a component of BICOMPONENT FIBER.

CHARACTERISTICS: PET polyester fibers are strong and have the useful ability to be engineered in production to have different degrees of modulus and elongation, which makes them suitable for a wide range of industrial applications as well as apparel, home furnishings, fiberfill, and floor coverings. The fibers have a very low moisture regain. Filament yarns are highly suitable for texturing. Fabrics made of polyester fiber are quick-drying, retain their shape, and tend to have wrinkle resistance and crease retention due to their ability to be heat-set in finishing. Polyester fiber is used alone and in blends and combinations with other fibers, especially in durable-press fabrics.

END USES: Polyester fiber is widely used in many types of apparel fabrics, both woven and knit, for shirtings, dress goods, blouses, menswear, sportswear, sleepwear, rainwear, underwear, and lingerie. It is used in a variety of home furnishings fabrics and floor coverings. And it is used extensively in diverse technical applications such as sewing thread, nonwoven fabrics, tire cord, industrial beltings and webbings, seat belts, ropes, roofing, and air-supported structures, to name a few. Polyester fiberfill is used in filled items such as quilted jackets, pillows, comforters, furniture cushions, and sleeping bags. (Also see POLYBUTYLENE TEREPHTHALATE FIBER and POLYETHYLENE NAPHTHALATE FIBER.)

POLYETHERETHERKETONE FIBER (PEEK): A manufactured fiber from polyetheretherketone polymer with high temperature and chemical resistance used in composites as a matrix material and in other industrial applications.

POLYETHERIMIDE FIBER (PEI): A manufactured fiber spun from polyetherimide polymer having high temperature resistance, excellent processibility, and toughness. Used for matrix materials in composites and in other industrial applications.

POLYETHERSULFONE FIBER (PES): High-molecular-weight fibers from polymers containing sulfone ($-SO_2-$) groups and aromatic nuclei. They demonstrate high thermal stability and chemical inertness.

POLYETHYLENE FIBER: A manufactured fiber made of polyethylene, often in monofilament form as well as continuous filament yarns and staple. Ethylene is polymerized at high pressures and the resulting polymer is melt-spun and cold drawn. It may also be dry-spun from xylene solution.

CHARACTERISTICS: Polyethylene fibers have a low specific gravity, extremely low moisture regain, the same tensile strength wet and dry, and are resistant to attack by mildew and insects. These qualities have made polyethylene fiber suitable for industrial applications, geotextiles, outdoor furniture, and similar applications. Polyethylene fiber does not dye, and in most cases, it is colored by the addition of pigments and dyes to the material prior to spinning. It has a low melting point, a property that has restricted its use in apparel. (Also see HIGH DENSITY POLYETHYLENE FIBER.)

POLYETHYLENE NAPHTHALATE FIBER (PEN): A type of polyester fiber distinguished by its high heat stability and developed for use in technical applications such as tire cord.

POLYETHYLENE TEREPHTHALATE FIBER (PET): See POLYESTER FIBER.

POLYIMIDE FIBER: Fully imidized, manufactured fiber formed from the condensation polymer of an aromatic dianhydride and an aromatic diisocyanate. The fiber is produced by dry spinning. It is a high-shrinkage fiber used in the formation of mechanically stable nonwoven fabrics. These fabrics are made without binders or resins; bonding apparently results from the local temperature and pressure that develop during shrinkage. The fiber is also used in technical applications such as molded components, hot gas filtration, and protective clothing.

POLYMER: A high molecular weight, chain-like structure from which manufactured fibers are derived; produced by linking together molecular units called monomers.

POLYMERIZATION: A chemical reaction wherein small molecules combine to form much larger molecules. (Also see ADDITION POLYMERIZATION and CONDENSATION POLYMERIZATION.)

POLYMERIZE: To undergo polymerization. To react molecules resulting in their combining and forming relatively long-chain, large molecules.

POLYNOSIC FIBER: A high-wet-modulus rayon staple having a microfibrillar structure of fibers. The molecular chain length of the cellulose forming the fiber is about twice as long as in conventional rayon. Polynosic fiber has higher tenacity, loop tenacity, and abrasion resistance than conventional rayon fiber. It has less tendency to swell and better alkali resistance, so it can be mercerized. Textile materials made from polynosic fiber have good dimensional stability due to its high modulus.

POLYOLEFIN FIBER: See OLEFIN FIBER.

POLYOXYAMIDE FIBER: Copolymeric fiber with good comfort properties, particularly high moisture absorption and transfer, and intrinsic softness.

POLYPEPTIDE FIBER: A manufactured protein-based fiber, including polyamide (nylon) and azlon.

POLYPHENYLENEBENZOBISOXAZOLE FIBER (PBO): A high-performance manufactured fiber with very high heat and flame resistance, as well as high modulus and tensile strength. It is designed for use in technical applications.

POLYPHENYLENE SULFIDE FIBER (PPS): See SULFAR FIBER.

POLYPROPYLENE FIBER: A manufactured, olefin fiber made from polymers or copolymers of propylene. Polypropylene fiber is produced by melt spinning the molten polymer, followed by stretching to orient the fiber molecules.

CHARACTERISTICS: Polypropylene fibers have a number of advantages over polyethylene fibers in the field of textile applications. The degree of crystallinity, 72% –75%, results in a fiber that is strong and resilient, and does not fibrillate like high density polyethylene. Polypropylene has a high work of rupture, which indicates a tough fiber, and may be made with tenacities as high as 8.0–8.5 grams per denier. The melting point of polypropylene is 165°C, which is low by comparison with nylon or polyester, but is high enough to make it suitable for most textile applications. So light that it actually floats, polypropylene fiber provides greater coverage per pound than any other fiber. It is highly resistant to mechanical abuse and chemical attack.

END USES: Polypropylene fibers are widely used in industrial, carpet, and geotextile applications. They have found important uses in fishing gear, in ropes, and for filter cloths, laundry bags and dye bags. The excellent chemical resistance of polypropylene fiber is of advantage in filtration and protective clothing applications. Fibrillated polypropylene yarns are widely used in indoor-outdoor carpets. Staple fiber finds application in needlepunched floor coverings, socks, medium to heavyweight underwear, blankets, nonwovens, and paper reinforcement.

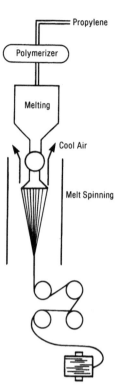

Polypropylene Fiber Production

POLYTETRAFLUOROETHYLENE FIBER (PTFE): Fluorine-containing manufactured fibers characterized by high chemical stability, relative inertness, and high melting point. Made by emulsion spinning, a process that essentially results in fusion of fibrils by passing an emulsion through a capillary, then drawing the resulting fiber. The fiber has a moderate tensile strength and is particularly resistant to the effect of high temperatures and corrosive chemicals. Having very low frictional coefficients, it has a slippery hand. It also has good electrical insulating capacity. The fiber has an inherent dark brown color and is difficult to dye. Its principal uses are for technical textile such as protective clothing, filtration media, and electrical insulation. (Also see FLUOROCARBON FIBER.)

POLYTRIMETHYLENE TEREPHTHALATE FIBER (PTT): A manufactured fiber produced by the reaction of 1,3-propanediol and terephthalic acid. It is distinguished by its high elastic recovery and resilience. Carpets made from PTT fiber have good crush, stain, static and soil resistance. Fabrics have inherent comfort-stretch and easy-care properties. PTT fiber has good dyeability and colorfastness.

POLYURETHANE FIBER: See SPANDEX FIBER.

POLYVINYL ALCOHOL: A colorless, water-soluble resin made by the hydrolysis of a polyvinyl ester (usually the acetate). Polyvinyl alcohol is used in textile processing as a size, frequently for nylon, and in fiber manufacture as a raw material for the production of polyvinyl alcohol fibers.

POLYVINYL ALCOHOL FIBER: See VINAL FIBER.

POLYVINYL CHLORIDE FIBER (PVC): See VINYON FIBER.

POLYVINYLIDENE CHLORIDE FIBER (PVDC): See SARAN FIBER.

PONGEE: 1. A thin, naturally tan-colored silk fabric with a knotty, rough weave. **2.** A cotton fabric made from yarns spun from fine-combed staple and finished with a high luster. This fabric is used for underwear. **3.** Fabrics like cotton pongee made from manufactured fibers.

PONTE DI ROMA: A common double-knit fabric construction with a four-feed repeat produced with the dial and cylinder needles in interlock gating. The fabric is plain and looks the same on both sides.

POPCORN: 1. A special-effect yarn containing short, thick spots. **2.** In polymer manufacture a term used to describe oversize, deformed chip.

POPLIN: A plain-weave fabric of various fibers characterized by a rib effect in the filling direction.

POROSITY: The ratio of the volume of air or void contained within the boundaries of a material to the total volume (solid matter plus air or void) expressed as a percentage.

$$\% \text{ Porosity} = \frac{V_v \times 100}{V_t}$$

where: V_v = volume of voids
V_t = total volume

POSITIVE DRIVE: In yarn winding, a mechanically driven system for controlling the velocity of the yarn package.

POSITIVE FEED: In weft knitting, metering a predetermined length of yarn to the needles.

POSTBOARDING: Boarding hosiery after dyeing. (Also see BOARDING.)

POTASH: A common name for potassium or potassium compounds. Generally used to mean potassium carbonate.

POT SPINNING: A method formerly used for making viscose rayon. The newly spun yarn was delivered into the center of a rapidly rotating, centrifugal pot, where it received twist and centrifugal force caused it to go to the wall of the pot. The yarn package so formed was called a cake.

POWDER-BONDING: See BONDING, 2.

POWER FACTOR: Of an insulating material, the ratio of the power in watts dissipated in a capacitor in which the material is dielectric, to the product of the sinusoidal voltage and current, expressed in effective volt-amperes.

POWER STRETCH: Fabric stretch, normally in the range of 30%–50% with good recovery, for figure-controlling purposes, as is required in such apparel applications as active sportswear and foundation garments. (Contrast with COMFORT STRETCH.)

POY: See PARTIALLY ORIENTED YARN.

PPS: Acronym for polyphenylene sulfide. See SULFAR FIBER.

PREBOARDING: Boarding hosiery before dyeing. (Also see BOARDING.)

PRECISION WINDING: A process for building yarn packages in which the wind is constant and the angle of the wind decreases as the diameter of the package increases. (Contrast with RANDOM WIND.)

PRECONDITIONING: Bringing a sample or specimen of textile material to a relatively low moisture content (approximate equilibrium in an atmosphere between 5% and 25% relative humidity) prior to conditioning in a controlled atmosphere of higher humidity for testing. (While preconditioning is frequently translated as predrying, specimens should not be brought to the over-dry state.)

PREFORM: 1. Fabrics that have been stacked in multiple layers and bonded with a stitching yarn or by other means. The preform may be cut into a shape for subsequent molding into a composite part. **2.** A preshaped nonwoven made by distributing fibers over a screen in the approximate contour of the finished part. **3.** A preshaped, three-dimensional reinforcement made via braiding, weaving, knitting, or some combination of these. **4.** A formed but not fully consolidated stack of prepreg layers which have the contour of the finished product. **5.** The first stage in the production of blow-molded products such as PET bottles.

PREMETALIZED DYES: See DYES.

PREOXIDIZED FIBER: In carbon fiber production, a fiber that results from a relatively low-temperature (200°–500°C) heat treatment in the presence of oxygen which converts the precursor fiber, PAN or rayon, to an infusible fiber that is stable to further processing.

PREPREG: Ready-to-mold, reinforcing material, either fiber, fabric, or mat, that is fully impregnated with resin and in some cases, partially cured. Prepregs are then used by fabricators in laying-up and molding composites after which curing is completed.

PRESHRUNK: A term used to describe fabric that has been treated to induce shrinkage prior to cutting.

PRESSLEY INDEX: A measure of the breaking load of a fiber bundle 0.465-inch long determined at essentially zero gauge length.

PRESSURE DROP: 1. A decrease in pressure that is caused by friction between a flowing liquid and a constricting container. The pressure drop is increased by a reduction in diameter of the container. **2.** The change in pressure across a filter.

PRESSURE DYEING: See DYEING.

PRESSURE MARK: See FINGER MARK.

PRETENSION: The relatively low tension applied to remove kinks and crimp when mounting a specimen preparatory to making a test or to a textile processing operation, etc.

PRIMARY BACKING: The material, usually woven or nonwoven polypropylene or jute, into which a carpet is tufted. The primary backing allows the positioning of each tuft and holds the tufts in position during processing, after which a SECONDARY BACKING is applied to provide dimensional stability.

PRIMARY COLORS: Magenta, yellow, and cyan (red, yellow, blue); these are the subtractive primaries used when mixing dyes, paints, etc., to make all other colors. In the CIE (Commission Internationale de l'Eclairage) system of color measurement, which is the international system most widely used today, the primary color vectors are red, green, and blue-violet. These are additive primaries based on the perception of color of reflected light by the human eye.

PRIMARY CREEP: The recoverable component of creep. (Also see DELAYED DEFORMATION.)

PRINT: A fabric with designs applied by means of dyes or pigments used on engraved rollers, blocks, or screens. (Also see PRINTING.)

PRINT BONDING: See BONDING, 2.

PRINTCLOTH: A mediumweight, plain-weave fabric made of carded yarns, usually cotton or polyester/cotton blends, with counts from 28's to 42's. Millions of yards of printcloth are printed annually and other millions are finished as white goods. Large amounts of the goods are also used in the greige for bags, containers, and base fabric for coated materials.

PRINTED YARN: See PRINTING, 1. WARP PRINTING.

PRINTING: A process for producing a pattern on yarns, warp, fabric, or carpet by any of a large number of printing methods. The color or other treating material, usually in the form of a paste, is deposited onto the fabric which is then usually treated with steam, heat, or chemicals for fixation. Various types of printing are described below:

1. Methods of Producing Printed Fabrics:

   Block Printing: The printing of fabric by hand, using carved wooden or linoleum blocks, as distinguished from printing by screens or rollers.

   Blotch Printing: A process in which the background color of a design is printed rather than dyed.

   Burn-Out Printing: A method of printing to obtain a raised design on a sheer ground. The design is applied with a special chemical onto a fabric woven of pairs of threads of different fibers. One of the fibers is then destroyed locally by chemical action. Burn-out printing is often used on velvet. The product of this operation is known as a burnt-out print.

Direct Printing: A process in which the colors for the desired designs are applied directly to the white or dyed cloth, as distinguished from discharge printing and resist printing.

Discharge Printing: In "white" discharge printing, the fabric is piece dyed, then printed with a paste containing a chemical that reduces the dye and hence removes the color where the white designs are desired. In "colored" discharge printing, a color is added to the discharge paste in order to replace the discharged color with another shade.

Duplex Printing: A method of printing a pattern on the face and the back of a fabric with equal clarity.

Electrostatic Printing: A process in which an electrostatically charged plate is positioned behind the print cloth to attract powdered dyes to the fabric surface. A stencil of the print pattern is placed between the fabric and the powder supply.

Etching: See PRINTING, 1. BURN-OUT PRINTING.

Extract Printing: See PRINTING, 1. DISCHARGE PRINTING.

Flat-Bed Screen Printing: A type of screen printing in which the print paste is squeegeed through a flat screen that is then lifted and moved forward one pattern repeat to print again. A different screen is used for each color in the pattern. The process may be manual or automatic.

Flock Printing: A type of printing, usually on sheer or lightweight fabrics, in which small patterns are produced by flocking. The adhesive print pattern is applied in the design areas, and the flock is embedded in the adhesive. (Also see FLOCKING.)

Heat-Transfer Printing: A method of printing fabric of polyester or other thermoplastic fibers with disperse dyes. The design is transferred from preprinted paper onto the fabric by contact heat which causes the dye to sublime. Having no affinity for paper, the dyes are taken up by the fabric. The method is capable of producing well-defined, clear prints.

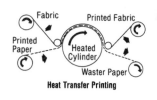

Heat Transfer Printing

Ink-Jet Printing: Non-contact printing that uses electrostatic acceleration and deflection of ink particles released by small nozzles to form the pattern. (Also see BUBBLE-JET PRINTING.)

Overprinting: A textile printing process in which a pattern is printed over another pattern or a dyed ground.

Photographic Printing: A method of printing from photoengraved rollers. The resultant design looks like a photograph. The designs may also be photographed on a silk screen which is used in screen printing.

Pigment Printing: Printing by the use of pigments instead of dyes. The pigments do not penetrate the fiber but are affixed to the surface of the fabric by means of synthetic resins which are cured after application to make them insoluble. The pigments are insoluble, and application is in the form of water-in-oil or oil-in-water emulsions of pigment pastes and resins. The colors produced are bright and generally fast except to crocking.

Resist Printing: A printing method in which the design can be produced: (1) by applying a resist agent in the desired design, then dyeing the fabric, in which case, the design remains white although the rest of the fabric is dyed; or (2) by including a resist agent and a dye in the paste which is applied for the design, in which case, the color of the design is not affected by subsequent dyeing of the fabric background.

Roller Printing: The application of designs to fabric, using a machine containing a series of engraved metal rollers positioned around a large padded cylinder. Print paste is fed to the rollers and a doctor blade scrapes the paste from the unengraved portion of the roller. Each roller supplies one color to the finished design, and as the fabric passes between the roller and the padded cylinder, each color in the design is applied. Most machines are equipped with eight rollers, although some have sixteen rollers.

Rotary Screen Printing: A printing system in which a perforated screen in the form of a cylinder is used to apply color. The print paste is fed automatically to a squeegee located inside the cylinder. Color is forced through the screen onto the cloth. Each color in the pattern requires a different rotary screen.

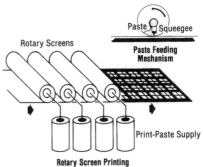

Rotary Screen Printing

Screen Printing: A method of printing similar to using a stencil. The areas of the screen through which the coloring matter is not to pass are filled with a waterproof material. The printing paste which contains the dye is then forced through the untreated portions of the screen onto the fabric below. Each color in the pattern requires a different screen. (Also see PRINTING, 1. FLAT-BED SCREEN PRINTING and ROTARY SCREEN PRINTING.)

Vigoreux Printing: See PRINTING, 1. WARP PRINTING.

Warp Printing: The printing of a design on a sheet of warp yarns. The filling is either white or a neutral color. Conventionally, warp printing is done before weaving, but some modern equipment allows the warp sheet to be printed during weaving.

2. Methods of Producing Printed Carpets:

Millitron® Process: A computer-controlled, non-contact spray printing process that allows the production of intricate multicolored designs. Although this process was developed for carpets by Milliken & Co., it can also be used for upholstery, pile fabrics, and other textiles.

Mitter Printing Machine: A rotary carpet printing machine with up to eight stainless-steel mesh screens, and with cylindrical squeegees of moderately large diameter in each rotary screen. The unit has a steaming zone for dye fixation.

Stalwart Printing Machine: A carpet printing machine in which color is applied to the carpet with a neoprene sponge laminated to the pattern. The pattern is cut in a rubber base attached to a wooden roll. It is very similar to relief printing. Used primarily for overprinting random patterns on dyed carpets. Suitable for shags and plush carpets as well as level loop and needletuft types.

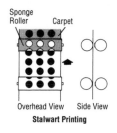

Overhead View   Side View

Stalwart Printing

Zimmer Flatbed Printing Machine (Peter Zimmer): A carpet printing machine that uses flat screens and dual, metal-roll squeegees. The squeegees are operated by electromagnets to control the pressure applied. The unit also has a steamer for dye fixation. The Zimmer flatbed machine is normally used for carpets of low to medium pile heights. Very precise designs are possible, but speeds are slower than with rotary screen printers.

Zimmer Rotary Printing Machine (Johannes Zimmer): A three-step, rotary carpet printing machine consisting of: (1) rotary screens with small-diameter steel-roll squeegees inside, with pressure adjusted electromagnetically for initial dyestuff application; (2) infrared heating units to fix dyes on the tips of the tufts; and (3) application of low-viscosity print paste, followed by steaming for complete penetration of dyes into tufts.

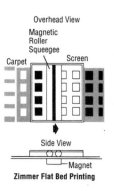

Zimmer Flat Bed Printing

Zimmer Rotary Printing Machine (Peter Zimmer): A rotary carpet printing machine in which each rotary screen has a slotted squeegee inside to feed print pastes through the screens to the carpet. Pressure of the print paste is adjusted by hydrostatic head adjustments.

PRINT PASTE: The mixture of gum or thickener, dye, and appropriate chemicals used in printing fabrics. Viscosity varies according to the types of printing equipment, the type of cloth, the degree of penetration desired, etc.

PRODUCER-COLORED: See DYEING, MELT DYEING and SOLUTION DYEING.

PRODUCER-TEXTURED YARN: Continuous filament yarn that has been bulked during manufacturing by the fiber producer. (Also see TEXTURING.)

PRODUCER TWIST: Small amounts of twist, usually ½ turn per inch or less, applied to yarns by the manufacturer to provide cohesion of filaments for further processing.

PROFILED FIBER: See CROSS SECTION.

PROGRESSIVE SHRINKAGE: Fabric shrinkage that continues during successive laundering or dry cleaning cycles.

PROJECTILE LOOM: A shuttleless loom that uses small, bullet-like projectiles to carry the filling yarn through the shed. Fill is inserted from the same side of the loom for each pick. A tucked selvage is formed. (Also see WEFT INSERTION, 1.)

PTFE: Acronym for polytetrafluoroethylene. See POLYTETRAFLUOROETHYLENE FIBER.

PTT: Acronym for polytrimethylene terephthalate. See POLYTRIMETHYLENE TEREPHTHALATE FIBER.

PTY: Acronym for PRODUCER-TEXTURED YARN.

PUCKER: Uneven surface caused by differential shrinkage of the yarns in a fabric or differential shrinkage of the fabric and sewing thread. May be desirable and planned, or undesirable.

PULLED-IN FILLING: An extra thread dragged into the shed with the regular pick and extending only a part of the way across the fabric.

PULLED WOOL: Wool pulled from the pelts of slaughtered sheep. It can be more difficult to process into fabric than shorn wool because of the presence of the root end of the fiber.

PULP: The end product of cooking wood chips, cotton, or some source of cellulose with water and appropriate chemicals. Used in the manufacture of cellulosic fibers, paper, and other cellulose-based products.

PULTRUSION: The production of continuous lengths of fiber-reinforced advanced composites. Fibers are fed as roving, fabric, mat, or some combination of these, through a resin impregnation process, to a forming guide, then to a heated die to produce a specific shape, and finally to a puller where the structure is pulled through different forming and cooling stages. Thermoplastic fibers may be substituted for the resin in the pultrusion process.

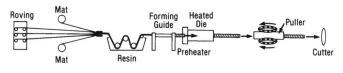

Pultrusion

PUMP CAPACITY: In extrusion of manufactured fibers, the volume of melt or polymer solution delivered by one revolution of the spinning metering pump.

PURL: 1. A knitting stitch that results in horizontal ridges across the fabric. It is made by drawing alternate courses through each side of the fabric. **2.** A picot or small loop that edges needlework, lace, or ribbon. Sometimes spelled pearl. (Also see PICOT.) **3.** Coiled gold or silver thread used for embroidery.

Purl

PURL GATING: See GATING.

PVA: Acronym for polyvinyl alcohol. (Also see VINAL FIBER.)

PVC: Acronym for polyvinyl chloride. (Also see VINYON FIBER.)

PVDC: Acronym for polyvinylidene chloride. (Also see SARAN FIBER.)

PYROLYSIS: A chemical change brought about by the action of heat, usually in the absence of a reactive medium. Complex chemical molecules are reduced to simpler chemical units as a result of pyrolysis.

Q

QR: Acronym for QUICK RESPONSE.

QUADRIPOLYMER: A polymer made from four distinct monomers.

QUALITENS®: See ON-LINE TESTING.

QUALITY: See SECONDS and YARN QUALITY.

QUALITY ASSURANCE: A system to assure that products and services meet customer requirements.

QUALITY CONTROL: A system applied to manufacturing operations to monitor and regulate production processes continually so that products meet specifications. (Also see STATISTICAL QUALITY CONTROL.)

QUARTZ FIBER: See SILICA FIBER.

QUENCH: 1. A box filled with water into which fabric is run after singeing to prevent sparks or fire. **2.** See CABINET. (Also see QUENCHING.)

QUENCHING: The cooling of fiber filaments after extrusion by carefully controlled air flow. (See CROSS-FLOW QUENCH, INFLOW QUENCH, and OUTFLOW QUENCH.)

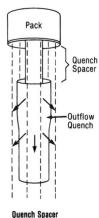

Quench Spacer

QUENCH SPACER: The "quiet" zone below the spinneret in which there is no quench air flow. Quench spacer distance is important in controlling fiber orientation and birefringence.

QUETSCH: The nip rollers of a padding machine.

QUICK RESPONSE: An initiative of the American textile industry involving streamlining of operations so that products are shipped to customers in a fraction of the previous time. For example, turnaround time from receipt of order to shipment might be days instead of weeks or even months. The system is highly dependent on computer linkages and "partnerships" between manufacturer and customer. (Also see JUST-IN-TIME.)

QUILL: A light, tapered tube of wood, metal, paper, or plastic on which the filling yarn is wound for use in the shuttle during weaving.

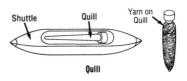

QUILLING: The process of winding filling yarns onto filling bobbins, or quills, in preparation for use in the shuttle for weaving.

QUILTING: 1. A fabric construction consisting of a layer of padding, frequently down or fiberfill, sandwiched between two layers of material and held in place by stitching or sealing in a regular pattern across the body of the composite. (Also see PINSONIC® THERMAL JOINING MACHINE.) **2.** The process of stitch bonding a batting or composite.

R

RACE PLATE: A flat wooden piece in front of the reed of the loom that functions to direct the shuttle or rapier when it passes through the shed.

RACK: A warp-knitting measure consisting of 480 courses. Tricot fabric quality is judged by the number of stitches per rack.

RACKED STITCH: A knitting stitch that produces a herringbone effect with a ribbed back. It is employed in sweaters for decorative purposes or to form the edge of garments. The racked stitch is a variation of the half-cardigan stitch; it is created when one set of needles is displaced in relation to the other set.

RACKING: A term referring to the side-to-side movement of the needles of the needle bed of a knitting machine. Racking results in inclined stitches and reduced elasticity.

RADIANT PANEL TEST: See FLAMMABILITY TESTS.

RADIO-FREQUENCY DRYING: Use of radio-frequency electromagnetic radiation for drying textiles. The application of RF to wet goods results in the selective heating of the water, which has a partial polarity, because the molecule must do work to align in the RF field causing heat generation within the water droplets. Non-polar materials, i.e., fabrics, are unaffected. RF drying is very uniform and energy efficient when air flow patterns through the dryer are properly designed and controlled.

RAILS: The metal bars on which the spindles of a downtwister are mounted.

RAIN TEST: A method to predict the resistance of a fabric to water penetration under conditions simulating actual rain.

RAMIE: A bast fiber similar to flax obtained from the stalk of a plant grown in China, the U.S., and Japan. It is widely used in industrial products such as twine and packings but is also blended with cotton or other fibers for knit apparel such as sweaters.

RANDOM CREELING: A creeling method in which the yarn supply packages are replaced individually as they become empty or unusable. (Contrast with BLOCK CREELING.)

RANDOM-SHEARED CARPET: A pile carpet with a textured face produced by shearing some of the loops and leaving others intact.

RANDOM TUMBLE PILLING TESTER: An apparatus to simulate fabric pilling propensity in actual use. Pills are generated by a random rubbing action produced by tumbling specimens in a horizontal cylindrical chamber lined with a gentle abrasive material.

RANDOM WINDING: A process for building yarn packages in which the angle of wind is kept constant. (Contrast with PRECISION WINDING.)

RAPIER LOOMS: Looms in which either a double or single rapier (thin metallic shaft with a yarn gripping device) carries the filament through the shed. In a single rapier machine, the yarn is carried completely across the fabric by the rapier. In the double machine, the yarn is passed from one rapier to the other in the middle of the shed. (Also see WEFT INSERTION, 1.)

RASCHEL KNITTING: See KNITTING, 1.

RATINÉ: 1. A plain-weave, loosely constructed fabric having a rough, spongy texture which is imparted by the use of nubby plied yarns. It is made from worsted, cotton, or other yarns. **2.** A variant of spiral yarns in which the outer yarn is fed more freely to form loops that kink back on themselves and are held in place by a third binder yarn that is added in a second twisting operation.

RAVEL: A type of comb or rail with projecting teeth for separating and guiding warp ends.

RAVELING: The process of undoing or separating the weave or knit of a fabric.

RAW FIBER: A textile fiber in its natural state, such as silk "in the gum" and cotton as it comes from the bale.

RAW SILK: Silk filaments as they are reeled from the cocoon, before degumming.

RAW WOOL: See GREASE WOOL.

RAYON FIBER: A manufactured fiber composed of regenerated cellulose, including substitutions for not more than 15% of the hydrogens of the hydroxyl groups. Includes high wet modulus fiber (FTC definition). Rayon fibers include yarns and fibers made by the viscose process, the cuprammonium process, and the now obsolete nitrocellulose and saponified acetate processes. Generally, in the manufacture of rayon, cellulose derived from woodpulp, cotton linters, or other vegetable matter is dissolved into a viscose spinning solution. The solution is extruded into an acid-salt coagulating bath and drawn into continuous filaments. Groups of these filaments may be made in the form of yarns or cut into staple.

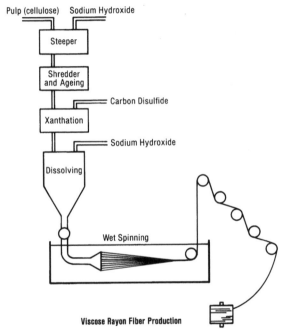

Viscose Rayon Fiber Production

CHARACTERISTICS: Rayon yarns are made in a wide range of types in regard to size, physical characteristics, strength, elongation, luster, handle, suppleness, etc. They may be white or solution dyed. Strength is regulated by the process itself and the structure of the yarn. (Also see POLYNOSIC FIBER.) Luster is reduced by including delustering materials such as titanium dioxide pigments in the fiber when it is extruded. The suppleness of the yarn is controlled by the number of filaments in the yarn, the denier or gauge of the individual filaments or fibers, and the fiber cross-section. Rayon fiber has a high moisture regain of 11%.

END USES: Rayon is used in home furnishings such as draperies, bedspreads, upholstery, blankets, dish towels, curtains, throw rugs; in tire cord and other industrial products; in nonwovens such as wipes and medical products; and in apparel fabrics for sport shirts, slacks, suitings, dresses, blouses, and linings. Rayon fiber is often blended or combined with other fibers to enhance functional and aesthetic qualities, e.g., with polyester in durable-press fabrics.

REACTION SPINNING: See SPINNING, 2.

REACTIVE DYES: See DYEING, FIBER REACTIVE DYES.

REAMING: Further plying of a two-ply yarn with a singles yarn. Reaming is not the same as plying three singles yarns in one operation.

RECONSTITUTED FIBERS: Fibers made from recovered waste polymer or blends of virgin polymer and recovered waste polymer.

RECOVERY: See ELASTIC RECOVERY.

RECREATIONAL SURFACES: Manufactured surfaces providing consistent properties, durability, and special characteristics as needed for the specific application. Included are artificial turf, pool decks, indoor-outdoor carpeting, tennis court surfaces, etc. Most types of constructions (knit, woven, tufted, and nonwoven), and most polymer types find use in this market. The polyolefins are particularly prominent in these applications.

RECYCLED MANUFACTURED FIBER: Fiber produced from recycled post-consumer products such as polyester fiber made from recycled soft drink bottles.

REDEPOSITION: A term used in laundering of textiles to describe soil deposited back onto fibers from the wash water.

REDUCTION CLEARING: The removal of unabsorbed disperse dye from the surface of polyester at the end of the dyeing or printing process by treatment in a sodium hydroxide/sodium hydrosulfite bath. A surface-active agent may be employed in the process.

REED: A comb-like device on a loom that separates the warp yarns and also beats each succeeding filling thread against that already woven. The reed usually consists of a top and bottom rib of wood into which metal strips or wires are set. The space between two adjacent wires is called a dent (or split) and the warp is drawn through the dents. The fineness of the reed is calculated by the number of dents per inch.

REED MARKS: A fabric defect consisting of warpwise light and heavy streaks in a woven fabric, caused by bent, unevenly packed, or weak reed wires.

REEL: 1. A revolving frame on which yarn is wound to form hanks or skeins. **2.** The frame on which silk is wound from the cocoon. **3.** A linen yarn measure of 72,000 yards. **4.** The large wheel in a horizontal warper onto which the warp sections are wound in the indirect system of warping. **5.** A spool of large capacity used to wind yarn or wire. **6.** A large revolving frame in a dye beck that circulates the fabric in the dyebath.

REELING: In silk fiber production, the process of unwinding the cocoon.

REFRACTIVE INDEX: See INDEX OF REFRACTION.

REFRACTORY FIBER: Oxide or non-oxide, amorphous or crystalline, manufactured fiber generally used for applications at temperatures greater than 1093°C in both oxidizing and non-oxidizing atmospheres, i.e., Al_2O_3, ZrO_2, $Al_2O_3 \bullet SiO_2$. Both types of refractory fibers are used in technical applications. The oxide fibers are used in needled constructions, felts, ropes, and other textiles; the nonoxide fibers are used primarily in fiber-reinforced composites.

REGAIN: See MOISTURE REGAIN and STANDARD MOISTURE REGAIN.

REGAIN STANDARD: See STANDARD MOISTURE REGAIN.

REGENERATED CELLULOSE: A material which begins as cellulose but at some stage in the chemical processing takes the form of another chemical compound, then appears again in its completed state as cellulose. Viscose and cuprammonium rayons are regenerated cellulose.

REINFORCEMENT FABRICS: See GEOTEXTILES.

RELATED SHADES: Colors of similar tone in the same or different depths.

RELATIVE HUMIDITY: The ratio of the actual vapor pressure of moisture in air to the saturation vapor pressure at ambient temperature.

RELATIVE VISCOSITY: Ratio of the viscosity of a polymer in solution to that of the solvent expressed as time of efflux of the solution divided by the time of efflux of the solvent at constant temperature.

RELAXATION SHRINKAGE OR GROWTH: Dimensional change in fabrics, yarns, or fibers that occurs when strain introduced during previous processing is relieved.

RELAXED YARN: A yarn treated to reduce tension and produce more uniform shrinkage or torque. Relaxation produces more uniform dyeing characteristics in regular filament yarns of nylon or polyester.

RELSET® PROCESS: A process of Richen, Inc., for continuous heat-setting of carpet or other heavy yarns. Individual ends are continuously fed into a heat-setting chamber and withdrawn into take-up cans or fed to winders.

REP: A plain-weave fabric with a narrow ribbed effect in the filling direction.

REPACK ORDER: 1. An order requiring special packaging, as for export. **2.** A small order for a number of items requiring a breakdown of large cases.

REPEAT: The distance covered by a single unit of a pattern that is duplicated over and over, measured along the length of a fabric.

REPELLENCY: The ability to resist wetting and staining by oils, water, soils, and other materials.

RESERVE DYEING: See DYEING.

RESIDUAL SHRINKAGE: A term describing the amount of shrinkage remaining in a fabric after finishing, expressed as a percentage of the dimensions before finishing.

RESILIENCY: Ability of a fiber or fabric to spring back when crushed or wrinkled.

RESIN: 1. A general term for solid or semi-solid natural organic substances, usually of vegetable origin and amorphous and yellowish to brown, transparent or translucent, and soluble in alcohol or ether but not in water. **2.** Any of a large number of manufactured products made by polymerization or other chemical processes and having the properties of natural resins.

RESIN-BONDED: A term used to describe material(s) held together by a polymeric agent, e.g., a nonwoven web, pigments on fabric, or one or more layers of material bonded to a substrate.

RESIN-TREATED: Usually, a term descriptive of a textile material that has received an external resin application for stiffening or an internal fiber treatment (especially of cellulosics) to give wrinkle resistance or durable-press characteristics.

RESIST DYEING: See DYEING, RESERVE DYEING.

RESIST PRINTING: See PRINTING, 1.

RESTRAINT SYSTEMS: An end use for textile fibers; restraint systems are devices such as air bags, seat belts, and shoulder harnesses for passenger protection in automobiles, trucks, airplanes, etc.

RETARDER: A chemical that, when added to the dyebath, decreases the rate of dyeing but does not affect the final exhaustion.

RETRO DYE SYSTEM: The tradename for a wet-processing system for combined dyeing and surface treatment with a cellulase enzyme for altering fabric aesthetics. The process is suitable for cotton-containing fabrics. (Also see ENZYME FINISHING.)

RETTING: A process for separating bast fibers from other constituents of the stalk, using moisture or chemicals to promote rotting of the nonfibrous material to facilitate removal of the fibrous portion.

REVERSIBLE BONDED FABRIC: A bonded structure in which two face fabrics are bonded together so that the two sides may be used interchangeably. There are limitations to the fabrics that may be used because of increased fabric stiffness resulting from bonding.

REVOLVING FLAT CARD: See FLAT CARD.

REVOLVING SPINNING RING: A driven ring that rotates in the direction of the traveler on a ring spinning frame. Since both the ring and the yarn package turn when this ring system is used, productivity is increased.

RHEOLOGICAL PROPERTIES: The properties of viscous substances including polymers that deal with deformation and flow. Includes viscosity and flow rate measurements.

RIBBING: A corded effect in a woven fabric that can be either lengthwise, crosswise, or diagonal.

RIBBON: Narrow fabric made in several widths and a variety of weaves and used as a trimming.

RIB GATING: See GATING.

RIB KNIT: A double-knit fabric in which the wales or vertical rows of stitches intermesh alternately on the face and the back. In other words, odd wales intermesh on one side of the cloth and even wales on the other. Rib-knit fabrics of this type have good elasticity, especially in the width.

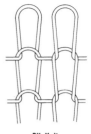

Rib Knit

RICKRACK: Flat braid in zigzag formation. It is produced by applying different tensions to individual threads during manufacture.

RIDGY BEAM: A beam of yarn on which the ends are not evenly distributed across the barrel, causing a profile of peaks (ridges) and valleys. A ridgy beam can give poor removal characteristics.

RIDGY CLOTH: See BAGGY CLOTH.

RIGHT-HAND TWILL: A twill construction in which the diagonal runs from the lower left to the upper right on the fabric face when viewed in the warp direction.

RIGHT-HAND TWIST: Z twist. See DIRECTION OF TWIST.

RING: 1. A narrow band around hosiery appearing different from the rest of the hose. Principal causes: variation in yarn size, dye absorption, or luster. **2.** The device that carries the traveler up and down the package in ring spinning. (Also see RING SPINNING and REVOLVING SPINNING RING.)

RING DOUBLING: See RING SPINNING.

RINGER: 1. On a section beam, ringer is a term used for one or more filaments that have left the parent end; as the beam revolves, the filaments continue to unwind, wrapping around the beam (hence the word "ringer"). The severity of a ringer is dependent upon the number of filaments contained in it at the time the filaments break. **2.** In slashing, the term ringer is often used when an end breaks on the slasher can, adheres to the can, and continues to wrap around it. This condition should not be confused with ringers on the section beam.

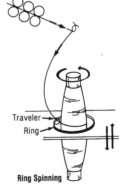

Traveler
Ring

Ring Spinning

RING SPINNING: A system of spinning using a ring-and-traveler take-up in which the drafting of the roving and the twisting and winding of the yarn onto the bobbin proceed simultaneously and continuously. Ring frames are suitable for spinning all counts up to 150's, and they usually give a stronger yarn and are more productive than mule spinning frames. Ring spinning equipment is also widely used to take-up manufactured filament yarns and insert producer-twist at extrusion. (Also see REVOLVING SPINNING RING.)

RING SPINNING FRAME: See SPINNING FRAME.

RING TWISTING: The process of plying yarns on equipment that uses a ring and traveler to twist and wind the yarn.

RIPENING: 1. Hydrolysis of cellulose acetate after acetylation to obtain the desired acetyl value. This is generally accomplished by heat and agitation of the acid cellulose acetate solution under controlled conditions of time, temperature, and acidity. Rapid ripening is accomplished by using increased temperature for the reaction. **2.** A stage in viscose rayon fiber manufacture in which the spinning solution is stored for a given period to allow it to reach the viscosity required for extrusion.

RIP OUT: See PICK-OUT MARK.

RIPPED SELVAGE: See CUT SELVAGE.

RISER: In textile fabric designing, a colored or darkened square on the design paper which indicates that the warp end is over the filling pick at that point. The opposite of riser is sinker.

ROAD MEMBRANE: A type of coarse geotextile fabric used to reinforce asphalt surfaces, e.g., highways, airport runways, and parking lots.

ROBOTICS: 1. The use of robot devices to perform automatic tasks or operate manufacturing equipment. **2.** The science or technology of designing robots for specific uses.

ROLLED ENDS: 1. On a section beam, rolled ends are adjacent ends that do not unwind parallel to each other. Rolled ends can be caused by such factors as uneven tension, ridgy beams, and static. **2.** The ends can also roll behind the hook reed in slashing and can tangle with each other, resulting in broken ends and ends doubling.

ROLLED SELVAGE: A curled selvage.

ROLLER CARD: Generally, any type of card in which rollers do the carding. Usually this refers to a woolen card with a main cylinder and four to seven stripper rolls and worker rolls working in pairs.

ROLLER PRINTING: See PRINTING, 1.

ROLL GOODS: Fabric rolled up on a core after it has been produced. It is described in terms of weight and width of the roll and length of the material on the roll.

ROLL LAPPING: A condition in which groups of fibers attach themselves to the drafting rolls instead of following the normal path through the drafting system. These fibers cause the trailing fibers to wind around the rolls and to break the end down completely. Cleaning of the rolls is required to remove the accumulated fiber.

ROOFING FABRIC: 1. A reinforcing component of single-ply coated or laminated roofing membranes. It can be weft-insertion warp-knit, laid scrim, woven, or nonwoven. **2.** A fabric, generally a nonwoven, used in layered systems site-assembled with roofing cement, usually asphaltic.

ROPE FORM: A term used to describe fabric bunched together in the width direction for processing, as compared with OPEN-WIDTH PROCESSING.

ROPE MARK: A fabric defect consisting of long, irregular, longitudinal markings on dyed or finished goods. A principal cause is abrasion while wet processing the fabric in rope form. Rope marks are often related to over-loading of the fabric during wet processing.

ROPE (TEXTILE): 1. A heavy, strong cord made from natural or manufactured fibers in a wide range of diameters, depending on the demands of the intended use. Ropes are constructed by twisting or braid-ing in a process called laying. Yarns are twisted together to form strands, which are then twisted together in the opposite di-rection to form the rope. Alternating the twist directions at different stages of rope assembly as-sures that the rope will be twist stable and will not kink during use. Some ropes con-sist of a core covered with a braided or polymer sheath. **2.** See ROPE FORM.

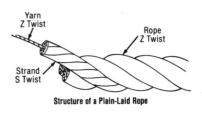

Structure of a Plain-Laid Rope

End View

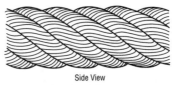

Side View

Structure of a Seven-Strand Rope

ROTARY-PLATFORM DOUBLE-HEAD ABRASER: An abrasion tester for fabric that applies rotary rubbing action. One abrading wheel abrades the fabric specimen outward, while another abrades toward the center.

ROTARY SCREEN PRINTING: See PRINTING, 1.

ROTOFLEX: A fatigue or endurance test developed by Goodyear for indus-trial yarns or cords.

ROTOR SPINNING: See OPEN-END SPINNING.

ROT RESISTANCE: The ability of textile materials to resist physical deterio-ration resulting from the action of bacteria and other destructive agents such as sunlight or sea water.

ROUGH: A fabric condition in which the surface resembles sandpaper. Prin-cipal causes are the shuttle rebounding in the box, jerky or loose shuttle tension, an incorrectly timed harness, and wild twist in the filling.

ROUGH SELVAGE: See LOOPY SELVAGE.

ROVING: 1. In spun yarn production, an intermediate state between sliver and yarn. Roving is a condensed sliver that has been drafted, twisted, doubled, and redoubled. The product of the first roving operation is sometimes called slubbing. **2.** The operation of producing roving. (See diagram on the next page.) **3.** In the manufacture of composites, continuous strands of parallel filaments.

ROVING FRAME: A general name for all of the machines used to produce roving, different types of which are called slubber, intermediate, fine, and jack. Roving frames draft the stock by means of drafting rolls, twist it by means of a flyer, and wind it onto a bobbin.

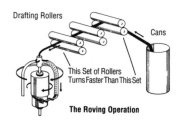

Drafting Rollers

Cans

This Set of Rollers Turns Faster Than This Set

The Roving Operation

ROWS: In pile floor covering, the average number of tufts or loops per inch in the warpwise direction.

RUB: See ABRASION MARK.

RUBBER FILAMENT: A filament extruded from natural or synthetic rubber and used as the core of some elastic threads. Because of their inferior ageing and storage properties, rubber filaments have been largely replaced by other elastic materials such as SPANDEX FIBER.

RUNNER: A break in the yarn of a knit fabric that causes the stitch to "run" along the needle line (wale) in a vertical direction. (Also see END OUT.)

RUNNER LENGTH: In knitting, the number of inches of yarn from a warp to make one rack of fabric.

RUN-OF-THE-MILL: See MILL RUN.

RUN-PROOF: A knitted construction in which the loops are locked to prevent runs.

RUN-RESISTANT: A type of knitting stitch that reduces runs.

S

SACKING: Tied wool fleeces weighing 200–400 pounds packed in large bags for shipping.

SAILCLOTH: Any heavy, strongly made woven canvas of cotton, linen, jute, polyester, nylon, aramid, etc., that is used for sails. Laminated fabrics are also finding use in this market. Sailcloth is used for apparel, particularly sportswear.

SAND: Used as a filter medium in fiber manufacture, particularly used in spinning packs for nylon or polyester production.

SANDING: An abrasive finishing operation used to alter the surface of fabrics, primarily those made of manufactured fibers.

SAND WASHING: A finish process in which garments are washed in a bath containing sand or another abrasive to produce a soft hand and a frosted appearance. (Also see STONE WASHING.)

SANDWICH BLEND: A method of preparing fiber mixtures by layering them horizontally in alternating layers with all elements in the proper proportion. Vertical sections are cut and fed to the next machine in the process, where blending is effected.

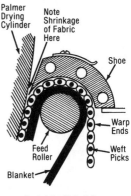

Sandwich Blend

SANFORIZED®: A trademark of Cluett, Peabody & Co., Inc., denoting a controlled standard of shrinkage performance. Fabrics bearing this trademark will not shrink more than 1% because they have been subjected to a method of compressive shrinkage involving feeding the fabric between a stretched blanket and a heated shoe. When the blanket is allowed to retract, the cloth is physically forced to comply.

SANFOR-SET®: A trademark of Cluett, Peabody & Co., Inc., denoting a controlled standard of fabric shrinkage performance originally developed for denims. Fabrics bearing this trademark will not shrink under home-wash, tumble-dry conditions because they have been subjected to a liquid ammonia treatment and compressive shrinkage.

SAPONIFICATION: Specifically in relation to manufactured fibers, saponification is the process of removing part or all of the groups from acetate or triacetate fiber, leaving regenerated cellulose. (Also see S-FINISHING.)

Sanforizing Method of Producing Shrinkage

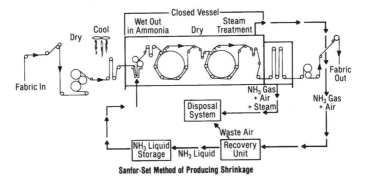

Sanfor-Set Method of Producing Shrinkage

SARAN FIBER: A manufactured fiber in which the fiber-forming substance is any long chain synthetic polymer composed of at least 80% by weight of vinylidene chloride units ($-CH_2-CCl_2-$) (FTC definition). Saran fiber is abrasion resistant and has excellent resistance to sunlight, weathering, and rotting. It is available primarily as monofilament. Principal end uses are for lawn furniture, upholstery, carpeting, ropes, netting, and bristles.

167

SASE: Acronym for stress at specified elongation; the stress experienced by a yarn or cord at a given elongation.

SATEEN: A strong, lustrous cotton fabric made in a satin weave.

SATIN WEAVE: One of the basic weaves, plain, satin, and twill. The face of the fabric consists almost completely of warp or filling floats produced in the repeat of the weave. The points of intersection are distributed as evenly and widely separated as possible. Satinweave fabric has a characteristic smooth, lustrous surface and has a considerably greater number of yarns in the set of threads, either warp or filling, that forms the face than in the other set.

4 x 1 Satin Weave

SATURATION: 1. The maximum intensity or purity of a color. If the color is as brilliant as possible, it is at saturation; if the color is subdued or grayed, it is dull, weak, and low in intensity. **2.** The upper limit concentration of a solute in a solvent, i.e., no more solute can be dissolved at a fixed temperature and pressure.

SATURATION BONDING: See BONDING, 2.

SATURATION VALUE: The maximum amount of dye that can be absorbed by a textile fiber under defined conditions.

SATURATOR: A machine for thoroughly wetting fabrics in an aqueous bath.

SAXONY: 1. A high-grade fabric for coats, made from Saxony Merino wool. **2.** A soft woolen with fancy yarn effects, used in sport-coat fabric. **3.** A highly twisted worsted knitting yarn. **4.** A term describing a cut-pile carpet having highly twisted, evenly sheared, medium-length pile yarns.

SCAFFOLDING YARN: See CARRIER YARN.

SCALE: See CUTICLE and CORTEX.

SCALLOPED SELVAGE: A fabric defect consisting of an abrupt, narrow place along the selvage. Principal cause is the failure of the clip on the tenter frame to engage or hold the fabric.

SCHAPPE: A yarn from partly degummed silk waste.

SCHAPPING: A method of degumming silk waste by means of a fermentation process.

SCHREINER: A type of calender that produces a highly lustrous finish on fabrics. It employs a smooth roll paired with a roll engraved with very fine lines at an angle to the machine direction. The fabric passes through the rolls under heavy pressure, producing a surface with greater light reflectance.

SCORCHING: The tendering of a fiber surface by heat so as to change the color and texture of the surface.

SCOTCHGARD®: A registered trademark of the 3M Company for a fluoride-based finish used to produce oil and water repellency on fabrics and floor coverings.

SCOURING: 1. An operation to remove the sizing and tint used on the warp yarn in weaving and, in general, to clean the fabric prior to dyeing. **2.** Washing of grease wool to remove oil, vegetable matter and other impurities before further processing.

SCRAY: On continuous processing ranges, a curved trough for accumulating fabric that is awaiting further processing.

SCREEN: 1. A hollow, cylindrical, coarse-mesh wire device used in pickers and certain openers to form the loose staple stock into a sheet, or lap. The screen is mounted horizontally on a shaft on which it revolves freely. **2.** A stencil used in screen printing. It is made of fine cloth, usually of silk or nylon, finely perforated in areas to form a design and mounted on a frame. The paste containing the dye is forced through the perforations onto the fabric, leaving the design. A series of screens, one for each color, is used for multicolored designs. (Also see PRINTING, 1.)

SCREEN PRINTING: See PRINTING, 1.

SCREW EXTRUDER: In manufactured fiber production, a pump for feeding polymer melt or polymer solution to the spinnerets. (Also see SCREW MELTER.)

SCREW FEEDS: Feed systems in which the action of the screw generates pressure that causes flow. This system usually consists of a container with a closely fitting screw unit.

SCREW MELTER: 1. Screw extruder in which frictional forces between the screw and the heated barrel contribute to rapid melting of solid polymer. This configuration is capable of high throughput. **2.** System in which a screw feed is used to feed polymer to a melt grid and to maintain a constant pressure at the grid.

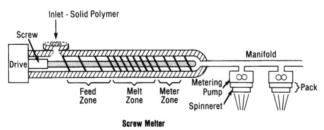

Screw Melter

SCRIM: 1. A lightweight, open-weave, coarse fabric; the best qualities are made with two-ply yarns. Cotton scrim usually comes in white, cream, or ecru and is used for window curtains and as backing for carpets. **2.** Fabric with open construction used as base fabric in the production of coated or laminated fabrics. **3.** A fabric made with two yarn sheets laid perpendicular to each other and bonded with an adhesive.

SCROLL PATTERN: A pattern on acetate film that activates clutch feed mechanisms photoelectrically on a tufting machine to generate a carpet pattern.

SCROOP: The sound of rustle or crunch that is characteristic of silk. Scroop is a natural property of silk, but may be induced in other fabrics to a degree by various treatments.

SCULPTURED: A term describing a carpet with areas of contrasting depth produced by mixing cut pile and loops.

SCUTCHING: The process, manual or mechanical, of separating bast fibers from the woody components of the plant stem after RETTING.

SEAM BINDING: A folded narrow woven fabric attached to a fabric seam or edge for reinforcement or to prevent raveling.

SEAMING: Joining the overlap of two pieces of fabric, usually near their edges.

SEAMLESS: A term that describes a tubular knit fabric without seams, e.g., seamless hosiery.

SEAM MARK: A particular type of pressure mark in the finished fabric. It is produced during finishing operations by the thickness of the seam used to join pieces for processing.

SEAM SLIPPAGE: A defect consisting of separated yarns occurring when sewn fabrics pull apart at the seams. Seam slippage is more prone to occur in smooth-yarn fabrics produced from manufactured filament yarns.

SEAM WELDING: Any stitchless procedure for joining fabrics based on the use of thermoplastic resins or the direct welding of thermoplastic materials. Seam welding is an alternative to conventional needle-and-thread seaming operations that is extremely popular in the nonwoven field.

SEAT BELT WEBBING: A heavy, woven narrow fabric, usually of polyester, used for body restraint.

SECANT MODULUS: The ratio of change in stress to change in strain between two points on a stress-strain diagram, particularly the points of zero stress and breaking stress.

SECONDARY BACKING: Woven or nonwoven fabric reinforcement laminated to the back of tufted carpet to enhance dimensional stability, strength, stretch resistance, and stiffness. Most secondary backings are woven jute, or woven or nonwoven polypropylene. The term is also sometimes used to describe attached polymeric back coatings such as latex foam.

SECONDARY COLORS: Green, orange, and violet, each of which is obtained by mixing two primary colors.

SECONDARY CREEP: The nonrecoverable component of creep. (Also see DELAYED DEFORMATION.)

SECOND-ORDER TRANSITION TEMPERATURE: The temperature at which the noncrystalline (amorphous) portions of a polymer melt or become plastic. An inflection point or change in stress-strain properties occurs at this point; however, for most fibers, this change is small.

SECONDS: 1. Imperfect fabrics (woven or knitted) containing flaws in the weave, finish, or dyeing, and sold as "seconds." **2.** Off-quality, defective, or substandard carpet. **3.** See YARN QUALITY.

SECTION BEAM: 1. A large, flanged roll upon which warp yarn is wound at the beam warper in preparation for slashing. **2.** Small flanged or unflanged beams assembled side-by-side on the shaft of a warp beam for further processing.

SECTION MARK: A fabric defect consisting of marks running warpwise in an evenly repeating pattern, caused by the improper setting of sections in silk-system (or indirect) warping.

SECTION WARPING: A two-stage operation for winding warp yarns in preparation for weaving. The yarns are first wound in sections on a large reel. When the required length has been wound for the first section, the reel is moved and the second section is wound beside the first. After all sections are built across the reel, they are wound simultaneously onto a beam for weaving.

SEERSUCKER: Lightweight fabric, made of cotton or manufactured fiber, having crinkled stripes made by weaving some of the warp threads slack and others tight. Woven seersucker is more expensive than imitations made by chemical treatment.

SELF-EXTINGUISHING: A term used to describe a material that will not support combustion after a flame source is removed.

SELF-TONE: See TONE-ON-TONE.

SELF-TWIST YARN: An inherently twist-stable, two-ply structure having a ply twist that is alternately S- and Z-directed along the yarn.

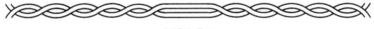

Self-Twist Yarn

SELVAGE or SELVEDGE: The narrow edge of woven fabric that runs parallel to the warp. It is made with stronger yarns in a tighter construction than the body of the fabric to prevent raveling. A fast selvage encloses all or part of the picks, and a selvage is not fast when the filling threads are cut at the fabric edge after every pick.

**Shuttle Loom
Selvage Formation**

SEPARATING COURSE: A course of weft-knit loops between knit garments or garment components that allows the garments or pieces to be separated when the course is removed.

SEQUESTRANT: Any compound that will inactivate a metallic ion by forming a water-soluble complex in which the metal is held in a nonionizable form. This results in prevention of the usual precipitation reactions of the metal.

SERGE: Any smooth-faced cloth made with a two-up and two-down twill weave.

SERGING: 1. Overcasting the cut edge of a fabric to prevent raveling. **2.** Finishing the edge of a carpet by oversewing rather than binding. Generally, the sides of a carpet are serged and the ends bound.

SERICIN: Silk gum. The gelatinous protein that cements the fibroin filaments in a silk fiber. It is removed in the process called degumming.

SERVED YARN: In aerospace textiles, a reinforcing yarn such as graphite or glass around which two different yarns are wound, i.e., one in the Z direction and one in the S direction, for protection or compaction of the yarn bundle.

End View

Served Yarn

SET MARK: A fabric defect consisting of narrow bars or bands across the full width of the fabric that may appear either as a tight, loose, or corduroy effect caused by loom stops improperly reset by the weaver. Set marks are sometimes caused by the weaver ripping out filling yarn and then not properly adjusting the pick wheel to obtain the proper relation between the fell of the cloth and the reed.

SET POINT: An input in process control that defines the desired value or range of values of the variable that is being controlled.

SET YARN: See TEXTURED YARNS, 8.

SEWING THREAD: See THREAD.

SEYDEL CONVERTER: Tow-to-top processing equipment. Seydel combines the prestretching and breaking process in one machine.

S-FINISHING: A finishing process applied to acetate and triacetate fabrics using a sodium hydroxide solution to give surface saponification; i.e., the fiber "skin" is converted to cellulose. It improves the hand and reduces the tendency to acquire a static charge.

SHADE BAR: See MIXED END OR FILLING.

SHADECLOTH: 1. A plain-weave cotton or linen fabric that is heavily sized and is often given oil treatment to make it opaque. This fabric is used for curtains and shades. **2.** An open fabric used to protect plants from sunlight and other weather conditions such as rain, hail, and frost.

SHADED FILLING: A defect consisting of a bar running across the fabric caused by a difference in appearance of the filling yarn, and occurring at a quill change or knot.

SHADING: In cut-pile fabrics, an apparent change in color when the pile is bent, caused by differences in the way light is reflected off the bent fibers. This phenomenon is a characteristic of pile fabrics, not a defect.

SHADOW PRINTING: See PRINTING, 1. WARP PRINTING.

SHADOW WEAVE: A woven fabric effect in which stripes, plaids, or checks are produced by the use of yarns twisted in the direction opposite to the yarns in the ground fabric. The differences in light reflection create the appearance of shadows.

SHAFT: 1. A term often used with reference to satins indicating the number of harnesses employed to produce the weave. **2.** See HARNESS.

SHAFT MARK: A fabric defect characterized by a number of floating ends, usually caused by a broken harness strap on the loom.

SHAG CARPET: A loosely tufted carpet construction with cut pile 1 to 5 inches in length and with greater than normal spacing between tufts.

SHANTUNG: Plain-weave fabric with unevenly ribbed surface and crisp texture.

SHARKSKIN: 1. A hard-finished, twill fabric, woolen or worsted, made of simple weaves with a two-color arrangement of warp and filling yarns. **2.** A plain-weave sportswear fabric made of dull-luster acetate or triacetate yarns.

SHEARING: 1. Cutting the fleece from sheep. **2.** A dry finishing operation in which projecting fibers are mechanically cut or trimmed from the face of the fabric. Woolen and worsted fabrics are almost always sheared. Shearing is also widely employed on other fabrics, especially on napped and pile fabrics where the amount varies accord-

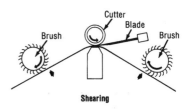

Shearing

ing to the desired height of the nap or pile. For flat-finished fabrics such as gabardine, a very close shearing is given. **3.** A carpet finishing process to create a smooth carpet face by removing surface fuzz. (Also see RANDOM-SHEARED CARPET.)

SHEATH-CORE BICOMPONENT FIBER: See BICOMPONENT FIBER.

SHEATH-CORE YARN: A bulk yarn made by wrapping high-shrinkage filaments with filaments of comparably lower shrinkage. The yarn bulks when treated to induce shrinkage.

SHED: A path through and perpendicular to the warp in the loom. It is formed by raising some warp threads by means of their harnesses while others are left down. The shuttle passes through the shed to insert the filling.

SHEDDING: 1. The operation of forming a shed in weaving. **2.** A loss of nominal length staple at any process in a staple yarn plant.

SHEERS: Transparent, lightweight fabrics of different constructions and yarns, especially those of silk and manufactured fibers. Examples are chiffons, some crepes, georgette, and voile.

SHETLAND: A term originally used for hand-spun yarn from sheep grown in the Shetland Islands. Today, it is used for 100% wool yarns spun on the woolen system with characteristics that can produce fabrics having the same tactile qualities as those made from Shetland wool.

SHIER: A short length of a single pick that appears to be cut out of the plane of the fabric.

SHINER: A relatively short streak caused by a lustrous section of a filament yarn. The principal cause is excessive tension applied to a yarn during processing.

SHIRE: See SHIER.

SHOE FOLD: A manner of folding fabric. The piece is folded from both ends into twelve or sixteen folds. The length of the fold depends upon the length of the piece.

SHOGGED STITCH: See RACKED STITCH.

SHORT-CUT STAPLE: Staple fiber less than 0.75-inch long. Typically used in wet-laid nonwoven processes to make fabrics, or as reinforcement in plastics, concrete, asphalt, and other materials.

SHORT HEATER: Device for heating the yarn on high-speed drawtexturing machines.

SHORT-LIQUOR DYEING: See DYEING.

SHOT: 1. See PICK. **2.** In woven pile floor coverings, the number of filling yarns per row of tufts.

SHREDDING: The separation of compressed fibers in pulp sheets prior to acetylation in acetate manufacture.

SHRINKAGE: Widthwise or lengthwise contraction of a fiber, yarn, or fabric, usually after wetting and redrying or on exposure to elevated temperature.

SHRINKAGE FORCE: The force generated by thermoplastic materials when they are subjected to elevated temperatures.

SHRINKAGE RESISTANCE: A property of textiles with good dimensional stability, usually as determined by standard tests. It can be an inherent property or induced by treatment.

SHUTTLE: A boat-shaped device, usually made of wood with a metal tip, that carries filling yarns through the shed in the weaving process. It is the most common weft-insertion device. The shuttle holds a quill, or pirn, on which the filling yarn is wound. It is equipped with an eyelet at one end to control rate. The filling yarn is furnished during the weaving operation.

Quill

Shuttle

SHUTTLE CHAFE MARK: A fabric defect that is usually seen as groups of short, fine lines across the fabric, often running for some distance in the piece and usually in the same area. Although these marks run in the direction of the filling, they are actually caused by the shuttle rubbing across and damaging the warp ends, producing a dull, chalky appearance.

SHUTTLELESS LOOM: A loom in which some device other than a shuttle is used for weft insertion. (Also see LOOM and WEFT INSERTION, 1.)

SIDE-BY-SIDE BICOMPONENT FIBER: See BICOMPONENT FIBER.

SILICA FIBER: A high-performance, glass-like fiber made by melt spinning and drawing almost pure silica. Silica fiber has high temperature resistance and high dielectric strength. It is used in technical applications such as fiber-reinforced composites, electrical and thermal insulation, and filtration.

SILICONE: One of a group of polymeric organic silicon compounds obtained as oils, greases, or plastics and applied to textile material as water- and heat-resistant lubricants and finishes.

SILK FIBER: A fine, strong, continuous filament produced by the larva of certain insects, especially the silkworm, when constructing its cocoons. The silkworm secretes the silk as a viscous fluid from two large glands in the lateral part of the body. The fluid is extruded through a common spinneret to form a double filament cemented together. This double silk filament, which is composed of the protein fibroin, ranges in size from 1.75–4.0 denier, depending upon the species of worm and the country of origin. The filament of the cocoon is softened and loosened by immersion in warm water and is then reeled off. Although raw silk contains 20%–30% of sericin, or silk glue, and is harsh and stiff, silk is soft and white when all of the glue has been removed by steeping and boiling in soap baths. Ecru silk is harsher, as it has only about 5% of the sericin removed. Silk is noted for its strength, resiliency, and elasticity. The major sources of commercial silk are Japan and China.

SI METRIC SYSTEM: A modern metric system developed for worldwide scientific usage. (See SI Metric Units in the Appendix.)

SIMULATED SPUN YARNS: Filament yarns that have been modified to have aesthetics similar to those of spun yarns. Simulated spun yarns have looped or hairy surfaces.

SINGEING: The process of burning off protruding fibers from yarn or fabric by passing it over a flame or heated copper plates. Singeing gives the fabric a smooth surface and is necessary for fabrics that are to be printed and for fabrics where smooth finishes are desired.

SINGLE JERSEY: See SINGLE-KNIT FABRIC.

SINGLE-KNIT FABRIC: Also called plain knit, a fabric constructed with one needle bed and one set of needles.

SINGLES YARN: The simplest strand of textile material suitable for operations such as weaving and knitting. A singles yarn may be formed from fibers with more or less twist; from filaments with or without twist; from narrow strips of material such as paper, cellophane, or metal foil; or from monofilaments. When twist is present, it is all in the same direction. (Also see YARN.)

SINGLING: A yarn defect caused by the breaking of one or more strands in a plying operation, with resulting unevenness in the finished product.

SINKER: In weave design, a blank square indicating a filling thread over a warp thread at the point of intersection.

SINTERING: Forming a bonded mass or fiber by heating the constituents of the mass or fiber without melting.

SISAL: A strong, white, bast fiber produced from leaves of the Agave plant, which is found in Central America, West Indies, and Africa. Sisal is used chiefly for cordage and twine.

SIZE: See SIZING.

SIZE MARK: A fabric defect that consists of a rough or frosted spot caused by uneven application or drying of the size.

SIZING: 1. A generic term for compounds that are applied to warp yarn to bind the fiber together and stiffen the yarn to provide abrasion resistance during weaving. Starch, gelatin, oil, wax, and manufactured polymers such as polyvinyl alcohol, polystyrene, polyacrylic acid, and polyacetates are employed. **2.** The process of applying sizing compounds. (Also see SLASHING.) **3.** The process of weighing sample lengths of yarn to determine the count.

SKEIN: A continuous strand of yarn or cord in the form of a collapsed coil. It may be of any specified length and is usually obtained by winding a definite number of turns on a reel under prescribed conditions. The circumference of the reel on which yarn is wound is usually 45–60 inches. (Also see HANK.)

SKEIN BREAK FACTOR: The comparative breaking load of a skein of yarn adjusted for the linear density of the yarn expressed in an indirect system. It is the product of the breaking load of the skein and the yarn number expressed in an indirect system (e.g., pounds times cotton count). A statement of the skein break factor must indicate the number of wraps in the skein, if this is not otherwise apparent. Without specifying the number of wraps, a statement of the skein break factor is meaningless.

SKEIN BREAKING TENACITY: The skein breaking load divided by the product of the yarn number in a direct numbering system and the number of strands placed under the tension (twice the number of wraps in the skein); preferably expressed in newtons per tex.

SKEIN DYEING: See DYEING.

SKEWNESS: The distance measured parallel to and along a selvage between the point at which a filling yarn meets this selvage and a perpendicular to the selvage from the point at which the same filling yarn meets the other selvage. Skewness may be expressed directly in inches or as a percentage of the width of the fabric at the point of measurement.

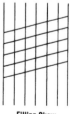

Filling Skew

SLACK END: An end woven under insufficient tension.

SLACK FILLING: See SLACK PICK.

SLACK MERCERIZATION: A process for producing stretch in cellulosic fabrics.

SLACK PICK: A single filling yarn woven under insufficient tension.

SLACK SELVAGE: A self-descriptive fabric defect caused by incorrect balance of cloth structure between the ground and selvage or by the selvage ends being woven with insufficient tension.

SLACK THREAD: See SLACK END.

SLACK TWIST: A term used to describe a plied yarn in which the twist is insufficient or nonexistent.

SLACK WARP: See SLACK END.

SLAM-OFF: See SMASH, 1.

SLASHER: A machine used to apply size to the warp ends, while transferring the warp yarns from section beams to the loom beam.

SLASHER SIZING: See SLASHING.

SLASHING: A process of sizing warp yarns on a slasher. (Also see SIZING, 2. and SLASHER.)

SLAT PATTERN: A mechanism on a tufting machine that meters yarn between two slats to generate a carpet pattern.

SLEAZY: Thin, lacking firmness, open-meshed; usually describes poor-grade fabrics.

SLEEVING: A braided, knit, or woven product or fabric in tubular or cylindrical form that is less than 4 inches in width (i.e., 8 inches in circumference).

SLEY: The number of warp yarns per inch in a woven cloth on or off the loom.

SLIDE WASTE: A yarn defect that is similar in appearance to a slub. It consists of a mass of fiber encircling the yarn end and can be slid freely along the end.

SLIPPAGE: Sliding or slipping of the filling threads over the warp ends (or vice versa), which leaves open spaces in the fabric. Slippage results from a loose weave or unevenly matched warp and filling.

SLIT-FILM YARN: Yarn of a flat, tape-like character produced by slitting an extruded film.

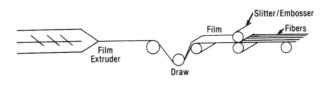

Slit-Film Process

SLIT TAPE: A fabric, 12 inches or less in width, made by cutting wider fabric to the desired width. Slit tapes are made primarily of cotton, linen, jute, glass, or asbestos and are used principally for functional purposes.

SLIVER: A continuous strand of loosely assembled fibers without twist. Sliver is delivered by the card, the comber, or the drawing frame. The production of sliver is the first step in the textile operation that brings staple fiber into a form that can be drawn (or reduced in bulk) and eventually twisted into a spun yarn.

SLIVER KNITTING: Circular knitting coupled with the drawing in of a sliver by the needles to produce a pile-like fabric. Sliver-knit fabrics are used in outer shell fabrics, heavy linings, simulated fur fabrics, skiwear, and area rugs.

SLIVER-TO-YARN SPINNING: A ring-spinning method of converting sliver directly into spun yarn, eliminating the roving operation.

SLOUGHED FILLING: See LOOPED FILLING.

SLUB: A yarn defect consisting of a lump or thick place on the yarn caused by lint or small lengths of yarn adhering to it. Generally, in filament yarn, a slub is the result of broken filaments that have stripped back from the end to which they are attached.

SLUBBER: A machine used in textile processes prior to spinning that reduces the sliver and inserts the first twist.

SLUBBING: The product of the slubber, it is the intermediate stage between sliver and roving.

SLUBBING FRAME: See SLUBBER.

SLUB CATCHER: A mechanical or electronic device designed to aid in the detection and removal of slubs or neps in yarns, usually during coning.

SLUB YARN: Any type of yarn that is irregular in diameter; the irregularity may be purposeful or the result of error. (Also see NOVELTY YARN, NUB YARN, and SLUB.)

SLUG: A thick place in a yarn or a piece of lint entangled in yarn, cord, or fabric.

SLURRY: A watery or solvent suspension; e.g., titanium dioxide mixed with water for addition to polymers.

SMASH: 1. A large hole in woven fabric with many broken warp ends and floating picks. One cause is the breaking of one or both harness straps, permitting the harness to drop and break out warp ends. **2.** The breaking of many yarn ends in a beaming operation, usually as a result of mechanical failures.

SMOKE CHAMBER TEST: See FLAMMABILITY TESTS.

SMOULDERING: A slow, flameless, smoking burning of a fabric.

SNAG: A pulled thread in knits. It is in the wale direction in warp knits and in the course direction in weft knits.

SNARL: A short length of warp or filling yarn that has twisted on itself because of lively twist or insufficient tension. The snarling may occur during or prior to the weaving process.

SNOW BALL: See BALLING UP.

SOAKING: 1. Treatment of rayon yarns in a lubricating and sizing solution preparatory to hard twisting. **2.** A treatment to soften raw silk by steeping in an oil or surfactant emulsion before throwing.

SOAP: The detergent obtained by the formation of a sodium or potassium salt of a fatty acid or mixture of fatty acids.

SOFTENER: 1. A product designed to impart a soft mellowness to the fabric. Examples are glucose, glycerine, tallow, or any one of a number of quaternary ammonium compounds. **2.** A substance that reduces the hardness of water by removing or sequestering the calcium and magnesium ions. **3.** A substance used to reduce friction during mixing and processing when dry powders are added to polymers.

SOFTENING POINT: The temperature at which substances without a sharp melting point change from viscous to plastic flow.

SOFT FLOW JET DYEING MACHINE: A type of jet dyeing machine that employs a driven reel to lift the fabric out of the dyebath and feed it to the air jet that transports it back to the dyeing chamber.

SOFT TWIST: A term, usually applied to spun yarn, to describe a yarn with a low number of turns of twist per unit length.

SOIL BURIAL TEST: A test of resistance of textile materials to certain micro-organisms present in soil. The samples are buried in soil for an extended period, then removed and measured for strength loss.

SOILING: The staining or smudging of textile materials resulting from the deposit of dirt, oil, undesirable dye, etc.

SOIL REDEPOSITION: See REDEPOSITION.

SOIL-RELEASE FINISH: A finish for textiles that makes it easier to remove stains and soil in laundering.

SOLID-STATE POLYMERIZATION: Reaction of the active end-groups within a solid polymer. It may be intentional as in heating and drying nylon 66 to increase the final degree of polymerization; or it may be undesirable such as that which occurs in fibers under high-temperature conditions in tires that leads to increased degree of polymerization, cross-linking, and subsequent brittleness and loss of strength.

SOLUBLE: Capable of being dissolved, i.e., passing into solution.

SOLUTION-DYEING: See DYEING.

SOLVENT BONDING: See BONDING, 2.

SOLVENT DYEING: See DYEING.

SOLVENT SPINNING: See SPINNING, 2. DRY SPINNING.

SORBENT: A nonwoven material used to attract and/or contain fluid.

SOURING: Any treatment of textile materials in dilute acid. Its purpose is the neutralization of any alkali that is present.

SPACE DYEING: See DYEING.

SPANDEX FIBER: A manufactured fiber in which the fiber-forming substance is a long chain synthetic polymer composed of at least 85% of a segmented polyurethane (FTC definition).

CHARACTERISTICS: Spandex is lighter in weight, more durable, and more supple than conventional elastic threads and has between two and three times their restraining power. Spandex is extruded in a multiplicity of fine filaments which immediately form a monofilament. It can be repeatedly stretched over 500% without breaking and still recover instantly to its original length. It does not suffer deterioration from oxidation as is the case with fine sizes of rubber thread, and it is not damaged by body oils, perspiration, lotions, or detergents.

END USES: Spandex is used in foundation garments, bathing suits, hose, and webbings.

SPC: Acronym for STATISTICAL PROCESS CONTROL.

SPECIFIC GRAVITY: Ratio of the mass of a material to the mass of an equal volume of water at 4°C. The range for modern fibers is not too great and is dependent to some extent on the liquid used as an immersant in measurements, because of fiber swelling and of possible absorption of liquid into fiber voids. (Also see DENSITY.)

SPECIFIC HUMIDITY: The weight of water vapor per unit weight of dry air.

SPECK: 1. A contaminant in polymer such as gels, metal, or dirt that shows up as a dark spot. **2.** A small particle of foreign substance that has not been removed from the stock before spinning.

SPECKING: The removal of burrs, knots, and other objects that impair the finished appearance of woolens and worsteds.

SPECKY: A term used to describe dyed woolen fabric with specks of undyed vegetable matter on the face. The specks can be removed by carbonizing or covered by speck dyeing.

SPECTROGRAPH: A spectroscope equipped with a camera or some other device for recording the spectrum. (Also see SPECTROSCOPE.)

SPECTROMETER: An instrument for identifying and comparing materials by the dispersing of light and the study of the spectra formed.

SPECTROPHOTOMETER: An instrument used to measure the transmission or reflectance of light as a function of wavelength.

SPECTROSCOPE: An instrument for forming a spectrum for visual examination.

SPECTROSCOPY: The identification of materials by the analysis of their spectra.

SPHERULITE: A common form of polymer crystallization from melts or concentrated solutions. These crystallites show a radial symmetry from a central point and have a distinctive maltese cross pattern of birefringence under the polarizing microscope.

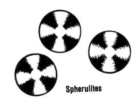

Spherulites

SPINDLE: A slender, upright, rotating rod on a spinning frame, roving frame, twister, winder, or similar machine. A bobbin is placed on the spindle to receive the yarn as the spindle is rotated at high speed.

SPIN-DRAWING: 1. The reduction of roving during spinning by a roller drafting mechanism similar to that used on the roving frame. **2.** Combined spinning and drawing in one operation in melt-spun fibers.

SPIN-DRAW-TEXTURING: A process for producing textured yarn by combining extrusion, drawing, and texturing on the same machine.

SPIN FINISH: See LUBRICANT.

SPIN MULTIPLIER: See TWIST MULTIPLIER.

SPINNERET: A metal disc containing numerous minute holes used in manufactured fiber extrusion. The spinning solution or melted polymer is forced through the holes to form the fiber filaments.

SPINNING: The process or processes used in the production of singles yarns or of fabrics generated directly from polymer.

Spinneret

1. Yarn from Staple Fiber: The formation of a yarn by a combination of drawing or drafting and twisting prepared strands of fibers, such as rovings.

2. Filament Yarn or Tow: In the spinning of manufactured filaments, fiber-forming substances in the plastic or molten state, or in solution, are forced through the fine orifices in a metallic plate called a spinneret, or jet, at a controlled rate. The solidified filaments are drawn-off by rotating rolls, or godets, and wound onto bobbins or pirns. There are several methods of spinning manufactured filaments:

Dry Spinning: The process in which a solution of the fiber-forming substance is extruded in a continuous stream into a heated chamber to remove the solvent, leaving the solid filament, as in the manufacture of acetate.

Gel Spinning: A spinning process in which the primary mechanism of solidification is the gelling of the polymer solution by cooling to form a gel filament consisting of precipitated polymer and solvent. Solvent removal is accomplished following solidification by washing in a liquid bath. The resultant fibers can be drawn to give a product with high tensile strength and modulus.

Melt Spinning: The process in which the fiber-forming substance is melted and extruded into air or other gas, or into a suitable liquid, where it is cooled and solidified, as in the manufacture of polyester or nylon.

Phase-Separation Spinning: Extrusion of polymer and solvent at high temperature into a cooling zone. During the cooling process, a phase separation occurs, usually accompanied by crystallization of the solvent. Solvent can be removed before or after drawing.

Reaction Spinning: A method of producing manufactured fiber in which polymerization and spinning of the filaments occur simultaneously when one reactant is extruded into a bath containing another reactant.

Wet Spinning: The process in which a solution of the fiber-forming substance is extruded into a liquid coagulating medium where the polymer is regenerated, as in the manufacture of viscose or cuprammonium rayon.

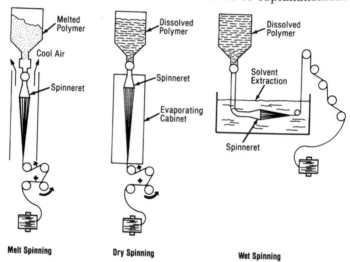

| Melt Spinning | Dry Spinning | Wet Spinning |

3. Spun Yarn from Leaf and Bast Fiber: In the manufacture of leaf and bast fiber yarns, the terms "wet spinning" and "dry spinning" refer to the spinning of fibers in the wet state and in the air-dry state, respectively.

4. Spun Yarn from Filament Tow: The formation of a yarn from filament tow by a combination of cutting or breaking, drafting, and twisting in a single series of operations. Also known as converting.

5. Nonwoven Fabrics: Fabrics can be produced directly from molten or dissolved fiber-forming substances by several continuous processes:

Flash Spinning: The process in which a fiber-forming substance in a volatile solvent is extruded from a high-temperature, high-pressure environment into lower temperature and pressure conditions, causing the solvent to rapidly evaporate, leaving a lacy, net-like fabric.

Spray Spinning: See SPUNBOND.

SPINNING BATH: 1. In wet spinning or dispersion spinning, the liquid co-agulating medium into which the fiber-forming material is extruded. **2.** In reaction spinning, the bath containing chemical components that react with other components extruded into it to effect polymerization and fiber formation.

SPINNING FRAME: A machine used for spinning staple yarn. It drafts the roving to the desired size, inserts twist, and winds the yarn onto a bobbin. The term is generally used to indicate a ring spinning frame, although it does cover flyer spinning and cap spinning on the worsted system.

SPINNING LIMIT: In staple yarn spinning, the yarn number of the finest yarn that can be satisfactorily spun from a given fiber lot under specified conditions.

SPINNING SOLUTION: A solution of a fiber-forming polymer (e.g., cellulose acetate) in a suitable condition to be extruded by either dry spinning or wet spinning.

SPINNING TWIST: The twist added to yarn during spinning to give it strength and other desired characteristics.

SPIRAL YARN: Specialty yarn made by winding hea-vier, slackly twisted yarn around a finer yarn with a hard twist to give a slubby appearance.

Spiral Yarn

SPLICING: 1. The joining of two ends of yarn or cordage. There are several methods used, e.g., by interweaving the strands, by the use of knots, by taper-ing, lapping, and cementing the ends, etc. **2.** A method of reinforcing knits, e.g., the heels and toes of hosiery, by introducing an additional yarn for strength.

SPLINTER: Two or more staple fibers adhering together, causing a stiff cluster that resists pulling apart in normal processing, and reacting in the yarn spin-ning process similarly to higher than nominal denier fiber.

SPLINTER COUNT: A measure of the number of coalesced fibers, mealy particles, or other such matter in staple fiber.

SPLIT: See REED.

SPLIT-DRAFT METIER: An extrusion cabinet for dry spinning in which the drying medium (hot air) is introduced between the jet and the yarn outlet and flows in both directions.

SPLIT END: 1. A defect in fabric caused by breakage of some of the singles yarns in a plied warp yarn. **2.** A defect in manufactured filament yarn caused by breakage of some of the filaments.

SPLIT-FLOW METIER: See SPLIT-DRAFT METIER.

SPLITTING: 1. In the processing of tow, a defect in which the integrity of opened tow is disturbed by separation or division into two or more segments longitudinally. Splitting can be continuous or intermittent, long or short term. **2.** In slashing, the separation of sized yarn ends before take-up on the slasher beam.

SPOOL: A flanged wooden or metal cylinder upon which yarn, thread, or wire is wound. The spool has an axial hole for a pin or spindle used in winding. (Also see BEAM.)

SPORTSWEAR: Garments designed for engaging in sports or for informal or casual wear. (Also see ACTIVEWEAR.)

SPOT BONDING: See BONDING, 2. POINT BONDING.

SPRAY BONDING: See BONDING, 2.

SPRAY SPINNING: See SPUNBOND.

SPREAD STITCH: See PINHOLE.

SPRING NEEDLE: A knitting machine needle with a long, flexible hook, or beard, that allows the hook to be closed by an action known as pressing so that the loops can be cast off. The hook springs back to its original position when the presser bar is removed. (Also see LATCH NEEDLE.)

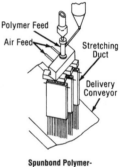

Head of Spring Needle

SPUNBOND: Nonwoven fabric formed by filaments that have been extruded, drawn, then laid on a continuous belt. Bonding is accomplished by several methods such as by hot-roll calendering or by passing the web through a saturated-steam chamber at an elevated pressure.

SPUN-DYED: See DYEING, MELT DYEING and DYEING, SOLUTION DYEING.

SPUN FABRIC: A fabric made from staple fibers that may contain one or a blend of two or more fiber types.

SPUNLACED FABRIC: A nonwoven fabric produced by entangling fibers in a repeating pattern to form a strong fabric free of binders.

Polymer Feed
Air Feed
Stretching Duct
Delivery Conveyor

Spunbond Polymer-to-Web Process

SPUNLIKE FILAMENT YARNS: See SIMULATED SPUN YARNS.

SPUN SILK: See SCHAPPE.

SPUN YARN: 1. A yarn consisting of staple fibers usually bound together by twist. **2.** A melt-spun fiber before it is drawn.

SQUARE CONSTRUCTION: See BALANCED WEAVE.

SQUEEGEE: The portion of a screen-printing apparatus consisting of a blade that forces the print paste through the screen onto the fabric.

SQUEEZE ROLLS: Rolls used to apply pressure for removal of water or chemicals from fabric.

STABILITY: A term used to describe the tendency of a fiber or fabric to return to its original shape after being subjected to external influence, such as tension, heat, or chemicals.

STABILIZED FIBER: Fiber that is heat or chemically treated to set the fiber properties and prevent deterioration, shrinkage, etc. (Also see HEAT STABILIZED, HEAT-SETTING, and UV ABSORBER.)

STAIN: See FINISHING SPOT.

STAINING: The undesired pickup of color by a fabric: (1) when immersed in water, dry-cleaning solvent, or similar liquid medium that contains dyestuffs or coloring material not intended for coloring the fabric; or (2) by direct contact with other dyed material from which color is transferred by bleeding or sublimation.

STAINLESS-STEEL FIBER: Textile fibers made of stainless steel. Steel fibers are used for antistatic purposes in carpets, for tire belt construction, and for high-temperature or heat-resistant end uses.

STALWART PRINTING MACHINE: See PRINTING, 2.

STANDARD ATMOSPHERE FOR TESTING: The atmospheric conditions maintained in the area where textile materials are tested, usually 65% ± 2% relative humidity and 21°C ± 1°C (70°F ± 2°F). For tire cord and industrial products, it is usually 55% ± 2% relative humidity and 24°C ± 1°C (75°F ± 2°F).

STANDARD CONDITION: Standard condition is that reached by a specimen when it is in moisture equilibrium with a standard atmosphere. Standard condition is seldom realized in practice since laboratory atmospheres are continually fluctuating between narrow limits, and it is not practical to wait for the attainment of moisture equilibrium which would require several days or more for tightly wound samples of high regain material. Practically, specimens are brought to moisture equilibrium in the standard atmosphere for testing as defined in these definitions. The term "standard condition" should not be used as a synonym for the concept of "standard atmosphere."

STANDARD DEVIATION: A measure of the dispersion of a set of numbers based on the difference of the individual numbers from the mean.

STANDARD MOISTURE REGAIN: Accepted moisture allowance for textile materials expressed in percentages of their dry weight.

STANDARD WEIGHT: The moisture-free weight of a textile material plus its standard moisture regain allowance.

STANDING WIRE: A broad term describing fixed rods or strips extending through the loom reed, that control the height of the pile in a woven pile fabric.

STAPLE: Natural fibers or cut lengths from filaments. The staple length of natural fibers varies from less than 1 inch as with some cotton fibers to several feet for some hard fibers. Manufactured staple fibers are cut to a definite length, from 8 inches down to about 1½ inches (occasionally down to 1 inch), so that they can be processed on cotton, woolen, or worsted yarn spinning systems. The term staple (fiber) is used in the textile industry to distinguish natural or cut length manufactured fibers from filament.

STAPLE FABRIC: See SPUN FABRIC.

STAPLE FIBER: See STAPLE.

STAPLE PROCESSING: The conversion of staple into spun yarns suitable in evenness, size, twist, and strength for use in the weaving or knitting of fabrics. (Also see TEXTILE PROCESSING.)

STAPLE YARN: See SPUN YARN.

STARCH LUMP: See HARD SIZE.

START-UP MARK: See SET MARK.

STATIC: An accumulation of negative or positive electricity on the surface of fibers or fabrics because of inadequate electrical dissipation during processing. Static results in an electrical attraction or repulsion of the fibers relative to themselves, to machine parts, or to other materials, preventing the fiber from traveling in a normal path in the process.

STATIC ADHESION: In tire cord, the measurement of the strength of a cord-to-rubber bond under static conditions or very low strain rate.

STATIC CRACK: See SHIER.

STATIC ELIMINATOR: 1. A chemical substance applied to a textile material to reduce or eliminate the buildup of static electricity. **2.** An electrically conductive attachment to textile machinery for preventing the buildup of static charges.

STATISTICAL PROCESS CONTROL: A system of applying statistical methods to control the quality of products made by a process. During the process, variability is determined by product testing, according to a specific sampling scheme, against pre-established limits plotted on a control chart. The data collected, when analyzed by statistical methods, help the operator to make decisions about how to adjust the process to keep the product within the acceptable variability limits.

STEAM CHEST: A steam-heated cabinet used in manufactured fiber production. Usually refers to the heated cabinet in which spin-drawing is done or to the cabinet around a stuffer-box crimper.

STEAM FIXATION: Processes for promoting fixation or penetration of dyes on dyed or printed textiles in a steam atmosphere. There are three main types of steaming conditions: (1) saturated steam, in which the water vapor is at the same temperature and pressure as the water droplets in equilibrium with it, (2) high-pressure steam, in which the elevated temperature is maintained by enclosing the water vapor in a sealed chamber at a pressure several times higher than ambient atmospheric pressure, and (3) superheated dry steam, which is steam at atmospheric pressure that is raised above the boiling point of water (100°C) by applying external heat.

STEEPING: 1. Prolonged soaking of a textile material without agitation in a treatment bath or in a wet state. **2.** In the manufacture of viscose rayon, the treatment of pulp in a caustic soda bath to produce alkali-cellulose. **3.** See RETTING.

STEINER TUNNEL TEST: See FLAMMABILITY TESTS, TUNNEL TEST.

STENTER: See TENTER FRAME.

STEPOVER MECHANISM: An attachment to a carpet tufting machine used to shift yarns back and forth over other yarns to break up visual streakiness or to generate a pattern.

STICKER: 1. A distortion in the weave characterized by tight and slack places in the same warp yarns. The principal causes are rolled ends on the beam, warp ends restricted by broken filament slubs, and knots catching at lease rods, drop wires, heddles, or reeds. (Also see DRAW-BACK.) **2.** See HARD SIZE.

STIFFNESS: The property of a fiber or fabric to resist bending or to carry a load without deformation. It is based on the fiber modulus.

STITCH-BONDED FABRIC: A composite nonwoven fabric formed by various methods of stitching through unconnected fibers, using techniques such as quilting or interlacing with a fine mesh to hold the construction together. (Also see BONDING, 2. STITCH BONDING.)

STITCH BONDING: See BONDING, 2.

STITCHING: The process of passing a fiber or thread through the thickness of fabric layers to secure them. In composite manufacture, stitching is used to make preforms or to improve damage tolerance of complex-shaped parts.

STITCH TRANSFER: In knitting, transferring a loop from one needle to another to effect a structural change in the fabric, e.g., rib to single knit, or in fashioning knit pieces.

STOCK DYEING: See DYEING.

STOCKINETTE: A knit fabric in tubular or flat form made with a plain stitch from yarns of wool, cotton, manufactured fibers, or a combination of these fibers. Stockinette fabrics are used for underwear, industrial applications, and other purposes. In heavier constructions, dyed and napped stockinette finds apparel uses. (Also spelled stockinet.)

STOLL-QUARTERMASTER UNIVERSAL WEAR TESTER: A versatile testing apparatus for measuring wear resistance of fabrics, yarns, thread, etc. It can be equipped with either of two testing heads, one for testing abrasion resistance of flat surfaces and the other for testing resistance to flexing and abrasion. (See diagram on the next page.)

STONE WASHING: A process to impart special color effects to fabric, particularly denim, by tumbling the wet fabric with pebbles to produce localized abrasion. The pebbles are sometimes soaked in a bleaching agent to lighten the fabric in random areas during tumbling. After the treatment, the fabric may be dyed to color the abraded areas. The effect is also achieved by ENZYME FINISHING.

STOP MARK: 1. See SET MARK. **2.** A defect in warp-knit fabric caused by differences in stitch length in the first few courses formed after a machine stop.

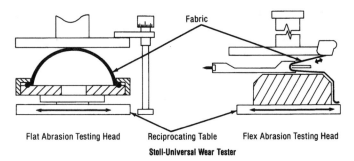

Flat Abrasion Testing Head   Reciprocating Table   Flex Abrasion Testing Head
Stoll-Universal Wear Tester

STOP MOTION: Any device that automatically stops a textile machine's operation on the occurrence of a yarn break, a high defect count, etc.

STOVING: A process for bleaching wool, silk, and other protein fibers in a chamber with sulfur dioxide.

STRAIGHT-BAR KNITTING MACHINE: A flat-knitting machine equipped with bearded needles used to produce fashioned pieces. (Also see FASHIONING.)

STRAIN RECOVERY CURVE: See TENSILE HYSTERESIS CURVE.

STRAND: 1. A single fiber, filament, or monofilament. **2.** An ordered assemblage of textile fibers having a high ratio of length to diameter and normally used as a unit; includes slivers, roving, singles yarns, plied yarns, cords, braids, ropes, etc.

STRAW: A general term for plant fibers obtained from stems, stalks, leaves, bark, grass, etc. They are made into hats, bags, shoes, mats, etc., by weaving, plaiting, or braiding.

STREAK: A discoloration (rust, oil, dye, grease, soap, etc.) extended as an irregular stripe in the cloth.

STRENGTH COUNT PRODUCT: See BREAK FACTOR.

STRESS: The resistance to deformation developed within a specimen subjected to an external force. Typical examples are tensile stress, shear stress, or compressive stress. Stress usually reaches a maximum at the time of rupture. When a textile material is subjected to a stress below that causing rupture, the stress gradually decreases or decays with time. Stress is expressed as force per unit linear density or unit of cross-sectional area.

STRESS-STRAIN CURVE: A graphical representation, showing the relationship between the change in dimension (in the direction of the applied stress) of the specimen from the application of an external stress, and the magnitude of that stress. In tension tests of textile materials, the stress can be expressed either in units of force per unit cross-sectional area, or in force per unit linear density of the original specimen, and the strain can be expressed either as a fraction or as a percentage of the original specimen length. (Also see LOAD-DEFORMATION CURVE.)

STRETCH BREAKING: In conversion of tow-to-top, fibers are hot stretched and broken rather than cut to prevent some of the damage done by cutting.

STRETCH GROWTH: See SECONDARY CREEP.

STRETCH SPINNING: A term used in the manufacture of rayon. Rayon filaments are stretched while moist and before final coagulation to decrease their diameter and increase their strength.

STRETCH YARN: Any yarn with the ability to stretch to a significant degree when tension is applied and contract when the tension is released, including (1) elastomeric filament yarns, and (2) manufactured filament yarns treated by various texturing processes to impart bulk and stretch. (Also see TEXTURED YARNS, 9.)

STRIATIONS: Streaks or bands of various nature in fibers or fabrics.

STRIÉ: A term describing any cloth having irregular stripes or streaks of practically the same color as the background.

STRIKE: The dye uptake of a textile material in the initial stage of dyeing. A rapid strike can result in uneven dyeing.

STRIKE-OFF: Printing of a test fabric length to check pattern registration and shade match prior to print production.

STRINGUP: See THREADUP.

STRINGY SELVAGE: See SLACK SELVAGE.

STRIPINESS: 1. Longitudinal streaks in a warp-knit fabric. **2.** Coursewise streaks in a weft-knit fabric.

STRIPPING: 1. A chemical process for removing color from dyed cloth by the use of various chemicals. Stripping is done when the color is unsatisfactory and the fabric is to be redyed. **2.** The physical process of removing fiber that is embedded in the clothing of a card. **3.** See DEGUMMING. **4.** Removal of grease from wool by scouring.

STRIP TEST: A tensile test using a strip of the fabric of specified width as the test specimen.

STROLL TEST: A method of determining the electrostatic propensity of a carpet by measuring the body voltage generated as a person walks on the carpet.

STUFFER BOX: A mechanism for crimping in which a fiber bundle (e.g., tow or filament yarn) is jammed against itself, causing it to crimp. By the suitable application of heat (usually wet steam) and pressure to the stuffed tow, a high and permanent crimp can be forced into the bundle. (Also see TEXTURING, STUFFER BOX METHOD.)

STUFFERS: Extra yarns running in the warp direction through a woven fabric to increase the fabric's strength and weight.

S TWIST: See TWIST, DIRECTION OF.

STYRENE: An unsaturated hydrocarbon (C_6H_5–$CH=CH_2$) prepared from coal tar. Polystyrene is a colorless, transparent plastic used for molding various articles for insulation, transparent parts, radio parts, etc.

SUBLIMATION: A phase change in which a substance, such as a dye, passes directly from the solid to the vapor phase without passing through a liquid phase. This process is the basis for transfer printing.

SUBLISTATIC® PROCESS: A method of applying print designs to fabrics containing manufactured fibers by paper-transfer techniques. Developed by Sublistatic Corp. (Also see PRINTING, HEAT-TRANSFER PRINTING.)

SUBSTANTIVITY: The selective attraction between a dye or other substance and a textile material (substrate). Substantivity allows preferential sorption of the substance by the substrate from an application medium (e.g., dyes from a dyebath).

SUBSTRATE: Fabric to which coatings or other fabrics are applied. It can be of woven, knit, nonwoven, or weft-insertion construction. Generally, substrate properties are dependent both on fiber type and fabric construction. Usually the fabric is scoured, heat-set, and otherwise finished prior to coating or bonding. Many smooth-surfaced manufactured fiber fabrics require impregnation with a latex prior to coating to ensure adequate adhesion.

SUBSURFACE STABILIZATION FABRICS: See GEOTEXTILES.

SUEDE FABRIC: Woven or knitted cloth finished to resemble suede leather, usually by napping, shearing, and sanding techniques.

SULFAR FIBER: A manufactured fiber in which the fiber-forming substance is a long chain, synthetic polysulfide in which at least 85% of the sulfide (–S–) linkages are attached to two aromatic rings (FTC definition). The raw material is polyphenylene sulfide which is melt spun and processed into staple fibers. These are high-performance fibers with excellent resistance to strong chemicals and high temperature. They show excellent strength retention in harsh environments; are flame retardant; and are non-conducting. They find use in high-temperature filter fabrics, electrical insulation, coal-fired boiler bag houses, papermaker's felt, and high-performance composites.

SULFATE PULP: See KRAFT PULP.

SULFONATED: A term describing a material that has been reacted with sulfonic acid, usually to impart solubility, dyeability with cationic dyes, or other properties.

SULFONIC ACID: Any acid containing the sulfonic group (SO_3H).

SULFUR DYES: See DYES.

SULFURING: See STOVING.

SUPERABSORBENT: A material that can absorb many times the amount of liquid ordinarily absorbed by cellulosic materials such as wood pulp, cotton, and rayon.

SUPERCRITICAL DYEING: See DYEING.

SUPERDRAWING: A process for drawing fiber beyond the NECKING stage to achieve maximum property values for specific uses. For example, acrylic filaments may be drawn many times their undrawn length to produce a precursor for the manufacture of CARBON FIBER.

SUPERFINE FIBER: See MICROFIBER.

SUPPORTED FABRIC: A fabric comprising a nonwoven web reinforced with a woven, knit, or stitch-bonded layer.

SURAH: A soft fabric of silk or filament polyester or acetate, usually a twill and often woven in a plaid. Surah is used for ties, scarves, blouses, and dresses.

SURFACE CHARGE: The electrical charge on the surface of a substance.

SURFACE ENERGY: 1. The free energy of the surfaces at an interface that arises because of differences in the tendencies of each phase to attract its own molecules. **2.** The work that would be required to increase the surface area of a liquid by one unit area.

SURFACE TENSION: Intermolecular forces acting on the molecules at the free surface of a liquid tend to minimize the surface area of the liquid and give the surface properties similar to those of an elastic skin under tension. When two dissimilar liquids make contact, these intermolecular forces will cause the shape of the interface to change until the potential energy of the entire molecular system is at a minimum.

SURFACE YARN WEIGHT: See PILE WEIGHT.

SURFACTANT: A surface-active agent, i.e., a product that acts by modifying the surface or boundary between two phases.

SWATCH: A piece of fabric used as a representative sample of any fabric.

SWELLING: 1. In textile usage, expanding of a fiber caused by the influence of a solvent or chemical agent. A property often used to facilitate dyeing. **2.** See DIE SWELL.

SWELL RATIO: See DIE SWELL.

SWIFT: 1. A large horizontal or vertical reel for winding warp yarns in indirect, or section, warping. **2.** A reel for winding and unwinding skeins of yarn. **3.** See CYLINDER, 1.

SWISS PIQUÉ: A type of DOUBLE PIQUÉ knit fabric.

SYNDIOTACTIC POLYMER: A polymer structure in which the atoms that are not part of the backbone chain are distributed in a symmetrical and recurring manner above and below the backbone chain when the latter is in a single plane. (Contrast with ATACTIC POLYMER, ISOTACTIC POLYMER, and TACTIC POLYMER.)

Syndiotactic Structure

SYNTHETIC FIBER: Another term for manufactured fiber.

SYSTÈME INTERNATIONALE D'UNITES: See SI METRIC SYSTEM.

T

TABLET TEST: See FLAMMABILITY TESTS, METHENAMINE PILL TEST.

TACKINESS: The property of being sticky or adhesive.

TACTIC POLYMER: A polymer whose molecular structure exhibits regularity or symmetry of non-backbone side groups rather than random ordering. (Contrast with ATACTIC POLYMER, ISOTACTIC POLYMER, and SYNDIOTACTIC POLYMER.)

TAFFETA: A plain-weave fabric with a fine, smooth, crisp hand and usually a lustrous appearance. Taffeta fabric usually has a fine cross rib made by using a heavier filling yarn than warp yarn. Taffetas are produced in solid colors, yarn-dyed plaids and stripes, and prints. Changeable and moiré effects are often employed. Although originally made of silk, manufactured fibers are now often used in the production of taffeta.

TAILING: A fabric defect that can occur in continuous dyeing. It consists of a gradual color change along the length of the cloth.

TAK® DYEING: See KÜSTERS DYEING RANGE.

TAKE-UP MOTION: A mechanism on a loom that controls the winding of the fabric produced during weaving.

TAKE-UP (TWIST): The change in length of a filament, yarn, or cord caused by twisting, expressed as a percentage of the original (untwisted) length.

TAKE-UP (YARN-IN-FABRIC): The difference in distance between two points in a yarn as it lies in a fabric and the same two points after the yarn has been removed from the fabric and straightened under specified tension, expressed as a percentage of the straightened length. In this sense, take-up is contrasted to the crimp of a yarn in a fabric, which is expressed as a percentage of the distance between the two points in the yarn as it lies in the fabric. Take-up is generally used in connection with greige fabric.

TANGENT MODULUS: The ratio of change in stress to change in strain derived from the tangent to any point on a stress-strain curve.

TANGLELACED FABRIC: See SPUNLACED FABRIC.

TAPE: 1. A narrow, woven fabric not over 8 inches in width. **2.** In slide fasteners, a strip of material, along one edge of which the bead and scoops are attached, the bead sometimes being integral with the strip. (Also see SLIT TAPE and NONELASTIC WOVEN TAPE.)

TAPESTRY: 1. A heavy woven fabric with decorative design, often scenes of important events, handwoven with colored filling yarns interlaced with the warp as required to create the design. **2.** A fabric based on the original handwoven tapestry that is produced on a jacquard loom, using colored yarns to form the design. It may have several sets of filling yarns.

TAPE YARN: See SLIT-FILM YARN.

TARE: The weight of all external and internal packing material (including bobbins, tubes, etc.) of a case, bale, or other type of container.

TARPAULIN: Water-resistant fabric used to protect loads or materials from the elements. May be a coated fabric, a fabric with water-proof finish, or a fabric that is tightly constructed to prevent water penetration.

TEAR STRENGTH: The force required to begin or to continue a tear in a fabric under specified conditions.

TEASEL BURR: See NAPPING.

TECHNICAL TEXTILES: Textile products that require special functionality such as those used in industrial, aerospace, military, marine, medical, construction, geotextile, transportation, and high-technology applications.

TEMPERATURE OF ZERO BIREFRINGENCE: The temperature at which the refractive indexes of a material are equal in two perpendicular directions (longitudinally and transversely for a fiber).

TENACITY: The tensile stress when expressed as force per unit linear density of the unstrained specimen (e.g., grams-force per denier or newtons per tex). (Also see BREAKING TENACITY.)

TENDER: A term used to describe a textile material that has been weakened.

TENSILE FACTOR: The empirical factor $T \times E^{1/2}$ that describes the tenacity-elongation exchange relationship for a large number of manufactured fiber systems.

TENSILE HYSTERESIS CURVE: A complex load-elongation, or stress-strain curve obtained: (1) when a specimen is successively subjected to the application of a load or stress less than that causing rupture and to the removal of the load or stress according to a predetermined procedure; or (2) when a specimen is stretched less than the breaking elongation and allowed to relax by removal of the strain according to a predetermined procedure.

TENSILE RECOVERY CURVE: See TENSILE HYSTERESIS CURVE.

TENSILE STRAIN: The relative length deformation exhibited by a specimen subjected to a tensile force. Strain may be expressed as a fraction of the nominal gauge length or as a percentage. (Also see ELONGATION.)

TENSILE STRENGTH: 1. In general, the strength shown by a specimen subjected to tension as distinct from torsion, compression, or shear. **2.** Specifically, the maximum tensile stress expressed in force per unit cross-sectional area of the unstrained specimen, e.g., kilograms per square millimeter, pounds per square inch. (For maximum stress per unit linear density, see BREAKING TENACITY or BREAKING LENGTH.)

TENSILE STRESS: The resistance to deformation developed within a specimen subjected to tension by external force. The tensile stress is commonly expressed in two ways: (1) as the tensile strength, i.e., the force per unit cross-sectional area of the unstrained specimen, or (2) as tenacity, i.e., the force per unit linear density of the unstrained specimen. The latter is more frequently used in textile testing.

TENSILE TEST: A method of measuring the resistance of a yarn or fabric to a force tending to stretch the specimen in one direction.

TENSION CONTROL: A device that reduces tension variability on a textile material during its passage through a machine.

TENTER FRAME: A machine that dries fabric to a specified width under tension. The machine consists essentially of a pair of endless chains on horizontal tracks. The fabric is held firmly at the edges by pins or clips on the two chains that diverge as they advance through the heated chamber, adjusting the fabric to the desired width.

TENTERING: See TENTER FRAME.

TENTER MARK: See CLIP MARK.

TEREPHTHALIC ACID: Para-phthalic acid [$C_6H_4(COOH)_2$]. Used to produce polyester resins, fibers, and films by combination with glycols.

TERPOLYMER: A product of the polymerization of three different monomers.

TERRY CLOTH: A cotton or cotton-blend fabric having uncut loops on one or both sides. Made on a dobby loom with a terry arrangement or on a jacquard loom. It is used for toweling, beach robes, etc.

TERTIARY COLORS: Shades that are obtained by mixing the three primary colors or by mixing one or more of the secondary colors with grey or black.

TETRACHLORIDE: A chloride, such as carbon tetrachloride, containing four atoms of chlorine.

TETRAFLUOROETHYLENE FIBER: See POLYTETRAFLUOROETHYLENE FIBER.

TEX: 1. A unit for expressing linear density, equal to the weight in grams of 1 kilometer of yarn, filament, fiber, or other textile strand. **2.** The system of yarn numbering based on the use of tex units. (Also see YARN NUMBER.)

TEXTILE: Originally, a woven fabric; now applied generally to any one of the following: **1.** Staple fibers and filaments suitable for conversion to or use as yarns, or for the preparation of woven, knit, or nonwoven fabrics. **2.** Yarns made from natural or manufactured fibers. **3.** Fabrics and other manufactured products made from fibers as defined above and from yarns. **4.** Garments and other articles fabricated from fibers, yarns, or fabrics when the products retain the characteristic flexibility and drape of the original fabrics.

TEXTILE COMPOSITE: See COMPOSITE.

TEXTILE FIBER: See FIBER.

TEXTILE FIBER PRODUCTS IDENTIFICATION ACT: U.S. legislation requiring that textile products be labeled with their fiber content and information about the manufacturer and country of origin. Similar information is required for advertisements for textiles. The Act also establishes generic names and definitions for manufactured fibers.

TEXTILE MATERIALS: A general term for fibers, yarn intermediates, yarn, fabrics, and products made from fabrics that retain more or less completely the strength, flexibility, and other typical properties of the original fiber or filaments.

TEXTILE PROCESSING: Any mechanical operation used to translate a textile fiber or yarn to a fabric or other textile material. This includes such operations as opening, carding, spinning, plying, twisting, texturing, coning, quilling, beaming, slashing, weaving, and knitting.

TEXTURE: A term describing the surface effect of a fabric, such as dull, lustrous, wooly, stiff, soft, fine, coarse, open, or closely woven; the structural quality of a fabric.

TEXTURED: An adjective used to describe continuous filament manufactured yarns (and woven and knit fabrics made from them) that have been crimped or have had random loops imparted, or that have been otherwise modified to create a different surface texture. (Also see TEXTURED YARNS and TEXTURING.)

TEXTURED YARNS: Yarns that develop stretch and/or bulk on subsequent processing. When woven or knitted into fabric, the cover, hand, and other aesthetics of the finished fabric better resemble the properties of a fabric constructed from spun yarn. (Also see TEXTURING.)

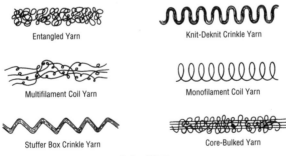

Entangled Yarn

Knit-Deknit Crinkle Yarn

Multifilament Coil Yarn

Monofilament Coil Yarn

Stuffer Box Crinkle Yarn

Core-Bulked Yarn

Textured Yarns

1. Bulked Yarn: Qualitative term to describe a textured yarn. A bulked yarn develops more bulk than stretch in the finished fabric.

2. Coil Yarn: A textured yarn that takes on a coil or spiral configuration when further processed. A coil yarn can be either a torque yarn or a nontorque yarn. A coil yarn can be formed by the false twist or edge crimping methods. Some side-by-side bicomponent fibers become coiled on further processing.

3. Core-Bulked Yarn: A bulky or textured yarn composed of two sets of filaments, one of which is straight to give dimensional stability and forms a core around and through which the other set is coiled or looped to give bulk.

4. Crinkle Yarn: A torque-free textured yarn that is characterized by periodic wave configurations. Crinkle yarns can be formed by the stuffer box, gear crimping, or knit-deknit methods.

5. Entangled Yarn: A textured yarn of one variant that develops bulk by the air jet texturing method.

6. Modified Stretch Yarn: A stretch yarn that develops more bulk than usual but less bulk than a bulked yarn in the finished fabric.

7. Nontorque Yarn: A yarn that does not rotate or kink when permitted to hang freely. A nontorque yarn may be the result of plying two equal but opposite torque yarns.

8. Set Yarn: A textured yarn that is heat relaxed to reduce torque. Set yarns are not stretch yarns.

9. Stretch Yarn: Qualitative term to describe a textured yarn. A stretch yarn develops more stretch than bulk in the finished fabric.

10. Torque Yarn: When a torque yarn is permitted to hang freely, it rotates or kinks to relieve the torque introduced into the yarn during texturing.

TEXTURING: The process of crimping, imparting random loops, or otherwise modifying continuous filament yarn to increase cover, resilience, abrasion resistance, warmth, insulation, and moisture absorption or to provide a different surface texture. Texturing methods can be placed roughly into six groups. (Also see TEXTURED YARNS.) (See diagram on the next page.)

1. Air Jet Method: In this method of texturing, yarn is led through the turbulent region of an air jet at a rate faster than it is drawn off on the far side of the jet. In the jet, the yarn structure is opened, loops are formed, and the structure is closed again. Some loops are locked inside and others are locked on the surface of the yarn. (Also see TEXTURED YARNS, 3. AND 6.)

2. Edge Crimping Method: In this method of texturing, thermoplastic yarns in a heated and stretched condition are drawn over a crimping edge and cooled. (Also see TEXTURED YARNS, 2.)

3. False-Twist Method: This continuous method for producing textured yarns utilizes simultaneous twisting, heat-setting, and untwisting. The yarn is taken from the supply package and fed at controlled tension through the heating unit, through a false-twist spindle or over a friction surface that is typically a stack of rotating discs called an aggregate, through a set of take-up rolls, and onto a take-up package. The twist is set into the yarn by the action of the heater tube and subsequently is removed above the spindle or aggregate resulting in a group of filaments with the potential to form helical springs. Much higher processing speeds can be achieved with friction false

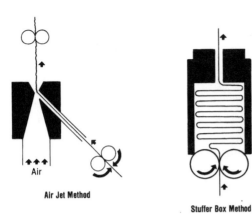

Air Jet Method

Air

Stuffer Box Method

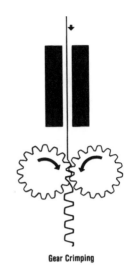

Gear Crimping

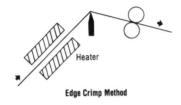

Heater

Edge Crimp Method

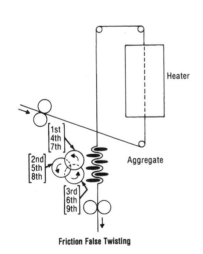

Heater

Aggregate

1st
4th
7th

2nd
5th
8th

3rd
6th
9th

Friction False Twisting

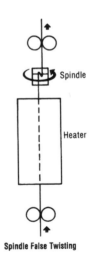

Spindle

Heater

Spindle False Twisting

twisting than with conventional spindle false twisting. Both stretch and bulked yarns can be produced by either process. (Also see TEXTURED YARNS, 2.)

4. Gear Crimping Method: In this texturing method, yarn is fed through the meshing teeth of two gears. The yarn takes on the shape of the gear teeth. (Also see TEXTURED YARNS, 4.)

5. Knit-deKnit Method: In this method of texturing, the yarn is knit into a 2-inch diameter hoseleg, heat-set in an autoclave, and then unraveled and wound onto a final package. This texturing method produces a crinkle yarn. (Also see TEXTURED YARNS, 4.)

6. Stuffer Box Method: The crimping unit consists of two feed rolls and a brass tube stuffer box. By compressing the yarn into the heated stuffer box, the individual filaments are caused to fold or bend at a sharp angle, while being simultaneously set by a heating device. (Also see TEXTURED YARNS, 4.)

TFPIA: Acronym for TEXTILE FIBER PRODUCTS IDENTIFICATION ACT.

THERMAL BONDING: See BONDING, 2. BONDING WITH BINDER FIBERS and BONDING, 2. POWDER BONDING.

THERMAL CHARACTER: A tactile property of a textile material. It is the difference felt in the temperature of the material and the skin of the person touching it.

THERMAL CONDUCTIVITY: A measure of heat flow through a material. It is the rate of heat transfer per unit area, across unit distance between two materials, per unit temperature difference. Low thermal conductivity indicates that a fabric has good insulating properties and therefore retains warmth.

THERMAL FINISHING: A general term for processes such as heat-setting, embossing, and calendering that employ heat to alter the final characteristics of a textile material.

THERMAL FIXATION: See DYEING.

THERMALLY STABILIZED: See HEAT STABILIZED.

THERMAL STABILITY: See HEAT RESISTANCE.

THERMOGRAVIMETRIC ANALYSIS: Analytical technique in which the rate of change in weight of a material undergoing continuous heating versus temperature is plotted. Used in analysis of polymers to provide information on such parameters as degree of crystallinity, glass transition temperature, thermal stability, etc.

THERMO-MAN: See FLAMMABILITY TESTS, THERMO-MAN.

THERMOPLASTIC: A term used to describe a plastic material that is permanently fusible. The term as applied to manufactured fibers describes their tendency to soften at higher temperatures.

THERMOSET: A term used to describe a plastic that, once formed, does not melt when heated.

THERMOSOL® PROCESS: Registered trademark of Du Pont for a thermal fixation dyeing process for textiles made of polyester or other thermoplastic fiber. (Also see DYEING, THERMAL FIXATION.)

THERMOTROPIC POLYMER: Polymer that exhibits liquid crystal formation in melt form. In thermotropic polymers there must be a balance between having the necessary degree of molecular perfection to preserve the liquid crystal formation and the amount of imperfection to permit melting at workable temperatures. These polymers give high-modulus, highly oriented extrusion products.

THICK-AND-THIN YARN: A novelty yarn of varying thicknesses.

THICKENER: A substance such as starch or gum that is added to print pastes to obtain the viscosity required to prevent the dyes from spreading outside the pattern area.

THICK FILLING: See COARSE THREAD.

THIN END: See FINE END, 1.

THREAD: 1. A slender, strong strand or cord, especially one designed for sewing or other needlework. Most threads are made by plying and twisting yarns. A wide variety of thread types are in use today, e.g., spun cotton and spun polyester, core-spun cotton with a polyester filament core, polyester or nylon filaments (often bonded), and monofilament threads. **2.** A general term for yarns used in weaving and knitting, as in "thread count" and "warp threads."

THREAD COUNT: 1. The number of ends and picks per inch in a woven cloth. **2.** The number of wales and courses per inch in a knit fabric.

THREADED-ROLL PROCESS: A high-speed method for converting crimped continuous filament tow into highly bulked, uniformly spread webs of up to 108-inch widths. The webs are useful in a variety of products, such as cigarette filters, sleeping pillows, and battings.

Threaded Roll Process

THREADLINES: The fiber lines of a manufactured fiber in extrusion or subsequent processes.

THREAD OUT: See END OUT.

THREADUP: The process of directing or threading fiber or fabric through all machine positions to start or restart a process, or the configuration which results.

THREE-BAR FABRIC: A tricot fabric made on a machine equipped with three guide bars.

THREE-DIMENSIONAL WEAVING: To produce three-dimensional textiles, yarns are simultaneously woven in three directions (length, width, and thickness) rather than in the conventional two. The types of structures that can be produced fall into four broad classes: (1) contoured fabrics, (2) expandable fabrics, (3) interwoven fabrics (also see DOUBLE WEAVE), and (4) contoured interwoven fabrics.

THREE-FOR-ONE TWISTER: A yarn twister that combines two-for-one twisting with uptwisting to insert three turns of twist for each revolution of the twisting elements.

THROUGHPUT: The amount of raw material processed in a specific time. This is the actual amount, not a percentage.

THROWING: The operation of doubling or twisting silk or manufactured filament yarns.

THROWSTER: A company that specializes in putting additional twist in yarn. More recently, the term also applies to a company that specializes in texturing yarns.

THRUM: The fringe of warp yarns that remains on the loom when the woven fabric has been cut free.

TICKING: A durable, closely woven fabric used for covering box springs, mattresses, and pillows. Ticking may be woven in a plain, satin, or twill weave, usually with strong warp yarns and soft filling yarns.

TIE-BACK: See STICKER, 1.

TIE DYEING: See DYEING.

TIGHT OR LOOSE END: A taut or slack warp end caused by too much or too little tension on an individual end while weaving, by ridgy section or warp beams, by incorrect tensions in beaming or sizing, or as a result of faulty fabric design.

TIGHT SPOT: See TWIT.

TIME-TO-BREAK: In tensile testing, the time interval during which a specimen is under prescribed conditions of tension and is absorbing the energy required to reach maximum load.

TINT: Coloration that produces a very pale shade. A tint usually represents the minimum amount of color that will give perceptible appearance of coloration. In yarn processing, fugitive tints are used for identification, then removed in wet processing.

TIP-SHEARED CARPET: A textured pile carpet similar to a random-sheared carpet, but with a less defined surface effect.

TIRE-BUILDER FABRIC: See TIRE FABRIC.

TIRE CONSTRUCTION: The geometry of the various layers of tire fabric in the final tire. Three constructions are commonly used:

Bias Tire   Bias/Belted Tire   Radial Tire

Tire Constructions

1. Bias Tire: In this construction, tire fabric is laid alternately at bias angles of 25°–40° to the tread direction. An even number of layers (or plies) is used.

2. Radial Tire: In a radial tire, tire fabric traverses the body of the tire at 90° to the tread direction. Atop the tire fabric are laid alternating narrow layers of fabric at low angles of 10°–30° to the tread direction; the belt that is formed around the tire body restricts the movement of the body.

3. Bias/Belted Tire: This tire construction combines features of the preceding two. The first layers of fabric are identical to the bias tire. The belt is added in alternating layers at 20° to the tread direction.

TIRE CORD: A textile material used to impart the flex resistance necessary for tire reinforcement. Tire yarns of polyester, rayon, nylon, aramid, glass, or steel are twisted to 5–12 turns per inch. Two or more of these twisted yarns are twisted together in the opposite direction to obtain a cabled tire cord. The twist level required depends on the material, the yarn linear density, and the particular application of the cord. Normally, tire cords are twisted to about the same degree in the S and Z directions, which means that the net effect is almost zero twist in the finished cord. (Also see TIRE FABRIC.)

TIRE FABRIC: A loose fabric woven to facilitate large-scale dipping, treating, and calendering of tire cords. Usually, 15–35 tire cords per inch of warp are woven into a tire fabric by 2–5 light filling yarns per inch. In these fabrics, the strength is in the warp and the filling only holds cords in position for processing. The filling yarns are normally broken during tire molding. The warp cords are polyester, rayon, nylon, aramid, glass, or steel and range in strength from 30 pounds to over 100 pounds per cord. A 60-inch fabric would normally have a warp strength of about 7,000 pounds. Such fabrics are used for tire carcasses and tire belts. More conventional square woven fabrics are used in certain parts of a tire such as the bead, chafer, and wrapping. (Also see TIRE CORD.)

TITANIUM DIOXIDE: A compound (TiO_2) that occurs naturally in three different forms (rutile, anatase, and brookite). It is used chiefly as a pigment or delusterant in paint or fiber.

TOBACCO CLOTH: A thin, lightweight, open cloth used to shade and protect tobacco plants.

TOE CLOSING: In knitting hosiery, this term refers to closing the toe opening. It may be knit closed, or in tube hosiery, sewn closed.

TOILE: 1. A broad term describing many simple plain- and twill-weave fabrics, especially those made from linen. **2.** Sheer cotton and linen fabrics.

TONE-ON-TONE: A term used to describe a pattern made with two different shades of the same color.

TONGUE TEAR STRENGTH: The average force required to tear a rectangular sample with a cut in the edge at the center of the shorter side. The two tongues are gripped in a tensile tester and the force required to continue the tear is measured.

TOP: 1. A wool sliver that has been combed to straighten the fibers and to remove short fiber; an intermediate stage in the production of worsted yarn. **2.** A similar untwisted strand of manufactured staple delivered by the comb or made directly from tow. **3.** A commercial weight measure, usually 5 to 15 pounds, for a ball of wool or manufactured fiber top.

TOP COLORS: Colors used on the ground color to form a design.

TOP DYEING: 1. The process of covering with an additional dye, not necessarily of the same color or class, to obtain the desired shade. **2.** Fiber in top form is placed in cans and dyed in a batch-dye vessel with reverse cycling capability. An expensive process that is used primarily for fancy yarns.

TORQUE: A force or a combination of forces that produces or tends to produce a twisting or rotating motion. In reference to yarn, torque refers to the yarn's tendency to turn on itself, or kink, as a result of twisting.

TORQUE YARN: See TEXTURED YARNS, 10.

TOTAL DENIER: See DENIER, TOTAL DENIER.

TOUGHNESS: 1. Ability of a material to endure large deformations without rupture. **2.** The actual work per unit mass required to rupture a fiber or a yarn.

TOW: A large strand of continuous manufactured fiber filaments without definite twist, collected in loose, rope-like form, usually held together by crimp. Tow is the form that most manufactured fiber reaches before being cut into staple. It is often processed on tow-conversion machinery into tops, sliver, or yarn, or on tow-opening equipment to make webs for various uses.

TOW CONVERSION: A spinning process for making spun yarns from tow. The filaments in the tow are broken or cut into lengths equivalent to staple lengths and are converted into top or sliver, which is fed to spinning equipment for yarn production. The process eliminates several operations required for spinning staple.

TOXIC SUBSTANCES CONTROL ACT: U.S. legislation empowering the Environmental Protection Agency to require the testing of chemical substances for health and environmental hazards.

TPCM: Acronym for turns per centimeter. See TWIST.

TPI: Acronym for turns per inch. See TWIST.

TPM: Acronym for turns per meter. See TWIST.

TQCA: Acronym for the Textile Quality Control Association.

TRANSESTERIFICATION: In the production of polyester from dimethyl terephthalate and ethylene glycol, the process of exchanging ethylene glycol for the methyl groups to obtain bis-β-hydroxyethyl terephthalate. The methanol generated in the reaction is removed as it is formed to drive the reaction to completion.

TRANSFER BAR: A bar containing metal points for holding knit loops so that pieced or ribbed borders can be transferred onto the needles of a straight-bar knitting machine.

TRANSFER PADDING: A process for applying finishes to fabric. The padding liquor is picked up by a continuous belt and transferred onto the dry fabric as it passes through the nip of the padder. The process gives a low wet pickup, which reduces drying time and thus energy costs.

TRANSFER TAIL: A long end of yarn wound at the base of a package that permits increased warping or transfer efficiency by providing an easily accessible connecting point for the succeeding package.

TRANSITION TEMPERATURE: A temperature at which some radical change, usually a phase change, in the appearance or structure of a substance occurs. Examples of transition temperatures are melting point, boiling point, and second-order transition temperature.

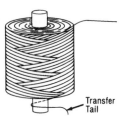

Transfer Tail

TRAPEZOID TEAR TESTER: See ELMENDORF TEAR TESTER.

TRAPPED END: An end that is unable to unwrap or unwind from the beam. Trapping of an end may be prolonged or intermittent depending upon the cause of trapping (e.g., rolled ends at the selvage, short ends, or mechanical difficulties).

TRAVELER: A C-shaped, metal clip that revolves around the ring on a ring spinning frame. It guides the yarn onto the bobbin as twist is inserted into the yarn.

TRAVERSE LENGTH: The lateral distance between the points of reversal of the wind on a yarn package.

TRAVERSE RATIO: See WIND RATIO.

TREE BARK: A term describing the rippled or wavy effect sometimes seen when a bonded fabric is stretched in the horizontal (widthwise) direction. This defect is caused by bias tensions present when two distorted or skewed fabrics are bonded.

TRI: Acronym for Textile Research Institute.

TRIACETATE FIBER: A manufactured fiber produced from cellulose triacetate in the forms of filament yarn, staple, and tow. Cellulose triacetate fiber differs from acetate fiber in that, during its manufacture, the cellulose is completely acetylated whereas acetate, which is diacetate, is only partially acetylated. The FTC notes that a fiber may be called triacetate when not less than 92% of the hydroxyl groups are acetylated. Fabrics of triacetate have higher heat resistance than acetate fabrics and can be safely ironed at higher temperatures. Triacetate fabrics that have been properly heat-set (usually after dyeing) have improved easy-care characteristics because of a change in the crystalline structure of the fiber. Triacetate fiber is not currently manufactured in the U.S. (Also see ACETATE FIBER.)

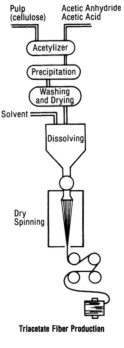

Triacetate Fiber Production

TRIACETIN: Glycerol triacetate. A type of plasticizer for acetate fibers. It is widely used to add firmness to cigarette filter rods.

TRIAXIAL FABRIC: Completely isotropic fabric made in a weaving process employing three yarns at 60° angles to one another. Triaxial fabric has no stretch or distortion in any direction. With equal sizes and number of yarns in all three directions, the fabric approaches equal strength and stiffness in all directions.

TRIAXIAL LOOM: A loom that weaves yarns in three directions. (Also see TRIAXIAL FABRIC.)

TRICK: A slot that holds the needles or other elements on a knitting machine.

TRICOMPONENT FIBER: A fiber spun from three different polymers. (Contrast with BICOMPONENT FIBER.)

Triaxial Weave

TRICOT: A generic term for the most common type of warp-knit fabric. It has fine wales on the face and coursewise ribs on the back. It can be made in a plain jersey construction or in meshes, stripes, and many other designs. Tricot is usually made of acetate, polyester, nylon, or rayon. (Also see JERSEY, 1. and KNITTING, 1.)

TRICOT BEAM: A metal flanged beam, commonly 42 inches in width, on which yarn is wound for use as a supply for the tricot machine.

TRICOT FABRIC YIELD: The number of square yards per pound of greige or finished tricot fabric.

TRICOT KNITTING: See KNITTING, 1.

TRICOT SECTION: See TRICOT BEAM.

TRILATERAL FIBER: A tricomponent fiber in which the polymer components are extruded in a side-by-side relationship.

TRILOBAL CROSS SECTION: Fiber cross-sectional shape having three lobes.

TRIMER: A polymer consisting of three monomer units. (Also see CYCLIC TRIMER.)

TRISKELION CROSS SECTION: A trilobal cross section in which the radiating arms are curved or bent. (Also see CROSS SECTION.)

TRISTIMULUS VALUES: In shade matching during dyeing, these values represent the amount of each of the three primary colors that, when mixed additively, will generate the desired shade.

TROPICAL WORSTED FABRIC: A lightweight worsted fabric in an open plain weave used in summer suitings.

TRUE: A term used to describe wool fibers with a uniform diameter.

TRUE TENSILE STRENGTH: The maximum tensile stress expressed in force per unit area of the specimen at the time of rupture. (Also see TENSILE STRENGTH.)

TTY: Acronym for throwster-textured yarn.

TUB: See BECK.

TUBE: 1. A cylindrical holder or bobbin used as a core for a cylindrical yarn package. **2.** A cylindrical yarn package.

TUBING: A woven, knit, or braided fabric of cylindrical form, having a width of over 4 inches.

TUBULAR FABRIC: A fabric woven or knit in a tube form with no seams, such as seamless pillowcases, some knit underwear fabrics, and seamless hosiery. (Also see CIRCULAR-KNIT FABRIC.)

TUCK STITCH: A knitting stitch made when a needle receives a new yarn without losing its old loop.

TUFT: 1. A cluster of soft yarns drawn through a fabric and projecting from the surface in the form of cut yarns or loops. **2.** The cut or uncut loops forming the face of a tufted or woven carpet. (Also see TUFTED FABRIC and TUFTED CARPET.)

TUFT BIND: The force required to pull a tuft or one side of a loop from a tufted carpet.

TUFTED CARPET: Carpet produced by a tufting machine instead of a loom. It is an outgrowth of hand-tufted bedspreads. Today, broadloom tufting machines produce over 70% of all domestic carpeting. Tufting machines are essentially multineedle sewing machines that push the pile yarns through a primary backing fabric and hold them in place to form loops as the needles are withdrawn. The loops are then either released for loop-pile carpets or cut for cut-pile carpets. The pile yarns may be either predyed or uncolored, in which case, the greige carpet is then piece-dyed or printed. In either case, a latex or other binding agent is applied to the back-stitch to lock the tufts in place and to secure the secondary backing fabric. Formerly, all carpets were woven, either by hand or machine. The significantly greater productivity of tufting has revolutionized the carpet industry and made soft floor coverings available to the mass market.

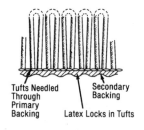

Tufted Carpet Construction

TUFTED FABRIC: Cotton sheeting, lightweight duck, or other fabric decorated with fluffy tufts of multiple-ply, soft-twist cotton yarns or manufactured fiber yarns closely arranged in continuous lines or spaced at intervals to produce the type of fabric called candlewick. The tufts are inserted and cut by machine in previously woven fabric or are woven in by the loom and afterwards cut to form the tufts. They have a chenille-like softness and bulk and are erroneously called chenille. Patterns vary from simple straight lines and elaborate designs to completely covered materials resembling long pile fabrics. They may be white, solid colored, or multicolored. Tufted fabrics are used for bedspreads, bath mats, and robes, etc.

TULLE: A fine, very lightweight, machine-made net usually having a hexagonal mesh effect. Tulle is used in ballet costumes and veils.

TUNNEL TEST: See FLAMMABILITY TESTS.

TURBIDITY: The decrease in optical transparency of a solution because of the presence of particulate matter.

TURBO PROCESS: A method of producing high-bulk spun yarn by stretch-breaking tow. (Also see TOW CONVERSION.)

TURN: The distance parallel to the axis of a yarn or rope in which a strand makes one complete spiral. (Also see TWIST.)

TURNED-OVER EDGE: A curled selvage.

TWEED: An irregular, soft, flexible, unfinished, shaggy wool or wool-blend fabric made with a 2 x 2 twill weave. Tweeds are used in all types of coat fabrics and suitings.

TWILL DIRECTION: See LEFT-HAND TWILL and RIGHT-HAND TWILL.

TWILL WEAVE: A fundamental weave characterized by diagonal lines produced by a series of floats staggered in the warp direction. The floats are normally formed by filling (filling-faced twill). A warp-face twill is a weave in which the warp yarns produce the diagonal effect. (See diagram on the next page.)

TWILO PROCESS: A spinning process in which yarn is made by binding fibers with an adhesive, then removing the adhesive after the yarn is made into fabric.

2 x 2 Twill Weave

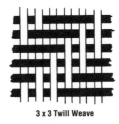

3 x 3 Twill Weave

TWINE: 1. A plied yarn made from medium-twist singles yarns with ply twist in the opposite direction. **2.** A single-strand yarn, usually 3 or 4 millimeters in diameter, made of hard fibers, such as henequen, sisal, or abaca, and sufficiently stiff to perform satisfactorily on a mechanical grain binder.

TWIST: The number of turns about its axis per unit of length of a yarn or other textile strand. Twist is expressed as turns per inch (tpi), turns per meter (tpm), or turns per centimeter (tpcm).

TWIST BLEED: See TWIT.

TWIST COUNTER: A device used to measure the number of twists per unit length in a yarn.

TWIST, DIRECTION OF: The direction of twist in yarns and other textile strands is indicated by the capital letters S and Z. Yarn has S twist if when it is held vertically, the spirals around its central axis slope in the same direction as the middle portion of the letter S, and Z twist if they slope in the same direction as the middle portion of the letter Z. When two or more yarns, either single or plied, are twisted together, the letters S and Z are used in a similar manner to indicate the direction of the last twist inserted.

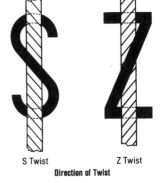

S Twist   Z Twist
Direction of Twist

TWISTING: 1. The process of combining filaments into yarn by twisting them together or combining two or more parallel singles yarns (spun or filament) into plied yarns or cords. Cables are made by twisting plied yarns or cords. Twisting is also employed to increase strength, smoothness, and uniformity, or to obtain novelty effects in yarn. **2.** A very high level of twist is added to singles or plied yarns to make crepe yarns. This operation generally is called creping or throwing. **3.** The process of adding twist to a filament yarn to hold the filaments together for ease in subsequent textile processing, etc.

TWIST MULTIPLIER: The ratio of turns per inch to the square root of the yarn count.

TWIST SETTING: A process for fixing twist in yarns to deaden torque and eliminate kinking during further processing. There are several methods that use steam to condition the packages of yarns.

TWIST TAKEUP: The difference in the length of a yarn before and after twisting, expressed as a percentage of the yarn before twisting.

TWIT: A short section of real twist in false-twist yarn that prevents crimp development and hence causes a pinhole effect in fabric. Also called twist bleed or tight spot.

TWO-FOR-ONE TWISTER: A twister that inserts twist at a rate of twice the spindle speed. For example, at a spindle speed of 2,000 rpm, 4,000 turns per minute are inserted in the yarn.

TWO-STAGE TWISTING: A method of producing plied yarns with a high level of twist by first inserting twist by ring twisting, followed by uptwisting.

TWO-TONE: A term used to describe a pattern made with two different colors. (Also see TONE-ON-TONE.)

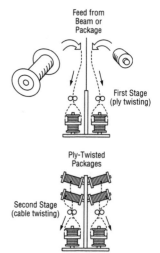

Two-Stage Twisting

TWO-WAY STRETCH: Woven fabric produced from textured stretch yarns in both warp and filling.

TYAA: Acronym for Textured Yarn Association of America.

TYING-IN: The process of joining the yarns of a new warp to each corresponding yarn of the current warp in a loom to eliminate the time-consuming process of threading the new warp through the eyes of the heddles and the dents of the reed.

U

U-BOX: A U-shaped holding device used in continuous wet processing of fabrics. It is similar to the J-BOX.

UCL: Acronym for upper control limit.

ULTIMATE TENSILE STRENGTH: See TENSILE STRENGTH, 2.

ULTRASONIC QUILTING: See PINSONIC® THERMAL JOINING MACHINE.

ULTRAVIOLET DEGRADATION: Weakening or deterioration caused by exposure to ultraviolet rays of sunlight or artificial light.

ULTRAVIOLET RESISTANCE: Ability to retain strength and resist deterioration on exposure to sunlight.

UNBALANCED PLAIN WEAVE: A weave with more or heavier yarns in one direction than the other direction. (Contrast with BALANCED WEAVE.)

UNCRIMPING ENERGY: See CRIMP ENERGY.

UNDRAWN TOW: See DRAWN TOW.

UNDRAWN YARN: Extruded yarn (filaments), the component molecules of which are substantially unoriented. Undrawn yarn exhibits predominantly plastic flow in the initial stages of stretching and represents an intermediate stage in the production of a manufactured yarn.

UNEVEN DYEING: A fabric dyeing that shows variations in shade resulting from incorrect processing or dyeing methods or from use of faulty materials.

UNEVEN SHRINKAGE: A wavy, warpwise condition in the fabric that prevents it from lying flat on a horizontal surface.

UNEVEN SURFACE: An irregular surface characterized by nonuniformity in the physical configuration of the yarns or fibers making up the surface of the fabric.

UNEVEN YARN: A yarn that varies in diameter to an abnormal degree.

UNFINISHED WORSTED: A worsted fabric with a relatively soft hand and a light nap.

UNIDIRECTIONAL FABRIC: A fabric having reinforcing fibers in only one direction.

UNIFIL WINDER: A device for automatic winding of yarn onto quills used for the filling yarn in shuttle looms. It allows the loom to run continuously.

UNIFORM ABRASION TESTING MACHINE: An abrasion tester for textile materials that applies abrasion action evenly in all directions over the surface of the specimen.

UNION CLOTH: A term describing a fabric woven from two or more types of yarn. For example, a union cloth may have a cotton warp and a wool filling. (Also see COMBINATION FABRIC.)

UNION DYEING: See DYEING.

UNITARY BACKED: A term used to describe a tufted carpet with a coating of high-rubber-content latex or a resin melt applied to the primary backing to increase tuft bind.

UNITENS®: See ON-LINE TESTING.

UNLEVELNESS: In textiles, uneven distribution of dyes or chemicals on a substrate.

UNOPENED STAPLE: Staple fiber in bunches or clusters in the bale in such a condition that it will not process smoothly through carding and subsequent operations in the spun-yarn plant.

UNRELAXED YARN: See RELAXED YARN.

UPDRAFT METIER: A dry spinning machine in which the air flow within the drying cabinet is countercurrent to the yarn path (upward).

UPPER CONTROL LIMIT: In statistical quality control, the highest value of a specific parameter that is acceptable for a process. On a control chart, it is represented by a straight line drawn parallel to the time axis 3 standard deviations above the expected mean value. (Also see STATISTICAL PROCESS CONTROL.)

UPTWISTER: A machine used for twisting yarns in an upward path from a rotating vertical supply package to a horizontal take-up package. Used for spun yarns and to a small extent for adding twist to some filament yarns.

UPTWISTING: The process of twisting yarn on the uptwister. The yarn to be twisted, which has been wound on a balanced support package, is placed on a revolving spindle. The yarn from the revolving supply package is fed upward through a gathering eye or guide, over a stop motion and a tension bar or bars, through a traversing guide, and onto the revolving collecting package.

Uptwister

URETHANE: The name of a group of organic chemical compounds or resins built from isocyanate, a very reactive material that liberates gas during reaction to produce foams of various types. Two types of compounds that react with isocyanate to form foam are polyesters and polyethers. Polyurethanes are used for foams and in other compounds in fiber form. The polyester variety should not be confused with polyester fibers. (Also see SPANDEX FIBER.)

USTER TESTER: An instrument that provides a continuous measurement of the variation in weight per unit length of sliver, roving, and yarn.

UV ABSORBER: Polymer additive that absorbs light in the UV region or that traps radicals produced in fiber during photooxidation. A UV absorber provides stabilization against actinic degradation. Some critical applications include geotextiles, recreational surface polymers and fabrics, tenting, tarpaulins, and other textiles that are exposed to sunlight.

V

VACUUM EXTRACTION: In wet processing of fabrics, use of a vacuum device to remove excess liquid before drying.

VACUUM IMPREGNATION: 1. A method of improving penetration of the dye liquor when dyeing heavy fabric. The fabric is wound on a heavy perforated cylinder, and the dye liquor is applied and drawn through the cloth by means of a vacuum. **2.** Application of dyes or chemicals to fabric followed by extraction of excess liquid as the fabric passes over a vacuum slot.

VAPOR-PHASE DYEING: See DYEING.

VARIANT: A manufactured fiber modified in polymer configuration or by additive during manufacture, resulting in a change in the properties of the fiber. Examples are flame-retardant variants, deep-dyeing variants, high-tenacity variants, low-pilling variants, and cotton- or wool-blending variants.

VAT DYES: See DYES.

V-BED FLAT-KNITTING MACHINE: A latch-needle weft-knitting machine with two needlebeds at a 90° angle to each other in the form of an inverted V. Each needlebed is at a 45° angle to the horizontal. These machines are used primarily to produce collars, sleeves, sweater strips, and rib trims.

V-BELT CORD: A cord made of tightly twisted, high-strength, low-elongation yarn used to reinforce belts for pulleys on power equipment.

VECTRAN® FIBER: Manufactured fiber spun from Ticona Vectra® liquid crystal polymer. These fibers have high-temperature resistance, high strength and modulus, and high resistance to moisture and chemicals, with good property retention in hostile environments. They are used as matrix fibers for advanced composites and as reinforcing fibers in advanced composites, ropes and cables, and in electronics applications.

VEGETABLE FIBER: A textile fiber of vegetable origin, such as cotton, kapok, jute, ramie, and flax.

VELOUR: 1. Generally, a soft, closely woven fabric with a short, thick pile, weighing about 10–20 ounces per yard and made in a plain or satin weave. Velour is usually made of cotton or wool, or with a cotton warp in wool, silk, or mohair velour. It is also made in blends of spun manufactured fiber and wool. Velours are used for coats, draperies, upholstery, powder puffs, and other pile items. **2.** A felt with velvet-like texture used for men's and women's hats.

VELVET CARPET: A woven carpet in which the pile ends are lifted over wires that are inserted in the same manner as the filling and that cut the pile as they are withdrawn. Velvet carpets are generally level loop, level cut loop, or plush.

VELVETEEN: A fabric with a low filling pile made by cutting an extra set of filling yarns woven in a float formation and bound to the back of the material at intervals by weaving over and under one or more warp ends.

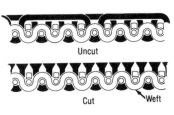

Velveteen: Section Through Warp

VELVET FABRIC: A warp-pile woven fabric with short, dense cut pile that produces a rich fabric appearance and soft texture. Two methods are used for weaving velvets. In the double-cloth method, two fabrics are woven face to face with the pile ends interlocking. A reciprocating knife cuts through these pile ends to produce two separate pieces of velvet. In the second method, pile ends are lifted over cutting wires that are inserted with the filling and that are withdrawn to cut the pile. Velvet is produced in a wide range of constructions and types. Originally made of silk, but now also of cotton or manufactured fibers giving fabrics that are sometimes washable. The fabric can be specially finished to make it crush-resistant and water-repellent or it may be embossed or patterned by burn-out printing.

VENTURI: A short tube with a constricted passage that increases the velocity and lowers the pressure of a fluid conveyed through it.

VERTICAL FLAME TEST: See FLAMMABILITY TESTS.

VIBROSCOPE: An instrument for determining the mass per unit length of a fiber.

VIGOREAUX PRINTING: See PRINTING, 1. WARP PRINTING.

VINAL FIBER: A manufactured fiber in which the fiber-forming substance is any long chain synthetic polymer composed of at least 50% by weight of vinyl alcohol units and in which the total of the vinyl alcohol units and any one or more of the various acetal units is at least 85% by weight of the fiber (FTC definition). It is made by dissolving polyvinyl alcohol in hot water and extruding this solution through a spinneret into a sodium sulfate coagulating bath. Vinal fibers show good chemical resistance but soften at comparatively low temperatures. Vinal fibers are used for apparel, industrial goods, and fishnets.

VINYL: A univalent radical (CH_2=CH–) derived from ethylene.

VINYLIDENE CHLORIDE: A chemical material obtained from ethylene, a petroleum product, and from chlorine. It is used for the manufacture of textile monofilaments and film. It is more commonly identified in the U.S. as saran. (Also see SARAN FIBER.)

VINYON FIBER: A manufactured fiber in which the fiber-forming substance is any long chain synthetic polymer composed of at least 85% by weight of vinyl chloride units (FTC definition). Although it has good flame resistance, the fiber has a high shrinkage capacity and is difficult to dye. It has found use in home furnishings fabrics, nonwovens, teabags, wigs, and bristles (monofilament) but is in very limited production today.

VIRGIN WOOL: The Wool Products Labeling Act of 1939 defines virgin wool as "wool that has never been used or reclaimed from any spun, woven, knitted, felted, manufactured or used product."

VISCOMETER: A device designed to measure the viscosity (resistance to flow) of a fluid. Many types exist from simple calibrated glass tubes to extensively instrumented, on-line shear viscometers.

VISCOSE PROCESS: 1. One of the methods of producing rayon. (Also see RAYON FIBER.) **2.** The chemical process used in the manufacture of cellophane. (Also see VISCOSE SOLUTION.)

VISCOSE RAYON: One type of rayon. It is produced in far greater quantity than cuprammonium rayon, the other commercial type. (Also see RAYON FIBER.)

VISCOSE SOLUTION: The solution obtained by dissolving cellulose xanthate in caustic soda, from which viscose filaments and cellophane are produced.

VISCOSITY: The internal flow resistance of a fluid. (Also see INTRINSIC VISCOSITY and RELATIVE VISCOSITY.)

VOILE FABRIC: A sheer spun cloth that is lightweight and soft. It is usually made with cylindrical, combed yarn. Voile is used for blouses, children's wear, draperies, and bedspreads, etc.

VOLATILE: Readily vaporized at a relatively low temperature.

VOLATILITY: Property of having a low boiling point or temperature of sublimation at normal pressure. Likewise, having a high vapor pressure at ambient conditions.

VOLUME RESISTIVITY: The ratio of the potential gradient parallel to the direction of current flow in a compound to the current density after a specified time of voltage application.

VULCANIZATION: See CURING, 2.

W

WALE: 1. In knit fabrics, a column of loops lying lengthwise in the fabric. The number of wales per inch is a measure of the fineness of the fabric. **2.** In woven fabrics, one of a series of ribs, cords, etc., running either warpwise or fillingwise.

WARP: 1. The set of yarn in all woven fabrics, that runs lengthwise and parallel to the selvage and is interwoven with the filling. **2.** The sheet comprising up to several thousand yarns wound together on a beam for the purpose of weaving or warp knitting.

WARP BAND: See SECTION MARK.

WARP BEAM: A large spool or flanged cylinder around which the warp threads, or ends, are wound in a uniform and parallel arrangement. (Also see BEAM.)

WARP-DRAWING: See DRAW-WARPING. Warp-drawn fibers may be taken up on packages other than beams.

WARP DYEING: See DYEING.

WARP HOLDING PLACE: See STICKER, 1.

WARPING: See BEAMING.

WARP-KNIT FABRIC: A fabric that is knit with the yarns running lengthwise, e.g., tricot, milanese, and raschel.

WARP KNITTING: See KNITTING, 1.

WARP PILE: The extra set of warp yarns that forms the surface in a double-woven pile fabric, including types such as velvet and velour. Upholstery fabrics such as mohair, plush, and frieze are produced by this method. (Also see PILE and VELVET FABRIC.)

WARP PREPARATION: A term that includes all the of operations that make the sheet of warp yarns ready for weaving.

WARP PRINTING: See PRINTING, 1.

WARP SHEET: See WARP, 2.

WARP SIZING: See SLASHING.

WARP STREAKS: A fabric fault that shows as bands or streaks running warpwise. Warp streaks should not be confused with reed marks.

WASH-AND-WEAR: A term applied earlier to garments made from fabrics treated to retain a neat appearance through laundering, with little or no pressing or ironing required. It has been largely replaced by other terminology. (Also see DURABLE PRESS and EASY-CARE.)

WASHFASTNESS: The resistance of a dyed fabric to loss of color or change in properties during home or commercial laundering.

WASTE: By-products created in the manufacture of fibers, yarns, and fabrics.

WATER IMBIBITION: See IMBIBITION.

WATER-JET LOOM: See JET LOOM.

WATERLESS DYEING: See DYEING, SOLVENT DYEING.

WATERPROOF: A term applied to materials that are impermeable to water; waterproof fabrics have had all their pores closed and are also impermeable to air and very uncomfortable.

WATER-REPELLENT: A term applied to fabrics that can shed water but are permeable to air and comfortable to wear. These fabrics are produced by treating the material with a resin, wax, or plastic finish that is not completely permanent.

WAVY CLOTH: See BAGGY CLOTH.

WAVY SELVAGE: See SLACK SELVAGE.

WEAK WEB: A web of fiber that, when being transferred from the card doffer to the calender rolls to form sliver, does not have sufficient strength from fiber cohesion or clinging entanglement to hold itself together while forming a continuous bridge in processing.

WEAK YARN: A yarn that is found to be either below standard breaking specifications or to be weak enough to cause an abnormally high degree of stops in textile processing.

WEAR TEST: A test for fabric wear, abrasion, flexibility, washing, crushing, creasing, etc., in which the fabric is made into a garment, worn for a specific time, then assessed for performance.

WEATHER-OMETER: An instrument used in measuring the weather resistance of textiles. It can simulate various weather conditions such as sunlight, rain, dew, and thermal shock. Weathering is accelerated to the degree that the effects of years of normal use are attained in only a few days.

WEATHER RESISTANCE: The ability of a textile material to resist the effects of climactic conditions. To assess weather resistance, materials are exposed to actual outdoor conditions for extended periods in specified locales, and detailed records are kept on sunlight hours, temperatures, humidity, and rainfall.

WEAVE: A system or pattern of intersecting warp and filling yarns. There are three basic two dimensional weaves: plain, twill, and satin. All other weaves are derived from one or more of these types. (Also see PLAIN WEAVE, TWILL WEAVE, and SATIN WEAVE.)

WEAVING: The method or process of interlacing two yarns of similar materials so that they cross each other at right angles to produce woven fabric. The warp yarns, or ends, run lengthwise in the fabric, and the filling threads (weft), or picks, run from side to side. Weaving can be done on a power or hand loom or by several hand methods. (Also see LOOM and WOVEN FABRIC.)

WEAVING EFFICIENCY: The ratio, expressed as a percentage, of the actual number of picks inserted per unit of time to the number that would have been inserted if the loom had operated for the same amount of time without stoppage for adjustments.

WEB: 1. The wide film of fibers that is delivered from the card. **2.** A similar product of other web-forming equipment, such as that formed by air deposition and used to make nonwoven fabrics. **3.** A term loosely used for lightweight nonwoven fabrics. **4.** See WEBBING.

WEBBING: Strong, narrow fabric, closely woven in a variety of weaves and principally used for belts and straps that have to withstand strain, e.g., automobile seat belts, cargo slings and tiedowns, and reinforcement of upholstery. Elastic webbing such as that used for suspenders is made with spandex or rubber yarns in part of the warp or filling, or both. (Also see WEB, 2.)

WEB CONSOLIDATION: A fiber interlocking process to provide integrity or strength to the web.

WEB FORMATION: Various processes by which fibers or filaments are arranged into a web structure to achieve specific physical properties, e.g., AIR LAYING, DRY LAYING, and WET LAYING.

WEFT: See FILLING.

WEFT INSERTION: 1. Any one of the various methods, shuttle, rapier, water jet, etc., for making a pick during weaving. **2.** A marriage of warp knitting and weaving brought about by inserting a length of yarn across the width of the knitting elements and fastening the weft yarn between the needle loop and the underlap. (See diagram on the next page.) (Also see METAP WEAVE-KNIT PROCESS.)

WEFT-KNIT FABRIC: A fabric that is knit with one continuous yarn forming the loops widthwise to form courses. It is one of the major types of knit fabrics and includes both FLAT-KNIT FABRICS and CIRCULAR-KNIT FABRICS. (See diagram on the next page.)

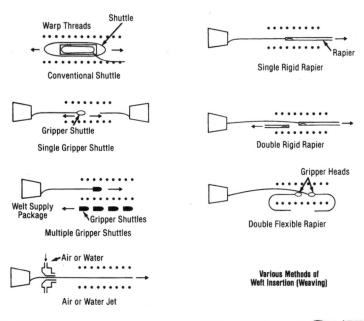

Conventional Shuttle

Single Gripper Shuttle

Multiple Gripper Shuttles

Air or Water Jet

Single Rigid Rapier

Double Rigid Rapier

Double Flexible Rapier

Various Methods of Weft Insertion (Weaving)

WEFT KNITTING: See KNITTING, 2.

WEIGHTED SILK: Silk that has been treated with metallic salts during dyeing and finishing to increase the fabric's weight and improve its drape. Overweighting can cause deterioration of the fabric.

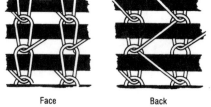

Face   Back

Fabrics Produced by Weft Insertion during Warp Knitting

WEIGHTING: 1. See LOADING. **2.** The application of metallic salts to silk to add weight and body.

WELT: 1. A finished edge on knit goods, especially hosiery. In women's stockings, it is a wide band knitted from heavier yarn than the leg and folded on itself. **2.** A small cord covered with fabric and sewn along a seam or border to add strength. **3.** A seam made by folding the fabric double, generally over a cord, and sewing it. **4.** A term sometimes used for piqué.

Weft-Knit Fabric

WET-LAID NONWOVEN: Fabric made by the wet-laying process. The short fibers typically have more random orientation in the web and the web has more isotropic properties than carded webs. (See diagram on the next page.)

WET LAYING: The production of a nonwoven fabric web from an aqueous suspension of fibers by filtering the short fibers onto a screen belt or perforated drum in a process similar to papermaking.

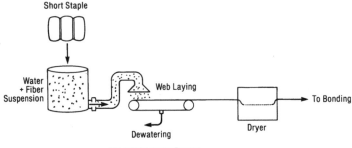

Wet-Laid Nonwoven Process

WET-ON-DRY: A term used to describe a wet processing sequence in which a textile material is dried between wet treatments.

WET-ON-WET: A term used to describe a wet processing sequence in which a wet textile material is not dried between wet treatments.

WET PICKUP: In wet processing, the total weight of treatment bath liquor, including additives, that is applied to a textile material, expressed as a percentage of the weight of the dry material.

WET PROCESSING: A general term for processes in which textile materials are treated with liquids or liquid-containing substances in a solution or dispersion, usually in water. Included are preparation, dyeing, printing, and finishing operations.

WET SPINNING: See SPINNING, 2.

WET STRENGTH: The measurement of the strength of a material when it is saturated with water, normally relative to the dry strength.

WETTING AGENT: A surfactant used to promote wetting of a textile material.

WHIPCORD: A compact woven fabric having a very steep twill on the face of the goods. Whipcord is used in dress woolens, worsteds, or wool blends and in many types of uniforms.

Whipcord

WHIPPED CREAM: A type of crepe fabric produced from false-twist-textured polyester yarn.

WHIPPED-IN FILLING: See PULLED-IN FILLING.

WHISKERS: Very fine fibrils or monocrystalline fibers. Whiskers of graphite, silicon carbide, silicon nitride, and aluminum oxide have been used for reinforcement of advanced composites.

WHITE GOODS: A broad term describing any goods that have been finished in the white condition.

WHITENING AGENT: See OPTICAL BRIGHTENER.

WICKING: 1. Cord, loosely woven or braided tape, or tubing to be cut into wicks. **2.** Dispersing or spreading of moisture or liquid through a given area, vertically or horizontally; capillary action in material.

WIDENING: In full-fashioned and V-bed flat knitting, shaping the fabric by increasing the number of wales.

WIDTH: A horizontal measurement of a material. In woven fabric, it is the distance from selvage to selvage, and in flat-knit fabric, the distance from edge to edge.

WILLIAMS UNIT: A wet-processing unit for open-width processing of fabric. The fabric passes up and down over rollers in the liquor. The unit is widely used for dyeing, washing, pretreating, and aftertreating.

WILTON CARPET: Woven carpet in which the pile yarns are woven in as an integral part of the carpet, being held in place by the filling, usually made on a loom with a jacquard head. The pile may be formed by wires and hooks or by weaving between two backings, in which case, the pile ends are cut to form two separate carpets. Wilton carpets are made in two types: (1) cut pile, e.g., tournia, Wilton moquette, plush, and velvet, and (2) loop pile, e.g., Brussels.

Wilton Loop Pile   Wilton Cut Pile

Wilton Carpets

WINCH: See BECK.

WINDING: Winding is the process of transferring yarn or thread from one type of package to another to facilitate subsequent processing. The rehandling of yarn is an integral part of the fiber and textile industries. Not only must the package and the yarn itself be suitable for processing on the next machine in the production process, but also other factors such as packing cases, pressure due to winding tension, etc., must be considered. Basically, there are two types of winding machines: precision winders and drum winders. Precision winders, used primarily for filament yarn, have a traverse driven by a cam that is synchronized with the spindle and produce packages with a diamond-patterned wind. Drum winders are used principally for spun yarns; the package is driven by frictional contact between the surface of the package and the drum.

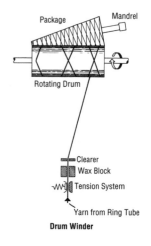

Drum Winder

WINDOW PANING: A fabric defect caused by nonuniform yarn. When thin sections of yarn become grouped together, the resultant increase in the transparency of the fabric is called window paning.

WIND RATIO: The number of wraps that an end or ends make in traversing from one side of a wound package to the other side and back to the first side.

WIRES: In woven carpet manufacturing, metal strips inserted in the weaving shed in Wilton and velvet constructions so that the surface yarns cross over them, forming loops of a specified height. In round-wire constructions, the loops are left uncut; in cut pile, flat wires with knife edges are used, cutting the loops as the wire is withdrawn.

WOOD GRAIN: A fabric defect that consists of fillingwise streaks resembling the irregular appearance of wood grain in lumber. Wood grain is usually caused by strained filling in quilling, the tension being more pronounced near the butt of the quill.

WOOD PULP: The cellulosic raw material for viscose rayon and for acetate.

WOOF: See FILLING.

WOOL: The term is usually used for the fleece of sheep, but according to the Textile Fiber Products Identification Act, wool is defined for purposes of labeling as: "The fiber from the fleece of the sheep or lamb or hair of the Angora or Cashmere goat (and may include the so-called specialty fibers from the hair of the camel, alpaca, llama, and vicuna) which has never been reclaimed from any woven or felted wool product."

Wool is one of the oldest fibers used by mankind. The fiber has been greatly improved over the centuries through crossbreeding of flocks. Today, wool is widely produced in many countries around the world. The major growers are Australia and New Zealand, South Africa, Argentina, and Russia.

CHARACTERISTICS: Wool fiber varies in diameter, color, and properties on different parts of the sheep's body and depending on other factors such as the breed of sheep, and where the sheep were raised. The fibers have overlapping scales on the surface that cause them to interlock binding the fibers together in a process called FELTING. This characteristic makes wool an excellent insulator because air is trapped between the fibers.

Shorter wool fibers with natural crimp are spun into yarns on the WOOLEN SPINNING SYSTEM, which produces a soft, hairy yarn. Longer, straighter fiber are spun on the WORSTED SPINNING SYSTEM, which produces smoother, denser yarns. In blends, particularly those with manufactured fibers, wool is used to improve the feel or appearance of finished products. Manufactured fibers are sometimes blended with wool to enable the spinning of very fine or loosely twisted yarns with increased tensile strength or to produce easy-care properties. A wide range of fabric types are produced by weaving, knitting, or felting. Woolen textiles are easily dyed with several classes of dyes and can be finished by various methods to alter the surface. The fiber is highly absorbent and swells when it absorbs moisture. Wool textiles can be treated to control shrinkage, to provide resistance to damage by moths, to impart stain resistance, and to set permanent creases in fabrics.

END USES: Wool is widely used in apparel such as coats, sweaters, suitings, and dresses, and to a lesser extent, in carpets and home furnishings, and in industrial uses such as felts. The fiber is used alone and in a variety of blends in which it is combined with nearly all natural or manufactured fibers.

WOOLEN CARD: A type of roller card used in the woolen spinning system, usually consisting of three cards in tandem: the breaker, intermediate, and finisher sections.

WOOLEN COUNT: The two systems used to determine woolen yarn counts in the U.S. are the run system and the cut system. The run system has a standard of 1600 yards per hank, while the cut system is based on 300 yards per hank.

WOOLEN CUT: A woolen yarn measure. A 1-cut woolen yarn has 300 yards in one pound of yarn.

WOOLEN RUN: A woolen yarn measure. A 1-run woolen yarn has 1,600 yards in one pound of yarn, a 2-run yarn has 3,200 yards, and so on.

WOOLEN SPINNING SYSTEM: The fundamental system of making yarns for woolen fabrics. In yarns spun on the woolen system, the fibers are not parallel but are crossed in what appears to be a haphazard arrangement. After blending, fibers produced on the woolen system are evenly distributed in carding on two, three, or even four cards. From here, the split web, called roving, goes to the spinning frame. In addition to wool, manufactured fibers, cotton, wastes, and noils can be processed on the woolen system. In general, the fibers used are shorter and more highly crimped than those used on the worsted system and are of the type that can be fulled.

WORKING LOSS: The irrecoverable loss of weight or yardage of a textile material that occurs during a textile process.

WORK RECOVERY: The ratio of recoverable work to the total work required to strain a fiber a specified amount under a given program of strain rate.

WORK-TO-BREAK: See ENERGY-TO-BREAK.

WORSTED: A general term applied to fabrics and yarns from combed wool and wool blends. Worsted yarn is smooth-surfaced, and spun from evenly combed long staple. Worsted fabric is made from worsted yarns and is tightly woven with a smooth, hard surface. Gabardine and serge are examples of worsted fabrics.

WORSTED CARD: A type of roller card used for worsted-system processing. It usually comprises two cards in tandem; the unit has a roller that carries the stock from the first card to the feed-in of the second card.

WORSTED COUNT: A woolen yarn measure. A 1's worsted yarn has 560 yards in one pound of yarn.

WORSTED SPINNING SYSTEM: A system of textile processing for manufacturing spun yarns from staple fibers usually over 3 inches in length. The main operations are carding, combing, drafting, and spinning. There are three basic systems of worsted yarn spinning: the bradford (or English system), the French (Alsatian or Continental system), and the American system.

WOVEN CARPET: Carpet produced on a loom. Weaving is a slower, more expensive, more labor intensive fabrication method than tufting. Woven carpet is distinguished by intricate patterns and tailored, controlled textures.

WOVEN FABRIC: Generally used to refer to fabric composed of two sets of yarns, warp and filling, that is formed by weaving, which is the interlacing of these sets of yarns. However, there are woven fabrics in which three sets of yarn are used to give a triaxial weave. In two dimensional wovens, there may be two or more warps and fillings in a fabric, depending on the complexity of the construction. The manner in which the two sets of yarns are interlaced determines the weave. By using various combinations of the three basic weaves, plain, twill, and satin, it is possible to produce an almost unlimited variety of constructions. Other effects may be obtained by varying the type of yarns, filament or spun, and the fiber types, twist levels, etc.

WRINKLE MARK: See SEAM MARK.

WRINKLE RECOVERY: That property of a fabric that enables it to recover from folding deformations.

WRINKLE RESISTANCE: That property of a fabric that enables it to resist the formation of wrinkles when subjected to a folding deformation. Wrinkle resistance in a fabric is a desirable attribute, but it is not easily measured quantitatively. Wrinkle resistance varies from quite low in many fabrics to very high in resilient fabrics. In order to form a wrinkle, a fabric's wrinkle resistance must be overcome. The fabric may, however, produce strains and store potential energy that can become evident as wrinkle recovery under suitable conditions.

WRONG COLOR PICK: See MIXED END OR FILLING.

WRONG DENTING: A defect in woven fabric caused when one or more warp ends are threaded through the reed incorrectly.

WRONG PICK: See MISPICK.

X

XANTHATING: A process in rayon manufacture in which carbon disulfide is reacted with alkali cellulose to produce bright orange cellulose xanthate.

XENON-ARC LAMP: A type of light source used in fading lamps. It is an electric discharge in an atmosphere of xenon gas at a little below atmospheric pressure, contained in a quartz tube.

Y

YARDAGE: The amount or length of a fabric expressed in yards.

YARD GOODS: Fabric sold on a retail basis by the running yard.

YARN: A generic term for a continuous strand of textile fibers, filaments, or material in a form suitable for knitting, weaving, or otherwise intertwining to form a textile fabric. Yarn occurs in the following forms: (1) a number of fibers twisted together (spun yarn); (2) a number of filaments laid together without twist (a zero-twist yarn); (3) a number of filaments laid together with a degree of twist; (4) a single filament with or without twist (a monofilament); or (5) a narrow strip of material, such as paper, plastic film, or metal foil, with or without twist, intended for use in a textile construction.

YARN CONSTRUCTION: A term used to indicate the number of singles yarns and the number of strands combined to form each successive unit of a plied yarn or cord.

YARN DENIER: See DENIER.

YARN-DYED FABRIC: A fabric constructed from yarns dyed prior to weaving or knitting.

YARN DYEING: See DYEING.

YARN DYEING DIFFERENCES: Variations in take-up of dyes by yarns, resulting in streaks in finished fabrics.

YARN INTERMEDIATE: A generic term for products obtained during the conversion of fibers to yarns, including card webs, laps, slivers, rovings, and tops.

YARN NUMBER: A relative measure of the fineness of yarns. Two classes of systems are in use: (1) Direct yarn number (equal to linear density) is the mass per unit length of yarn. This system is used for silk and manufactured filament yarns. (2) Indirect yarn number (equal to the reciprocal of linear density) is the length per unit mass of yarn. This system is used for cotton, linen, and wool-type spun yarns. (Also see COTTON COUNT.)

YARN NUMBER, EQUIVALENT SINGLE: The number of a plied yarn or cord determined by the standard methods used for singles yarns.

YARN QUALITY: Various grades of yarn designated by the producer with respect to performance characteristics, e.g., first quality, second quality, etc.

YARN SIZE: See YARN NUMBER.

YARN SLIPPAGE: In seamed fabrics, a gap on either side of the seam caused by yarn movement.

YARN-TO-CORD CONVERSION EFFICIENCY: In tire cord, this is a measurement relating tensile strength of untwisted yarn to tensile strength of cord.

Increasing cord twist or increasing yarn diameter lowers conversion efficiency.

YARN VARIATION: See RING, 1.

YELLOWNESS COEFFICIENT: Measure of the color of a molded acetate disc or dope solution. $Cy = 1 - T_{4400}/T_{6400}$ where Cy is the yellowness coefficient; T_{4400} is the transmission at 4400A (blue); and T_{6400} is the transmission at 6400A (orange).

YIELD: 1. Number of linear or square yards of fabric per pound of fiber or yarn. **2.** The number of finished square yards per pound of greige fabric.

YIELD POINT: Point on the stress-strain curve where the load and elongation stop being directly proportional. (Also see ELASTIC LIMIT.)

YOUNG'S MODULUS: A property of perfectly elastic materials, it is the ratio of change in stress to change in strain within the elastic limits of the material. The ratio is calculated from the stress expressed in force per unit cross-sectional area, and the strain expressed as a fraction of the original length. Modulus so calculated is equivalent to the force required to strain the sample 100% of its original length, at the rate prevailing below the elastic limit.

Z

ZD: Acronym for ZERO DEFECTS.

ZEIN FIBER: A manufactured fiber of regenerated protein derived from maize.

ZERO DEFECTS: In quality control, a goal to produce goods with no defects and to work without producing any errors.

ZERO-TWIST: Twistless, devoid of twist.

ZIMMER CARPET PRINTING MACHINES: See PRINTING, 2.

ZIPPERING: A carpet defect that occurs when tufts are not securely encapsulated by the backsizing compound. Tufts are easily pulled from the backing in long lengthwise runs.

Z TWIST: See TWIST, DIRECTION OF.

Appendix

Abbreviations and Symbols

General Units

Amperes	A	Ohms	Ω
Atmospheres	atm	Ounces	oz
Becquerels	Bq	Ounces per Linear Yard	oz/lin yd
British Thermal Unit	Btu	Ounces per Square Yard	oz/yd²
Calories	cal	Parts per Million	ppm
Candelas	cd	Pascals	Pa
Coulombs	C	Pounds	lb
Degrees Centigrade	°C	Pounds per Square Inch	psi
Degrees Fahrenheit	°F	Quarts	qt
Degrees Kelvin	K	Radians	rad
Degrees of Arc or Temperature	°	Relative Humidity	RH
Denier	d	Revolutions per Minute	rpm
Denier per Filament	dpf	Seconds	s or sec
Farads	F	Siemens	S
Feet	ft	Specific Gravity	sp gr
Fluid Ounces	fl oz	Standard Cubic Feet	
Foot-Pounds	ft-lb	per Minute	scfm
Gallons	gal	Steradians	sr
Grains	gr	Teslas	T
Grams	g	Turns per Inch	tpi
Grams per Denier	g/d	Turns per Meter	tpm
Grams per Linear Meter	g/m	Variation	δ
Grams per Liter	g/l	Wales x Courses	w x c
Grams per Square Meter	g/m²	Warp x Filling	w x f
Grays	Gy	Watts	W
Henries	H	Webers	Wb
Hertz	Hz	Yards	yd
Horsepower	hp	Yards per Minute	ypm
Hours	hr		
Inch-Pounds	in.-lb		
Inches	in.		
Intrinsic Viscosity	IV	**Metric Prefixes**	
Joules	J	Mega- (10^6)	M-
Liters	l	Kilo- (10^3)	k-
Lumens	lm	Hecto- (10^2)	h-
Lux	lx	Deka- (10^1)	da-
Meters	m	Deci- (10^{-1})	d-
Minutes	min	Centi- (10^{-2})	c-
Minutes of Arc	′	Milli- (10^{-3})	m-
Moles	mol	Micro- (10^{-6})	μ-
Newtons	N		

Abbreviations and Symbols (Continued)

Yarn Count

Cotton Count	c.c.	Plied Yarn	=	Singles denier/
Jute Count	j.c.			number of plies,
Linen Lea	l.l.			e.g., 70/3
Metric Count	m.c.			
Tex	tex	Cabled Yarn	=	Singles denier/
Wool Count	w			number of plies/
Woolen Cut	w/c			number of cabled
Woolen Run	w.r.			plies, e.g., 70/3/2
Worsted Count	w.c.			
		Filament Yarn	=	Total denier/
				filament count,
				e.g., 70/36

SI Metric Units

A new system of measurement is being adopted throughout the world. This modernized version of the kilogram-meter-second system bears the formal name "The International System of Units," and in all languages it has the short designation "SI," from the French name Le Systeme International d'Unités. On December 23, 1975, the United States of America became committed to a national program to make SI the predominant but not exclusive system of measurement when President Ford signed the "Metric Conversion Act of 1975" into Public Law 94-168.

SI is based on nine precisely defined base units that can be combined to form any number of derived units, and seventeen derived units have been given special names. The system has two distinct advantages. (1) There is only one unit for each physical quantity. Numerous, often confusing, units of pressure, energy, and power used in various fields are superseded by the pascal, the joule, and the watt, respectively. Moreover, SI has explicitly distinct units for mass (the kilogram) and force (the newton). (2) The definition of all derived units involves only multiplication and/or division of its component units: the numerical factor is always unity. Just as force equals mass times acceleration, the unit of force, the newton, is one kilogram meter per second squared.

SI Metric Units (Continued)

Physical Quantity	Unit Name	Formula	Symbol
Base Units			
Length	meter	—	m
Mass	kilogram	—	kg
Time	second	—	s
Electric Current	ampere	—	A
Temperature	degrees Kelvin	—	K
Amount of substance	mole	—	mol
Luminous Intensity	candela	—	cd
Plane Angle	radian	—	rad
Solid Angle	steradian	—	sr
Derived Units			
Force	newton	$kg \cdot m/s^2$	N
Pressure or Stress	pascal	N/m^2	Pa
Work, Energy, Quantity of Heat	joule	$N \cdot m$	J
Power, Radiant Energy, Flux	watt	J/s	W
Electric Potential, Potential Difference, Electromotive Force	volt	W/A	V
Conductance	siemens	A/V	S
Electric Resistance	ohm	V/A	Ω
Magnetic Flux	weber	$V \cdot s$	Wb
Inductance	henry	Wb/A	H
Magnetic Flux Density	tesla	Wb/m^2	T
Electric Charge, Quantity of Electricity	coulomb	$A \cdot s$	C
Capacitance	farad	C/V	F
Frequency (of a periodic phenomenon)	hertz	$cycles/s$	Hz
Activity (of radionuclides)	becquerel	$disintegrations/s$	Bq
Absorbed Dose of Radiation	gray	J/kg	Gy
Luminous Flux	lumen	$cd \cdot sr$	lm
Illuminance	lux	lm/m^2	lx

Measures, Weights, Equivalents

Units	Multiply By:	To Get:		Multiply By:	To Get:
Linear Measures					
feet	x 0.3048	= meters		x 3.281	= feet
inches	x 2.54	= centimeters		x 0.3937	= inches
inches	x 25.4	= millimeters		x 0.03937	= inches
miles	x 1.6093	= kilometers		x 0.6214	= miles
mils	x 0.0254	= millimeters		x 39.37	= mils
yards	x 0.9144	= meters		x 1.0936	= yards
Area Measures					
feet^2	x 0.0929	= meters^2		x 10.764	= feet^2
feet^2	x 144	= inches^2		x 0.00695	= feet^2
inches^2	x 6.452	= centimeters^2		x 0.155	= inches^2
inches^2	x 645.16	= millimeters^2		x 0.00155	= inches^2
yards^2	x 0.8361	= meters^2		x 1.196	= yards^2
yards^2	x 9	= feet^2		x 0.111	= yards^2
yards^2	x 1296	= inches^2		x 0.00077	= yards^2
Volume					
feet^3	x 28.317	= liters		x 0.03531	= feet^3
feet^3	x 7.481	= gallons		x 0.1337	= feet^3
feet^3	x 29.92	= quarts (liquid)		x 0.0334	= feet^3
feet^3	x 0.02832	= meters^3		x 35.315	= feet^3
feet^3	x 1728	= inches^3		x 0.00058	= feet^3

Measures, Weights, Equivalents (Continued)

Units	Multiply By:	To Get:		Multiply By:	To Get:
Volume (continued)					
fluid ounces	x 29.57	= milliliters		x 0.0338	= fluid ounces
fluid ounces	x 0.031	= quarts (liquid)		x 32	= fluid ounces
fluid ounces	x 29.57	= centimeters^3		x 0.0338	= fluid ounces
fluid ounces	x 1.805	= inches^3		x 0.554	= fluid ounces
gallons	x 3.7854	= liters		x 0.2642	= gallons
gallons	x 128	= fluid ounces		x 0.0078	= gallons
gallons	x 3785.4	= centimeters^3		x 0.00026	= gallons
gallons	x 231	= inches^3		x 0.00433	= gallons
inches^3	x 0.01639	= liters		x 61.024	= inches^3
inches^3	x 0.01732	= quarts (liquid)		x 57.75	= inches^3
inches^3	x 16.387	= centimeter^3		x 0.06102	= inches^3
inches^3	x 16387	= millimeters^3		x 0.000061	= inches^3
quarts (liquid)	x 0.94635	= liters		x 1.0567	= quarts (liquid)
quarts (liquid)	x 946.4	= centimeters^3		x 0.00106	= quarts (liquid)
yards^3	x 764.5	= liters		x 0.0013	= yards^3
yards^3	x 202	= gallons		x 0.00495	= yards^3
yards^3	x 0.7646	= meters^3		x 1.3080	= yards^3
yards^3	x 27	= feet^3		x 0.037	= yards^3

Measures, Weights, Equivalents (Continued)

Units	Multiply By:	To Get:	Multiply By:	To Get:
Mass				
grains	x 0.0648	= grams	x 15.43	= grains
grains	x 0.00229	= ounces	x 436.7	= grains
ounces	x 28.35	= grams	x 0.0353	= ounces
pounds	x 0.4536	= kilograms	x 2.2046	= pounds
pounds	x 453.6	= grams	x 0.0022	= pounds
Force				
kilograms(mass)	x 9.807	= newtons	x 0.10197	= kilograms (mass)
kilograms-force	x 2.2046	= pounds-force	x 0.4536	= kilograms-force
ounces-force	x 0.278	= newtons	x 3.597	= ounces-force
pounds-force	x 4.448	= newtons	x 0.2248	= pounds-force
Energy or Work				
Btu	x 1055	= joules	x 0.000948	= Btu
Btu	x 778	= foot-pounds	x 0.00129	= Btu
calories	x 4.187	= joules	x 0.2388	= calories
foot-pounds	x 1.3558	= joules	x 0.7376	= foot-pounds
watt-hours	x 3600	= joules	x 0.0002778	= watt-hours
watt-hours	x 2655	= foot-pounds	x 0.0003766	= watt-hours

Measures, Weights, Equivalents (Continued)

Units	Multiply By:	To Get:	Multiply By:	To Get:
Pressure or Stress				
atmospheres	x 101.3	= kilopascals	x 0.00987	= atmospheres
atmospheres	x 760	= mm Hg (0°C)	x 0.00132	= atmospheres
atmospheres	x 29.92	= inches Hg (0°C)	x 0.0334	= atmospheres
atmospheres	x 406.8	= inches H_2O (4°C)	x 0.00246	= atmospheres
atmospheres	x 14.7	= pounds per square inch	x 0.068	= atmospheres
inches Hg (0°C)	x 3.383	= kilopascals	x 0.2956	= inches Hg (0°C)
inches Hg (0°C)	x 0.491	= pounds per square inch	x 2.037	= inches Hg (0°C)
inches H_2O (4°C)	x 0.249	= kilopascals	x 4.016	= inches H_2O (4°C)
inches H_2O (4°C)	x 0.036	= pounds per square inch	x 27.78	= inches H_2O (4°C)
mm Hg (0°C)	x 0.134	= kilopascals	x 7.46	= mm Hg (0°C)
mm Hg (0°C)	x 0.019	= pounds per square inch	x 52.6	= mm Hg (0°C)
mm Hg (0°C)	x 13.596	= kilograms per square meter	x 0.073551	= mm Hg (0°C)
mm Hg (0°C)	x 1.3596	= grams per square centimeter	x 0.73551	= mm Hg (0°C)
pounds per square inch	x 6.895	= kilopascals	x 0.145	= pounds per square inch
torrs	x 1.0	= mm Hg (0°C)	x 1.0	= torrs
Power				
ft-lbf/min	x 0.0226	= watts	x 44.25	= ft-lbf/min
horsepower	x 0.746	= kilowatts	x 1.34	= horsepower
horsepower	x 33000	= ft-lbf/min	x 0.00003	= horsepower

Temperature Conversion Chart
Fahrenheit ⇔ Centigrade

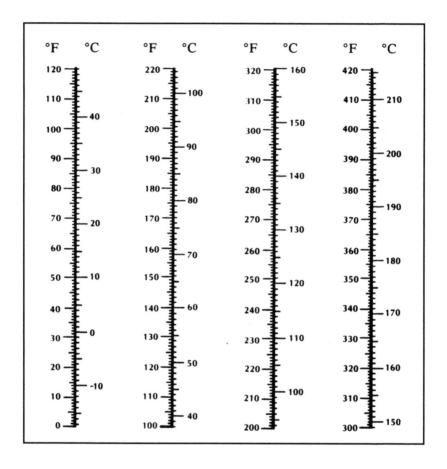

Steam Pressure—Temperature Table

Saturated Steam Gauge Pressure		Temperature		Saturated Steam Gauge Pressure		Temperature	
psi*	kPa*	°F	°C†	psi*	kPa*	°F	°C†
—	—	32	0	0	0	212	100
—	—	41	5	3	21	221	105
—	—	50	10	5	34	227	108
—	—	59	15	6	41	230	110
—	—	68	20	10	69	239	115
—	—	77	25	14	96	248	120
—	—	86	30	15	103	250	121
—	—	95	35	19	131	257	125
—	—	104	40	20	138	259	126
—	—	113	45	25	172	266	130
—	—	122	50	30	207	274	135
—	—	131	55	35	241	281	138
—	—	140	60	38	262	284	140
—	—	149	65	40	276	287	142
—	—	158	70	45	310	293	145
—	—	167	75	50	345	298	148
—	—	176	80	54	372	302	150
—	—	185	85	60	414	307	153
—	—	194	90	64	441	311	155
—	—	203	95	70	483	316	158

*psi x 6.895 = kPa   †°F = 9/5 °C + 32
kPa x 0.145 = psi   °C = 5/9 (°F - 32)

Steam Pressure—Temperature Table (Continued)

Saturated Steam Gauge Pressure		Temperature		Saturated Steam Gauge Pressure		Temperature	
psi*	kPa*	°F†	°C†	psi*	kPa*	°F†	°C†
75	517	320	160	260	1793	410	210
80	552	324	162	280	1931	415	213
87	600	329	165	291	2006	419	215
90	620	331	166	300	2068	422	217
100	690	338	170	320	2206	428	220
115	793	347	175	340	2344	433	223
120	827	350	177	355	2448	437	225
131	903	356	180	360	2482	438	226
140	965	361	183	380	2620	444	229
148	1020	365	185	390	2689	446	230
160	1103	371	188	400	2758	448	231
168	1158	374	190	430	2965	455	235
180	1241	380	193	440	3034	457	236
188	1296	383	195	470	3241	464	240
200	1379	388	198	480	3310	466	241
211	1455	392	200	515	3551	473	245
220	1517	395	202	520	3585	474	246
236	1627	401	205	560	3861	482	250
240	1655	403	206	600	4137	489	254

*psi x 6.895 = kPa   †°F = 9/5 °C + 32
kPa x 0.145 = psi   °C = 5/9 (°F - 32)

Specific Gravity and Moisture Content
of Common Natural and Manufactured Fibers
(70°F*, 65% Relative Humidity)

Fiber	Specific Gravity	Moisture Content (%)
Acrylic†	1.15	1-2
Cellulose Acetate	1.32	6
Cellulose Triacetate†	1.25	2.5-4.5
Cotton	1.54	7 (Commercial = 8.5)
Glass†	2.54	0
Polyamide† (nylon 6 and nylon 66)	1.14	4.1-4.5
Polyester†	1.38	0.4-0.5
Polyethylene†	0.92	0
Polypropylene†	0.90	0
Polyurethane†	1.21	1.0-1.5
Polyvinyl Chloride†	1.38	0-1
Polyvinylidene Chloride†	1.70	0
Protein†	1.25	10-18
Silk	1.37	9
Viscose Rayon	1.51	13
Wool	1.32	13-15

*21°C
†Average of major commercial brands

Yarn Number Conversion Table

Yards per Pound	Wool Runs (1600 yd per lb)	Cotton Count (840 yd per lb)	Worsted Count (560 yd per lb)	Metric Count (1000 m per kg)	Linen Count (300 yd per lb)	Grains per 100 Yards	Denier (g per 9000 m)	Tex (g per 1000 m)
300	0.188	0.357	0.536	0.605	1.000	2,333	14,890	1,654
372	0.233	0.443	0.664	0.750	1.240	1,882	12,000	1,333
447	0.279	0.532	0.798	0.901	1.390	1,566	10,000	1,111
560	0.350	0.667	1.000	1.129	1.867	1,250	7,972	885.2
600	0.375	0.714	1.071	1.210	2.000	1,167	7,441	826.7
840	0.525	1.000	1.500	1.694	2.800	833.3	5,315	590.5
1,120	0.700	1.333	2.000	2.258	3.733	625.0	3,986	442.9
1,600	1.000	1.905	2.857	3.226	5.333	437.5	2,790	310.0
1,680	1.050	2.000	3.000	3.388	5.600	416.7	2,658	295.3
2,030	1.269	2.417	3.625	4.093	6.767	344.9	2,200	244.4
2,232	1.395	2.657	3.986	4.500	7.440	313.6	2,000	222.2
2,240	1.400	2.667	4.000	4.516	7.467	312.5	1,994	221.6
2,520	1.575	3.000	4.500	5.081	8.400	277.8	1,771	196.8
2,800	1.750	3.333	5.000	5.645	9.333	250.0	1,595	177.2
3,200	2.000	3.810	5.714	6.452	10.67	218.8	1,395	155.0
3,360	2.100	4.000	6.000	6.774	11.20	208.3	1,328	147.6

Yarn Number Conversion Table (Continued)

Yards per Pound	Wool Runs (1600 yd per lb)	Cotton Count (840 yd per lb)	Worsted Count (560 yd per lb)	Metric Count (1000 m per kg)	Linen Count (300 yd per lb)	Grains per 100 Yards	Denier (g per 9000 m)	Tex (g per 1000 m)
4,060	2.538	4.833	7.250	8.183	13.53	172.4	1,100	122.2
4,200	2.625	5.000	7.500	8.468	14.00	166.7	1,063	118.1
4,211	2.632	5.013	7.520	8.490	14.04	166.2	1,060	117.8
4,464	2.790	5.315	7.971	9.000	14.88	156.8	1,000	111.1
4,480	2.800	5.333	8.000	9.032	14.93	156.3	996.5	110.7
4,699	2.937	5.594	8.391	9.474	15.67	149.0	950.0	105.6
4,800	3.000	5.714	8.571	9.677	16.00	145.8	930.1	103.3
4,960	3.100	5.905	8.857	10.00	16.53	141.1	900.0	100.0
5,040	3.150	6.000	9.000	10.16	16.80	138.9	885.8	98.4
5,252	3.283	6.252	9.378	10.59	17.51	133.3	850.0	94.4
5,581	3.488	6.644	9.966	11.25	18.60	125.4	800.0	88.9
5,600	3.500	6.667	10.00	11.29	18.67	125.0	797.2	88.6
5,880	3.675	7.000	10.50	11.86	19.60	119.0	759.3	84.3
5,953	3.721	7.087	10.63	12.00	19.84	117.6	750.0	83.3
6,160	3.850	7.333	11.00	12.42	20.53	113.6	724.8	80.6
6,378	3.986	7.593	11.39	12.86	21.26	109.8	700.0	77.8

Yarn Number Conversion Table (Continued)

Yards per Pound	Wool Runs (1600 yd per lb)	Cotton Count (840 yd per lb)	Worsted Count (560 yd per lb)	Metric Count (1000 m per kg)	Linen Count (300 yd per lb)	Grains per 100 Yards	Denier (g per 9000 m)	Tex (g per 1000 m)
6,400	4.000	7.619	11.43	12.90	21.33	109.4	697.6	77.5
6,720	4.200	8.000	12.00	13.55	22.40	104.2	664.4	73.9
6,869	4.293	8.177	12.27	13.85	22.90	101.9	650.0	72.2
7,280	4.550	8.667	13.00	14.68	24.27	96.16	613.3	68.1
7,440	4.650	8.857	13.29	15.00	24.80	94.09	600.0	66.7
7,560	4.725	9.000	13.50	15.24	25.20	92.59	590.5	65.7
7,840	4.900	9.333	14.00	15.81	26.13	89.29	569.4	63.2
8,000	5.000	9.524	14.29	16.13	26.67	87.50	558.1	62.0
8,117	5.073	9.663	14.49	16.37	27.06	86.24	550.0	61.1
8,400	5.250	10.00	15.00	16.94	28.00	83.33	531.5	59.0
8,929	5.581	10.63	15.94	18.00	29.76	78.40	500.0	55.6
8,960	5.600	10.67	16.00	18.06	29.87	78.13	498.3	55.4
9,000	5.625	10.71	16.07	18.15	30.00	77.78	496.1	55.1
9,240	5.775	11.00	16.50	18.63	30.80	75.76	483.2	53.7
9,300	5.813	11.07	16.61	18.75	31.00	75.27	480.0	53.3
9,520	5.950	11.33	17.00	19.19	31.73	73.53	469.0	52.1

Yarn Number Conversion Table (Continued)

Yards per Pound	Wool Runs (1600 yd per lb)	Cotton Count (840 yd per lb)	Worsted Count (560 yd per lb)	Metric Count (1000 m per kg)	Linen Count (300 yd per lb)	Grains per 100 Yards	Denier (g per 9000 m)	Tex (g per 1000 m)
9,600	6.000	11.43	17.14	19.35	32.00	72.92	465.1	51.7
9,900	6.188	11.79	17.68	19.96	33.00	70.71	451.0	50.1
9,921	6.200	11.81	17.72	20.01	33.07	70.56	450.0	50.0
10,080	6.300	12.00	18.00	20.32	33.60	69.45	442.9	49.2
10,200	6.375	12.14	18.21	20.56	34.00	67.07	437.7	48.6
10,500	6.563	12.50	18.75	21.17	35.00	66.67	425.2	47.2
10,640	6.650	12.67	19.00	21.45	35.47	65.79	419.6	46.6
10,800	6.750	12.86	19.39	21.77	36.00	64.82	413.4	45.9
10,920	6.825	13.00	19.50	22.02	36.40	64.10	408.8	45.4
11,160	6.975	13.29	19.93	22.50	37.20	62.72	400.0	44.4
11,200	7.000	13.33	20.00	22.58	37.33	62.50	398.6	44.2
11,400	7.125	13.57	20.36	22.98	38.00	61.40	391.6	43.5
11,760	7.350	14.00	21.00	23.73	39.20	59.47	379.3	42.1
12,000	7.500	14.05	21.08	23.80	40.00	59.31	378.3	42.0
12,400	7.750	14.76	22.14	25.00	41.33	56.45	360.0	40.0
12,600	7.875	15.00	22.50	25.40	42.00	55.56	354.3	39.3

Yarn Number Conversion Table (Continued)

Yards per Pound	Wool Runs (1600 yd per lb)	Cotton Count (840 yd per lb)	Worsted Count (560 yd per lb)	Metric Count (1000 m per kg)	Linen Count (300 yd per lb)	Grains per 100 Yards	Denier (g per 9000 m)	Tex (g per 1000 m)
12,760	7.975	15.19	22.73	25.73	42.53	54.86	350.0	38.9
12,800	8.000	15.24	22.86	25.81	42.67	54.69	348.8	38.8
12,880	8.050	15.33	23.00	25.97	42.93	54.35	346.6	38.5
13,200	8.250	15.71	23.57	26.61	44.00	53.03	338.2	37.6
13,440	8.400	16.00	24.00	27.10	44.80	52.08	332.2	36.9
13,500	8.438	16.07	24.11	27.22	45.00	51.85	330.7	36.7
14,000	8.750	16.67	25.00	28.23	46.67	50.00	318.9	35.4
14,280	8.925	17.00	25.50	28.79	47.60	49.02	312.6	34.7
14,400	9.000	17.14	25.71	29.03	48.00	48.61	310.0	34.4
14,560	9.100	17.33	26.00	29.35	48.53	48.08	306.6	34.0
14,880	9.300	17.71	26.57	30.00	49.60	47.04	300.0	33.3
15,120	9.450	18.00	27.00	30.48	50.40	46.30	295.3	32.8
15,300	9.563	18.21	27.32	30.85	51.00	45.75	291.8	32.4
15,680	9.800	18.67	28.00	31.61	52.27	44.64	284.7	31.6
15,960	9.975	19.00	28.50	32.18	53.20	43.86	279.7	31.0
16,000	10.00	19.05	28.57	32.26	53.33	43.75	279.0	31.0

Yarn Number Conversion Table (Continued)

Yards per Pound	Wool Runs (1600 yd per lb)	Cotton Count (840 yd per lb)	Worsted Count (560 yd per lb)	Metric Count (1000 m per kg)	Linen Count (300 yd per lb)	Grains per 100 Yards	Denier (g per 9000 m)	Tex (g per 1000 m)
16,240	10.15	19.33	29.00	32.74	54. 13	43. 10	274.9	30.5
16,500	10.31	19.64	29.46	33.27	55.00	42.43	270.6	30.0
16,800	10.50	20.00	30.00	33.87	56.00	41.67	265.7	29.5
17,100	10.69	20.36	30.54	34.48	57.00	40.94	261.1	29.0
17,360	10.85	20.67	31.00	35.00	57.87	40.32	257.2	28.6
17,600	11.00	20.95	31.43	35.48	58.67	39.77	253.7	28.1
17,860	11.16	21.26	31.89	36.00	59.53	39.19	250.0	27.8
17,920	11.20	21.33	32.00	36.13	59.73	39.06	249.1	27.7
18,480	11.55	22.00	33.00	37.26	61.60	37.88	241.6	26.8
18,600	11.63	22.14	33.21	37.50	62.00	37.64	240.0	26.7
19,040	11.90	22.67	34.00	38.39	63.47	36.76	234.5	26.0
19,200	12.00	22.86	34.29	38.71	64.00	36.46	232.5	25.8
19,500	12.19	23.21	34.82	39.32	65.00	35.90	228.9	25.4
19,600	12.25	23.33	35.00	39.52	65.33	35.71	227.8	25.3
20,160	12.60	24.00	36.00	40.65	67.20	34.72	221.5	24.6
20,400	12.75	24.29	36.43	41.13	68.00	34.31	218.8	24.3

Yarn Number Conversion Table (Continued)

Yards per Pound	Wool Runs (1600 yd per lb)	Cotton Count (840 yd per lb)	Worsted Count (560 yd per lb)	Metric Count (1000 m per kg)	Linen Count (300 yd per lb)	Grains per 100 Yards	Denier (g per 9000 m)	Tex (g per 1000 m)
20,800	13.00	24.76	37.14	41.94	69.33	33.65	214.6	23.8
21,000	13.13	25.00	37.50	42.34	70.00	33.33	212.6	23.6
21,280	13.30	25.33	38.00	42.90	70.93	32.90	209.8	23.3
21,840	13.65	26.00	39.00	44.03	72.80	32.05	204.4	22.7
22,320	13.95	26.57	39.86	45.00	74.40	31.36	200.0	22.2
22,400	14.00	26.67	40.00	45.16	74.67	31.25	199.3	22.1
23,520	14.70	28.00	42.00	47.42	78.40	29.76	189.8	21.0
24,640	15.40	29.33	44.00	49.68	82.13	28.41	181.2	20.1
24,800	15.50	29.53	44.29	50.00	82.67	28.23	180.0	20.0
25,200	15.75	30.00	45.00	50.81	84.00	27.78	177.2	19.7
25,760	16.10	30.67	46.00	51.94	85.87	27.17	173.3	19.2
26,260	16.41	31.27	46.90	52.94	87.53	26.66	170.0	18.9
26,880	16.80	32.00	48.00	54.19	89.60	26.04	166.1	18.4
27,200	17.00	32.38	48.57	54.84	90.67	25.74	164.1	18.2
27,720	17.33	33.00	49.50	55.89	92.40	25.25	161.1	17.9
28,000	17.50	33.33	50.00	56.45	93.33	25.00	159.4	17.7

Yarn Number Conversion Table (Continued)

Yards per Pound	Wool Runs (1600 yd per lb)	Cotton Count (840 yd per lb)	Worsted Count (560 yd per lb)	Metric Count (1000 m per kg)	Linen Count (300 yd per lb)	Grains per 100 Yards	Denier (g per 9000 m)	Tex (g per 1000 m)
28,560	17.85	34.00	51.00	57.58	95.20	24.51	156.3	17.3
28,800	18.00	34.29	51.43	58.06	96.00	24.31	155.0	17.2
29,760	18.60	35.43	53.15	60.00	99.20	23.52	150.0	16.7
30,000	18.75	35.71	53.57	60.48	100.0	23.33	148.8	16.5
30,400	19.00	36.19	54.29	61.29	101.3	23.03	146.9	16.3
32,000	20.00	38.10	57.14	64.52	106.7	21.88	139.5	15.5
32,480	20.30	38.67	58.00	65.49	108.3	21.55	137.5	15.2
33,600	21.00	40.00	60.00	67.74	112.0	20.83	132.9	14.8
34,440	21.53	41.00	61.50	69.44	114.8	20.33	129.6	14.4
34,720	21.70	41.33	62.00	70.00	115.7	20.16	128.6	14.2
35,840	22.40	42.67	64.00	72.26	119.5	19.53	124.6	13.8
36,000	22.50	42.86	64.29	72.58	120.0	19.44	124.0	13.8
36,800	23.00	43.81	65.71	74.19	122.7	19.02	121.3	13.4
37,200	23.25	44.29	66.43	75.00	124.0	18.82	120.0	13.3
38,080	23.80	45.33	68.00	76.78	126.9	18.38	117.2	13.0
39,200	24.50	46.67	70.00	79.03	130.7	17.86	113.9	12.6

Yarn Number Conversion Table (Continued)

Yards per Pound	Wool Runs (1600 yd per lb)	Cotton Count (840 yd per lb)	Worsted Count (560 yd per lb)	Metric Count (1000 m per kg)	Linen Count (300 yd per lb)	Grains per 100 Yards	Denier (g per 9000 m)	Tex (g per 1000 m)
40,320	25.20	48.00	72.00	81.29	134.4	17.36	110.7	12.3
42,000	26.25	50.00	75.00	84.68	140.0	16.67	106.3	11.8
44,640	27.90	53.15	79.71	90.00	148.8	15.68	100.0	11.1
45,920	28.70	54.67	82.00	92.58	153.1	15.24	97.22	10.8
47,040	29.40	56.00	84.00	94.84	156.8	14.88	94.91	10.5
49,600	31.00	59.05	88.58	100.0	165.3	14.11	90.00	10.0
50,400	31.50	60.00	90.00	101.6	168.0	13.89	88.58	9.84
53,760	33.60	64.00	96.00	108.4	179.2	13.02	83.05	9.22
55,800	34.88	66.43	99.65	112.5	186.0	12.54	80.00	8.88
58,800	36.75	70.00	105.0	118.6	196.0	11.90	75.93	8.43
59,530	37.21	70.87	106.3	120.0	198.4	11.76	75.00	8.33
61,600	38.50	73.33	110.0	124.2	205.3	11.36	72.48	8.05
63,780	39.86	75.93	113.9	128.6	212.6	10.98	70.00	7.77
64,000	40.00	76.19	114.3	129.0	213.3	10.94	69.76	7.75
67,200	42.00	80.00	120.0	135.5	224.0	10.42	66.44	7.38
74,410	46.51	88.58	132.9	150.0	248.0	9.407	60.00	6.66

Yarn Number Conversion Table (Continued)

Yards per Pound	Wool Runs (1600 yd per lb)	Cotton Count (840 yd per lb)	Worsted Count (560 yd per lb)	Metric Count (1000 m per kg)	Linen Count (300 yd per lb)	Grains per 100 Yards	Denier (g per 9000 m)	Tex (g per 1000 m)
75,600	47.25	90.00	135.0	152.4	252.0	9.259	59.05	6.56
81,170	50.73	96.63	144.9	163.6	270.6	8.624	55.00	6.11
84,000	52.50	100.0	150.5	169.4	280.0	8.333	53.15	5.90
89,290	55.81	106.3	159.5	180.0	297.6	7.840	50.00	5.55
92,400	57.75	110.0	165.0	186.3	308.0	7.576	48.32	5.36
97,440	60.90	116.0	174.0	196.5	324.8	7.184	45.82	5.09
99,210	62.01	118.1	177.2	200.0	330.7	7.056	45.00	5.00
100,800	63.00	120.0	180.0	203.2	336.0	6.945	44.29	4.92
111,600	69.75	132.9	199.4	225.0	372.0	6.272	40.00	4.44
148,800	93.00	177.1	265.7	300.0	496.0	4.704	30.00	3.33
223,200	139.5	265.7	398.6	450.0	744.0	3.136	20.00	2.22
446,500	279.1	531.5	797.3	900.0	1488.0	1.568	10.00	1.11

Yarn Number Conversion Formulas

Yarn Number System	Cotton Count	Denier	Worsted Count	Wool Count	Linen Lea	Woolen Cut
Cotton Count	—	$\dfrac{5{,}315}{d}$	c.c. x 1.50	c.c. x 52.5	c.c. x 2.80	c.c. x 2.80
Denier	$\dfrac{5{,}315}{d}$	—	$\dfrac{7{,}972}{d}$	$\dfrac{279{,}030}{d}$	$\dfrac{14{,}880}{d}$	$\dfrac{14{,}880}{d}$
Worsted Count	$\dfrac{\text{w.c.}}{1.50}$	$\dfrac{7{,}972}{\text{w.c.}}$	—	w.c. x 35.0	w.c. x 1.867	w.c. x 1.867
Wool Count	$\dfrac{w}{52.50}$	$\dfrac{279{,}030}{w}$	$\dfrac{w}{35.0}$	—	$\dfrac{w}{18.75}$	$\dfrac{w}{18.75}$
Linen Lea	$\dfrac{\text{l.l.}}{2.80}$	$\dfrac{14{,}880}{\text{l.l.}}$	$\dfrac{\text{l.l.}}{1.867}$	l.l. x 18.75	—	same
Woolen Cut	$\dfrac{\text{w/c}}{2.80}$	$\dfrac{14{,}880}{\text{w/c}}$	$\dfrac{\text{w/c}}{1.867}$	w/c x 18.75	same	—
Woolen Run	$\dfrac{\text{w.r.}}{0.525}$	$\dfrac{2{,}800}{\text{w.r.}}$	$\dfrac{\text{w.r.}}{0.350}$	w.r. x 100	w.r. x 5.33	w.r. x 5.33
Jute Count	$\dfrac{17.14}{\text{j.c.}}$	j.c. x 310	$\dfrac{25.71}{\text{j.c.}}$	$\dfrac{900}{\text{j.c.}}$	$\dfrac{48.0}{\text{j.c.}}$	$\dfrac{48.0}{\text{j.c.}}$
Metric Count	m.c. x 0.5905	$\dfrac{9{,}000}{\text{m.c.}}$	$\dfrac{\text{m.c.}}{1.129}$	m.c. x 31.00	$\dfrac{\text{m.c.}}{0.605}$	$\dfrac{\text{m.c.}}{0.605}$
Grains/120 Yards	$\dfrac{1{,}000}{\text{gr/120 yd}}$	$\dfrac{\text{gr/120 yd}}{0.1881}$	$\dfrac{1{,}500}{\text{gr/120 yd}}$	$\dfrac{52{,}500}{\text{gr/120 yd}}$	$\dfrac{2{,}800}{\text{gr/120 yd}}$	$\dfrac{2{,}800}{\text{gr/120 yd}}$
Tex	$\dfrac{590.5}{\text{tex}}$	$\dfrac{\text{tex}}{0.1111}$	$\dfrac{885.8}{\text{tex}}$	$\dfrac{31{,}000}{\text{tex}}$	$\dfrac{1{,}654}{\text{tex}}$	$\dfrac{1{,}654}{\text{tex}}$

Yarn Number Conversion Formulas (Continued)

Yarn Number System	Woolen Run	Jute Count	Metric Count	Grains/120 Yards	Tex
Cotton Count	c.c. x 0.525	$\dfrac{17.14}{\text{c.c.}}$	c.c. x 1.693	$\dfrac{1{,}000}{\text{c.c.}}$	$\dfrac{590.5}{\text{c.c.}}$
Denier	$\dfrac{2{,}800}{\text{d}}$	d x 0.003225	$\dfrac{9{,}000}{\text{d}}$	d x 0.1881	d x 0.1111
Worsted Count	w.c. x 0.350	$\dfrac{25.71}{\text{w.c.}}$	w.c. x 1.129	$\dfrac{1{,}500}{\text{w.c.}}$	$\dfrac{885.8}{\text{w.c.}}$
Wool Count	$\dfrac{w}{100}$	$\dfrac{900}{w}$	$\dfrac{w}{31.0}$	$\dfrac{52{,}500}{w}$	$\dfrac{30{,}975}{w}$
Linen Lea	$\dfrac{\text{l.l.}}{5.33}$	$\dfrac{48.0}{\text{l.l.}}$	l.l. x 0.605	$\dfrac{2{,}800}{\text{l.l.}}$	$\dfrac{1{,}654}{\text{l.l.}}$
Woolen Cut	$\dfrac{\text{w/c}}{5.33}$	$\dfrac{48.0}{\text{w/c}}$	w/c x 0.605	$\dfrac{2{,}800}{\text{w/c}}$	$\dfrac{1{,}654}{\text{w/c}}$
Woolen Run	—	$\dfrac{9.0}{\text{w.r.}}$	$\dfrac{\text{w.r.}}{0.31}$	$\dfrac{525.0}{\text{w.r.}}$	$\dfrac{310.0}{\text{w.r.}}$
Jute Count	$\dfrac{9.0}{\text{j.c.}}$	—	$\dfrac{29.03}{\text{j.c.}}$	j.c. x 58.33	j.c. x 34.45
Metric Count	m.c. x 0.310	$\dfrac{29.03}{\text{m.c.}}$	—	$\dfrac{1{,}693}{\text{m.c.}}$	$\dfrac{1{,}000}{\text{m.c.}}$
Grains/120 Yards	$\dfrac{525.0}{\text{gr/120 yd}}$	$\dfrac{\text{gr/120 yd}}{58.33}$	$\dfrac{1{,}693}{\text{gr/120 yd}}$	—	gr/120 yd x 0.5905
Tex	$\dfrac{310.0}{\text{tex}}$	$\dfrac{\text{tex}}{34.45}$	$\dfrac{1{,}000}{\text{tex}}$	$\dfrac{\text{tex}}{0.5905}$	—

Calculations for Fabric Weight

For Yards per Pound*:

(a) $\dfrac{\text{Total yards}}{\text{Net weight in pounds}}$

(b) $\dfrac{16}{\text{Ounces per linear yard}}$

(c) $\dfrac{\text{Total Yards}}{\text{Ounces}} \times 16$

(d) $\dfrac{\text{Square inch weighed}}{\text{Weight in grams (width)}} \times 12.60$

(e) $\dfrac{\text{Square inch weighed}}{\text{Weight in grams (width)}} \times 194.4$

(f) 12-inch square sample weighed in grains $= \dfrac{27{,}993.6}{\text{Grains} \times \text{width}}$

(g) 8-inch square sample weighed in grains $= \dfrac{12{,}441.6}{\text{Grains} \times \text{width}}$

(h) $\dfrac{576}{\text{Width (ounces per square yard)}}$

yd/lb x 2.016 = m/kg

For Ounces per Square Yard†:

(a) $\dfrac{\text{Weight in pounds (16) (36)}}{\text{Yards (width)}}$

(b) $\dfrac{\text{Weight in ounces (36)}}{\text{Yards (width)}} = \text{Ounces per linear yard} \left(\dfrac{36}{\text{Width}}\right)$

(c) $\dfrac{576}{\text{Width (yard per pound)}} \times 45.72$

(d) $\dfrac{\text{Grams weight of sample}}{\text{Square inch weighed}} \times 2.9622$

(e) $\dfrac{\text{Grains weight of sample}}{\text{Square inch weighed}}$

(f) 8-inch square used: Grain weight x 0.04628

(Continued on next page)

Calculations for Fabric Weight *(continued)*

(g)   12-inch square used: Grain weight x 0.02057

(h)   8-inch square used: Gram weight x 0.7144

(i)   12-inch square used: Gram weight x 0.3175

†oz/yd^2 x 0.03391 = kg/m^2

For Ounces per Linear Yard‡:

(a) $\dfrac{\text{Weight in ounces}}{\text{Yards weighed}}$

(b) $\dfrac{16}{\text{Yards per pound}}$

(c)   Ounces per square yard $\left(\dfrac{\text{Width}}{36}\right)$

(d) $\dfrac{\text{Weight in grams (width)}}{\text{Square inch weighed}}$ x 1.270

(e) $\dfrac{\text{Weight in grains (width)}}{\text{Square inch weighed}}$ x 0.0823

‡$oz/lin\ yd$ x 0.031 = kg/m

For Pile Density of Carpet:

$\dfrac{\text{Pile yarn weight in ounces per square yard x 36}}{\text{Thickness in inches}}$

Conversion of Nominal Denier per Filament (dpf) to Nominal Decitex per Filament (dxpf)

Nominal dpf	Nominal dxpf
1.5	1.7
2.0	2.2
2.25	2.5
2.5	2.8
3.0	3.3
4.0	4.4
4.5	5.0
5.0	5.6
5.5	6.1
6.0	6.7
8	9
10	11
11	12
12	13
13	14
15	17
16	18
17	19
18	20
21	23
26	29

Conversion of Nominal Denier to Nominal Decitex
(Based on ASTM Standard D 2260-89)

Nominal Denier (den)	Nominal Decitex (dtex)	Nominal Denier (den)	Nominal Decitex (dtex)
40	44	220	240
45	50	236	260
60	67	240	270
70	78	250	280
75	83	285	310
78	87	300	330
85	94	310	340
90	100	320	360
95	105	330	370
100	112	450	500
110	122	600	660
128	140	700	770
130	145	840	940
140	155	900	1000
150	167	1000	1100
160	175	1100	1200
170	190	1300	1450
180	200	1400	1600
200	220	1600	1750
204	225	1800	2000
210	235	2600	2800

Conversion of Nominal Total Denier to Nominal Kilotex Values for Tow Items

Nominal Denier (den)	Nominal Decitex (dtex)	Nominal Denier (den)	Nominal Decitex (dtex)
24000	2.7	53000	5.9
25000	2.8	64000	7.1
30000	3.3	65000	7.2
36000	4.0	70000	7.8
38000	4.2	87000	10
39000	4.3	100000	11
40000	4.4	108000	12
41000	4.5	137000	15
42000	4.7	150000	17
44000	4.9	180000	20
45000	5.0	211000	23
46000	5.1	216000	24
47000	5.2	225000	25
48000	5.3	234000	26
50000	5.5	450000	50
51000	5.7	500000	55

Stress-Strain Calculations

For tenacity at break:

$$\frac{\text{Gram load at break}}{\text{Denier}} = \text{tenacity (g/d)}$$

For tenacity at any elongation:

$$\frac{\text{Gram load at given elongation}}{\text{Denier}} = \text{tenacity (g/d)}$$

For elongation at break:

$$\frac{\text{Length at break} - \text{original length}}{\text{Original length}} \times 100 = \% \text{ elongation}$$

For elongation at any load:

$$\frac{\text{Length at given load} - \text{original length}}{\text{Original length}} \times 100 = \% \text{ elongation}$$

For elastic limit:

$$\frac{\text{Gram load at yield point}}{\text{Denier}} = \text{yield stress (g/d)}$$

$$\frac{\text{Elongation at yield point}}{\text{Original length}} \times 100 = \% \text{ yield strain}$$

For average stiffness per unit elongation (resistance to deformation):

$$\frac{\text{Gram load at break} \times 100}{\text{Denier} \times \% \text{ elongation}} = \text{average stiffness (g/d)}$$

For toughness index (work to break):

$$\frac{\text{Gram load at break} \times \% \text{ elongation at break}}{2(\text{Denier}) \times 100} = \text{toughness index} \left(\frac{\text{g} \cdot \text{cm}}{\text{d} \cdot \text{cm}} \right)$$

For energy to break:

$$\frac{\text{Breaking strength (lb)} \times \text{elongation (in.}}{2} = \text{energy to break (lb} \cdot \text{in.)}$$

Textile Moisture Calculations

For moisture content:

$$\frac{\text{Original wt.} - \text{dry wt.}}{\text{Original wt.}} \times 100 = \% \text{ moisture content}$$

For moisture regain:

$$\frac{\text{Original wt.} - \text{dry wt.}}{\text{Dry wt.}} \times 100 = \% \text{ moisture regain}$$

To determine moisture regain of blends:

$$\frac{\% \text{ Fiber A} \times R_a + (\% \text{ Fiber B} \times R_b) + \dots}{\% \text{ Fiber A} + \% \text{ Fiber B} + \dots} = \% \text{ regain of blend}$$

Where: R_a = commercial regain of Fiber A
R_b = commercial regain of Fiber B

Wet Processing Calculations

To convert from grams per liter to percent on weight of fiber:

$$\frac{\text{Liquor ratio}}{10} \times g/l = \% \text{ owf}$$

To convert from percent on weight of fiber to grams per liter:

$$\frac{\% \text{ owf} \times 10}{\text{Liquor ratio}} = g/l$$

For percent wet weight of fabric:

$$\frac{\text{Wet wt.} - \text{dry wt.}}{\text{Dry wt.}} \times 100 = \% \text{ wet wt.}$$

For percent wet pickup of fabric:

% Wet wt. − % dry wt. = % wet pickup

For percent dry solids add-on on fabric weight:

% Solids content of liquid x % wet pickup = % solids add-on

Weaving Guides

Diameters of Spun Yarns of Different Cotton Counts

Cotton Count	Diameter in.	mm	Cotton Count	Diameter in.	mm
80	0.00427	0.108	20	0.00847	0.215
75	0.00433	0.110	19	0.00876	0.222
70	0.00456	0.116	18	0.00900	0.229
65	0.00474	0.120	17	0.00926	0.235
60	0.00495	0.126	16	0.00957	0.243
55	0.00521	0.132	15	0.00990	0.251
50	0.00540	0.137	14	0.0102	0.259
48	0.00554	0.141	13	0.0106	0.269
46	0.00565	0.144	12	0.0110	0.279
44	0.00577	0.146	11	0.0115	0.292
42	0.00588	0.149	10	0.0120	0.305
40	0.00606	0.154	9	0.0126	0.320
38	0.00616	0.156	8	0.0135	0.343
36	0.00636	0.162	7	0.0145	0.368
34	0.00657	0.167	6	0.0156	0.381
32	0.00675	0.171	5	0.0171	0.434
30	0.00700	0.178	4	0.0191	0.485
28	0.00724	0.184	3	0.0221	0.561
26	0.00751	0.190	2	0.0274	0.696
24	0.00781	0.198	1	0.0382	0.970
22	0.00813	0.206			

Weaving Guides (Continued)

Loom Reed Air Space

Reed Dent	50% Air Space in.	mm	55% Air Space in	mm	60% Air Space in.	mm
10	0.0500	1.270	0.0550	1.397	0.0600	1.524
13	0.0385	0.978	0.0423	1.074	0.0462	1.173
15	0.0334	0.848	0.0367	0.932	0.0400	1.016
17	0.0294	0.747	0.0324	0.823	0.0353	0.897
20	0.0250	0.635	0.0275	0.698	0.0300	0.762
21	0.0238	0.604	0.0262	0.665	0.0286	0.726
23	0.0218	0.554	0.0239	0.607	0.0261	0.663
25	0.0200	0.508	0.0220	0.559	0.0240	0.610
26	0.0192	0.488	0.0211	0.536	0.0231	0.587
28	0.0179	0.455	0.0197	0.500	0.0214	0.544
30	0.0166	0.422	0.0183	0.465	0.0200	0.508
31	0.0161	0.409	0.0177	0.450	0.0193	0.490
34	0.0147	0.373	0.0162	0.411	0.0177	0.450
35	0.0143	0.363	0.0157	0.399	0.0171	0.434
36	0.0139	0.353	0.0153	0.389	0.0167	0.424
38	0.0132	0.335	0.0145	0.368	0.0158	0.401
40	0.0125	0.318	0.0137	0.348	0.0150	0.381
42	0.0119	0.302	0.0131	0.333	0.0143	0.363
44	0.0114	0.290	0.0128	0.325	0.0136	0.345
45	0.0111	0.282	0.0122	0.310	0.0133	0.338
47	0.0106	0.269	0.0117	0.297	0.0128	0.325
50	0.0100	0.254	0.0110	0.279	0.0120	0.305
53	0.0094	0.239	0.0104	0.264	0.0113	0.287
55	0.0091	0.231	0.0100	0.254	0.0109	0.277
57	0.0088	0.224	0.0096	0.244	0.0105	0.267
60	0.0084	0.213	0.0092	0.234	0.0100	0.254
61	0.0082	0.208	0.0090	0.229	0.0098	0.249
62	0.0081	0.206	0.0089	0.226	0.0097	0.246
65	0.0077	0.196	0.0085	0.216	0.0092	0.234